D1156377

AMINES AND SCHIZOPHRENIA

AMINES AND SCHIZOPHRENIA

Edited by

HAROLD E. HIMWICH

Galesburg State Research Hospital, Galesburg, Ill. (U.S.A.)

SEYMOUR S. KETY

National Institutes of Health, Bethesda, Md. (U.S.A.)

JOHN R. SMYTHIES

University of Edinburgh (Scotland)

SYMPOSIUM PUBLICATIONS DIVISION

PERGAMON PRESS

OXFORD · LONDON · EDINBURGH · NEW YORK

TORONTO · SYDNEY · PARIS · BRAUNSCHWEIG

Pergamon Press Ltd., Headington Hill Hall, Oxford
4 & 5 Fitzroy Square, London W.1
Pergamon Press (Scotland) Ltd., 2 & 3 Teviot Place, Edinburgh 1
Pergamon Press Inc., 44–01 21st Street, Long Island City, New York 11101
Pergamon of Canada, Ltd., 6 Adelaide Street East, Toronto, Ontario
Pergamon Press (Aust). Pty. Ltd., 20–22 Margaret Street, Sydney, New South Wales
Pergamon Press S.A.R.L., 24 rue des Écoles, Paris 5e
Vieweg & Sohn GmbH, Burgplatz 1, Braunschweig

First edition 1967

Library of Congress Catalog Card No. 66-23046

Printed in Great Britain by Alden Press Ltd., Oxford

(2990/67)

CONTENTS

LIST OF CONTRIBUTORS

BALDESSARINI, R. J., Section on Medicine, Laboratory of Clinical Science, National Institute of Mental Health, National Institutes of Health, Bethesda, Maryland 20014.

BERLET, H. H., Thudichum Psychiatric Research Laboratory, Galesburg State Research Hospital, Galesburg, Illinois.

BOURDILLON, R. E., Royal Southern Hospital, Caryl Street, Liverpool 8, England.

BRUNE, G. G., Neurologische Universitätsklinik, Hamburg-Eppendorf, Hamburg 20, Martinistr. 52, Germany.

COLE, J. O., Chief, Psychopharmacology Service Center, National Institute of Mental Health, National Institutes of Health, Bethesda, Maryland.

DURELL, J., Chief, Section on Psychiatry, Laboratory of Clinical Science, National Institute of Mental Health, National Institutes of Health, Bethesda, Maryland.

EFRON, D. H., Head, Pharmacology Program, Psychopharmacology Service Center, National Institute of Mental Health, National Institutes of Health, Bethesda, Maryland.

FORREST, A. D., Consultant Psychiatrist, Andrew Duncan Clinic, Royal Edinburgh Hospital, Morningside Terrace, Edinburgh, Scotland.

FRIEDHOFF, A. J., Co-Director of Center for the Study of Acute Psychotic Disorders, Department of Psychiatry and Neurology, New York University School of Medicine, 550 First Avenue, New York 16, New York.

HIMWICH, H. E., Director, Research Division, Galesburg State Research Hospital, Galesburg, Illinois.

HIMWICH, W. A., Thudichum Psychiatric Research Laboratory, Galesburg State Research Hospital, Galesburg, Illinois.

HOLMSTEDT, B., Professor, Department of Toxicology, Karolinska Institutet, Stockholm 60, Sweden.

HORWITT, M. K., Director, L. B. Mendel Research Laboratory, Elgin State Hospital, Elgin, Illinois.

JENNER, F. A., Physician in Charge, Medical Research Council Unit for Research on the Chemical Pathology of Mental Disorders, Hollymoor Hospital, Birmingham, England.

KETY, S. S., Chief, Laboratory of Clinical Science, National Institute of Mental Health, National Institutes of Health, Bethesda, Maryland.

KUEHL, F. A., Jr., Assistant Director, Bio-organic Chemistry, Merck Sharp Dohme Research Laboratories, Rahway, New Jersey.

LASTER, L., Chief, Gastroenterology Unit, National Institute of Arthritis and Metabolic Diseases, National Institutes of Health, Bethesda, Maryland.

LEBEDEV, B., Professor of Psychiatry and Director of Bechterev State Institute for Psychoneurological Research, Leningrad, U.S.S.R.

LEONARD, F., Program Head, Chemistry, Psychopharmacology Service Center, National Institute of Mental Health, National Institutes of Health, Bethesda, Maryland.

MANDELL, A., Assistant Professor, Department of Psychiatry, University of California School of Medicine, Center for Health Sciences, Los Angeles, California.

MUDD, S. H., Laboratory of General and Comparative Biochemistry, National Institute of Mental Health, National Institutes of Health, Bethesda, Maryland.

PERRY, T. L., Associate Professor, Department of Pharmacology, The University of British Columbia, Faculty of Medicine, Vancouver 8, Canada.

PSCHEIDT, G. R., Thudichum Psychiatric Research Laboratory, Galesburg State Research Hospital, Galesburg, Illinois.

RICHTER, D., Medical Research Council Laboratories, Woodmansterne Road, Carshalton, Surrey, England.

RIDGES, A. P., Department of Medicine, University of Liverpool, Ashton Street, Liverpool, England.

SCHILDKRAUT, J. J., Laboratory of Clinical Science, National Institute of Mental Health, National Institutes of Health, Bethesda, Maryland.

SMYTHIES, J. R., Senior Lecturer, Department of Psychological Medicine, University of Edinburgh, Edinburgh 8, Scotland.

SNYDER, S. H., Laboratory of Clinical Science, National Institute of Mental Health, National Institutes of Health, Bethesda, Maryland.

SPAIDE, J. K., Thudichum Psychiatric Research Laboratory, Galesburg State Research Hospital, Galesburg, Illinois.

SPRINCE, H., Chief Research Biochemist, Veterans Administration Hospital, Coatesville, Pennsylvania.

STRAUGHAN, D. W., Department of Psychiatry, University of Edinburgh, Edinburgh, Scotland.

SZARA, S., Chief, Section on Psychopharmacology, Clinical Neuropharmacology Research Center, CI, IR, NIMH, William A. White Building, Saint Elizabeth's Hospital, Washington 20, D.C.

WAISMAN, H. A., Professor of Pediatrics, University of Wisconsin Medical Center, Madison, Wisconsin.

PREFACE

THIS Preface, as usual, is written after all the rest of this volume had been put together, and in retrospect certain events in the achievement of this production are outstanding. In the first place, the project is the brainchild of John Smythies, who drew into it first Seymour Kety and then Harold Himwich, so that the final product reflects the combined endeavours of three different laboratories, all, however, deeply involved in the problem of schizophrenia. The wherewithal to make this project possible came from Grant No. MH 10999–01 and we are happy to acknowledge our gratitude to the National Institutes of Health. In all the many transactions involved in attaining the necessary funds, the procedures were greatly facilitated by the understanding cooperation and know-how of Dr. Daniel Efron, who also contributed significantly to the scientific discussions following presentation of papers. The encouragement and good offices of Dr. Thomas T. Tourlentes, Superintendent of the Galesburg State Research Hospital, in obtaining our grant, and the administrative cooperation of Miss Florence O. Johnson, Assistant Superintendent of the hospital, were invaluable.

This project was made possible by the good will and cooperation from many other sources. Perhaps first among them we should thank Mrs. Helena Lemp who made available at low costs the services, built up over a matter of years by the Federation of American Societies for Experimental Biology, in the recording of the discussions following the papers. The reader will see that they added significantly to the information contained within this volume. We found the management of the Dennis Hotel to be reasonable and helpful and we are happy to acknowledge this cooperation. In the management of the actual meetings, Dr. Williamina A. Himwich helped unobtrusively in many ways, and for one thing made it possible for Harold Himwich to act as Chairman during the second day of the meeting, undisturbed by exigencies associated with administrative detail. Seymour Kety not only was the Chairman on the first day of the meeting, but the reader will find a brilliant Summary and a heuristic hypothesis from his pen. The keynoter of the meeting was John Smythies who very ably set the groundwork for the discussions to follow in the Introduction. Without the cooperative efforts of all these individuals and others as well, this contribution could not have taken place, nor could we have had the informative and stimulating presentations and discussions enjoyed by the participants. We would like to believe that much of the exhilarating feeling which comes from the viewing of new vistas will be shared by the readers of this volume.

INTRODUCTION

J. R. SMYTHIES

Department of Psychological Medicine, University of Edinburgh, Scotland

THE AIMS of this present Symposium are to survey and discuss the possible biochemical basis of schizophrenia, with particular regard to the role that certain amines may play. The last ten years has witnessed a quantity of work in this field and I think it is fair to say that modest progress has been made. By this I do not mean that we can yet say with conviction what *are* the biochemical bases of schizophrenia, manic-depressive psychosis and kindred diseases. But we do have at last some interesting data and working hypotheses in this field and this enables us to give a reasonable account of what *could be* the biochemical mechanisms involved. These hypotheses account for the known phenomena and can be tested by experiment. Much of this Symposium will be concerned with attempts so to test these hypotheses. It may be helpful at this point to distinguish between: (1) demonstrated facts, (2) working hypotheses, and (3) experimental data still *sub judice*.

(1) The *demonstrated facts* I would take to be as follows:

(i) Three important amines—norepinephrine, serotonin and dopamine—occur in the brain, together with the enzymes for their syntheses and breakdown. Furthermore, the first two occur particularly in those parts of the brain concerned with emotion and the higher control of learning, motivation and behaviour (Smythies, 1965) that so manifestly are at fault in the psychoses. These amines presumably play an important role in neuronal function.

(ii) There is a group of drugs that produces psychoses in man. These reactions are somewhat similar, allowing for the many different environmental and situational parameters necessarily involved, to certain schizophrenic syndromes. These drugs include such agents as mescaline, dimethyltryptamine, psilocyn and LSD.

(iii) The agents in group (ii) are all either N-methyl or O-methyl derivatives of the neurohumours listed in (i). O-methylation is a normal route of metabolism in the body for catecholamines and Axelrod has discovered in mammalian tissues an N-methylating enzyme (capable of turning tryptamine into dimethyltryptamine).

(2) The three main *hypotheses* in this field, arising naturally from these established facts, are as follows:

(i) The hypothesis put forward in 1952 by Harley-Mason, Osmond and Smythies, based on the chemical relationship between mescaline and norepinephrine, suggested that schizophrenia may be associated with an abnormality of O-methylation of norepinephrine with the production in the body of some psychotoxic metabolite such as dimethoxyphenylethanolamine.

(ii) The hypothesis put forward by Gaddum and by Woolley and Shaw in 1954, based on the pharmacological antagonism between LSD and serotonin, that schizophrenia may be associated with some abnormality of serotonin metabolism. This was next developed by Szara and his co-workers, who discovered the psychotomimetic properties of the N-methyl derivatives of tryptamine and its analogs. This suggested that there might be an abnormal N-methylating process in schizophrenia with the production in the body of psychotoxic metabolites such as dimethyltryptamine. Irvine and Page combined these hypotheses to suggest that a compound like serotonin can be both N-methylated and O-methylated to yield a compound like 5-methoxy-N:N-dimethyltryptamine—which they proceeded to demonstrate was a very potent disrupter of conditioned avoidance behaviour in the rat.

(iii) The third hypothesis derives naturally from these first two by a change of emphasis from psychotoxic *compounds* to an aberrant biochemical *process* and was first put on the map by Kety and his co-workers. The basic biochemical mechanism at fault in schizophrenia may be transmethylation (for a variety of possible causes). This disorder of methylation by itself might lead to functional changes in neurones incompatible with their normal function and on the behavioral level with the production of a psychosis. This fault might also lead to the production of abnormally methylated compounds of the types already described which would aggravate the situation by adding their own psychotoxic effects to the neuronal function already disordered by the abnormal transmethylating mechanism.[1]

These three hypotheses can be called for convenience:

(i) the catechol amine hypothesis;

(ii) the tryptamine hypothesis, and, at a more profound level of generalization;

(iii) the transmethylation hypothesis.

[1] Smythies, J. R. (1965) *The Neurological Foundations of Psychiatry*, Oxford, Blackwell, 1965.

(3) An important topic for discussion at this meeting therefore must consist of the *experimental data* that have been put forward in attempts to confirm, refute, or generally test, these hypotheses. This data consist of the following:

(i) The experiments I have already referred to by Pollin, Cardon and Kety who showed that feeding the methyl-donor methionine to schizophrenics made their symptoms worse. This work has been confirmed by Brune and Himwich, and by Sprince's group. These findings have been further developed by Brune and Himwich. Methione has other functions besides being a methyl-donor and one of these other functions might have been responsible for exacerbating the schizophrenic symptoms. Brune and Himwich therefore fed another methyl-donor of a different chemical family—betaine. This also made schizophrenic symptoms worse. Therefore, the transmethylation hypothesis received support.

(ii) The reports by Friedhoff and Van Winkle that it is possible to isolate a metabolite predicted by theory (i) from schizophrenic urine—namely dimethoxyphenylethylamine (the di-O-methyl derivative of dopamine rather than norepinephrine). This is not apparently a normal metabolite. This report has been entirely confirmed by three groups (two of which are represented at this meeting) and partially confirmed by Takesada *et al.* It has been denied by Perry's group which is also represented at this meeting.

(iii) The experiments from Himwich's laboratory showing that certain amines particularly tryptamine are excreted in excess during a psychotic attack, and the levels returning to normal in the individual with clinical remission.

(iv) The reports that the plasma of schizophrenic patients is more toxic than the plasma of normal individuals (as measured by a variety of biological test mechanisms—particularly learned behaviour in rats as measured by the group led by Jack Bergen at the Worcester Foundation). This toxic agent may be a small molecule (perhaps an abnormal biogenic amine) linked to plasma protein.

Some of the papers to be presented at this Symposium will discuss these facts, these hypotheses and this experimental data directly—and we are most fortunate to have most of the people who have been active in this field present. Other papers will be concerned with biochemical data basic to these formulations. It therefore gives me much pleasure to hand over to our Chairman for today's proceedings, Dr. Seymour Kety.

STRUCTURE–ACTIVITY RELATIONSHIPS OF MESCALINE

J. R. Smythies and E. A. Sykes

Department of Psychological Medicine, University of Edinburgh, Scotland

It is generally agreed that mescaline produces a state of psychosis that has certain similarities to some aspects of the schizophrenic syndrome. It would therefore be of some theoretical interest for biological psychiatry to know on what biochemical system mescaline exerts its effects. One way of studying this is by the structure–activity relationships (SAR) method. We have explored the effect of various analogs of mescaline on animal behaviour. In our early work we used the Winter and Flataker test; latterly we have employed the conditioned-avoidance response (CAR).

Our first task was to determine the effects of mescaline itself on the CAR as the base-line for our subsequent studies. The literature at that date was somewhat confusing. Cook and Weidley (1957) using a pole-jump escape technique had failed to block the CAR in rats with dosages up to 100 mg/kg. Chorover (1960), however, using a shuttle box extinguished the CAR with a dosage of 25 mg/kg.

In our experiments we have used a shuttle box with a buzzer as the conditioned stimulus (CS) and shock as the unconditioned stimulus (UCS). The buzzer-shock interval was 5 sec and the rat had to learn to cross from one compartment of the box to the other within these 5 sec to avoid the shock. Normally this was quickly learned and the rat would cross with a regular buzzer-cross reaction time (RT) of some 4 sec. This leaves scope for detecting both an increase in RT (as produced by CPZ) or a decrease in RT (as produced typically by amphetamine). Each 2-hr experimental period consisted of seven runs of twenty trials each. The trials were randomly spaced and occupied 8 min, and were followed by 5 min time-out. We recorded the number of shocks received and the RT. The injection (of drug or saline) was given between the second and third runs. The first two runs in any experiment were discarded as the animals took some minutes to adapt to the experimental situation (and hence a few shocks were delivered before the CR and RT became stabilized). A series of saline controls was followed by a drug run and then another saline control. The results are expressed in D–S scores, i.e. as the difference between the drug score and the mean of the preceding and following saline scores for each "run" of twenty trials. The statistical significance of the results was assessed by Wilcoxon's non-parametric ranking method for paired replicates.

RESULTS

Mescaline has a biphasic effect on CAR performance. Different animals show widely different degrees of susceptibility to the drug. At 25 mg/kg the drug first inhibits the CAR (increased RT and shocks). This is followed by a *decrease* in RT (Fig. 1). Some animals are more sensitive than others, and Fig. 2 shows the reaction of the most sensitive ($n = 4$), and Fig. 3 that of the least sensitive ($n = 4$). At 12·5 mg/kg the inhibitory phase is less marked or absent and the excitatory phase is more marked. At these dosage levels there were no signs of ataxia or "toxic" effects of the drug. This was confirmed by

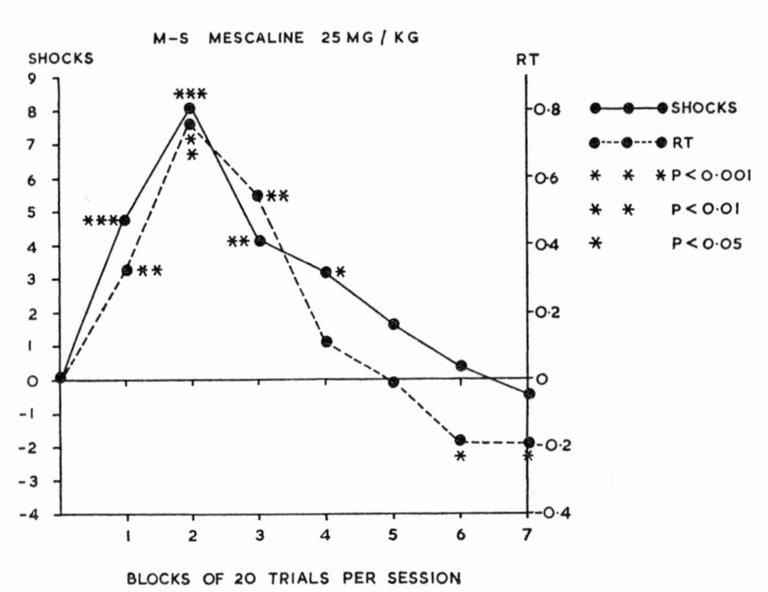

FIG. 1. The effect of mescaline 25 mg/kg on shocks and reaction time (RT: expressed in mm of kymograph paper; 1 mm = 2·5 sec).

the Rushton–Steinberg test for ataxia which showed no ataxia at 25 mg/kg. At 50 mg/kg, however, signs of paralysis of the hind legs appeared, so it seems that 25 mg/kg should normally be the maximum dose.

One first analog was trimethoxyphenylalanine (Fig. 4) which we supposed might cross the blood-brain barrier more easily than mescaline. However, it proved almost completely inactive even in a dosage of 100 mg/kg. This may be correlated with the report (Blaschko, 1965) that this substance is not a substrate for decarboxylase.

We then investigated two compounds: 3–4,dimethoxyphenylethylamine (d.m.p.e.) and N,N-dimethylmescaline (Fig. 4). The former was chosen because of its current interest as a possible abnormal metabolite in schizophrenia. Figures 5–7 show its effect on the CAR at 25, 50 and 100 mg/kg.

At each dose level there were two notable features about its effects: (i) it inhibited the CAR with little sign of the later excitatory action of mescaline, and (ii) the degree of inhibition has a bimodal distribution. This is not due to compounding the results from two populations of rats, one of which reacts earlier than the other, as Fig. 8 indicates that this "double hump" is present in the individual records from every rat. This suggests that the action of the drug itself may be followed by that of some metabolite. It is an effect that we

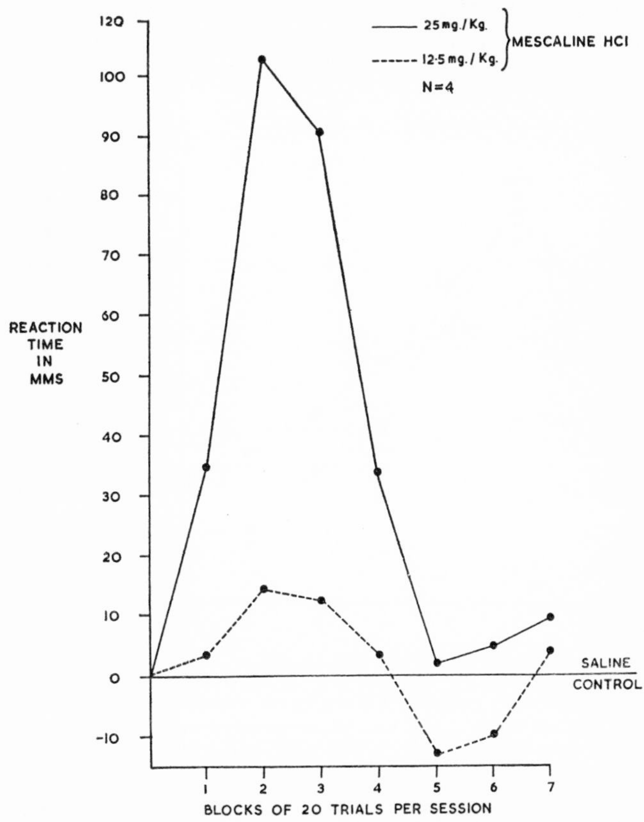

FIG. 2. The effect of two doses of mescaline on RT: Class I animals ($n = 4$).

have seen reported for no other drug. However, one of us (*in* Berger *et al.*, 1960) working at the Worcester Foundation on the effect of plasma protein fractions from schizophrenic patients on a mouse behaviour test, noted a very similar effect, as shown in Fig. 9. The test was a modification for mice of the Winter and Flataker test, and the same bimodal curve is noticeable. The difference in time course may be accounted for by the different metabolic rates of rats and mice. This suggests that the active fraction in toxic schizophrenic serum, shown by the Worcester group to be a small molecule, may

25 mg. / Kg
12·5 mg. / Kg
MESCALINE HCl
N = 4
REACTION TIME IN MMS
40
30
20
10
0
-10
-20
SALINE CONTROL
1
2
3
4
5
6
7
BLOCKS OF 20 TRIALS PER SESSION

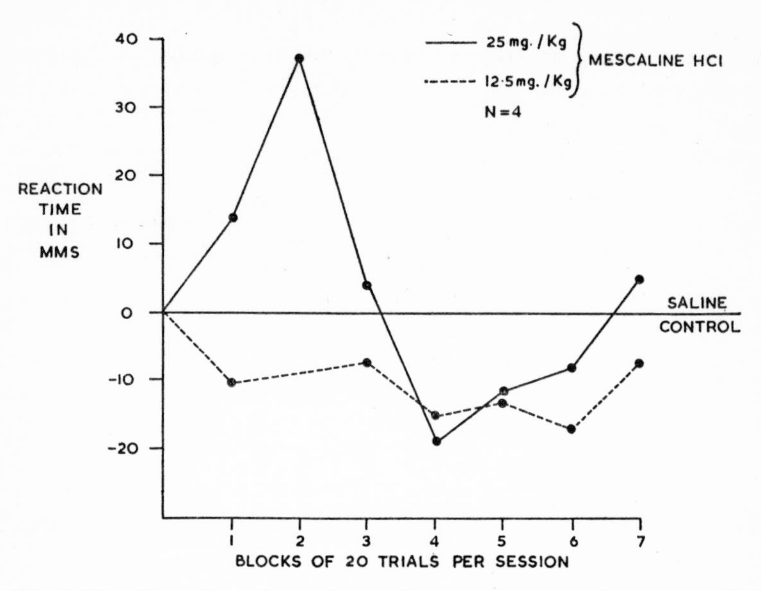

FIG. 3. The effect of two doses of mescaline on RT: Class II animals ($n = 4$).

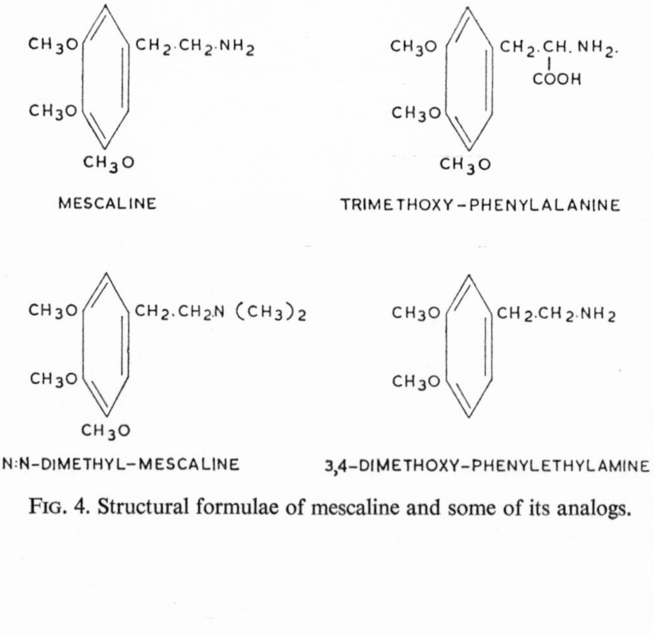

CH3O
CH3O
CH3O
CH2.CH2.NH2
MESCALINE
CH3O
CH3O
CH3O
CH2.CH.NH2.
COOH
TRIMETHOXY-PHENYLALANINE
CH3O
CH3O
CH3O
CH2.CH2N (CH3)2
N:N-DIMETHYL-MESCALINE
CH3O
CH3O
CH2.CH2.NH2
3,4-DIMETHOXY-PHENYLETHYLAMINE

FIG. 4. Structural formulae of mescaline and some of its analogs.

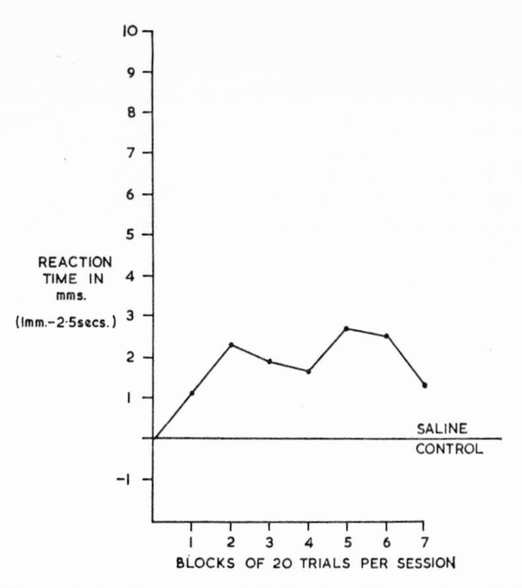

FIG. 5. The effect of dimethoxyphenylethylamine (d.m.p.e.) on RT: 25 mg/kg ($n = 8$).

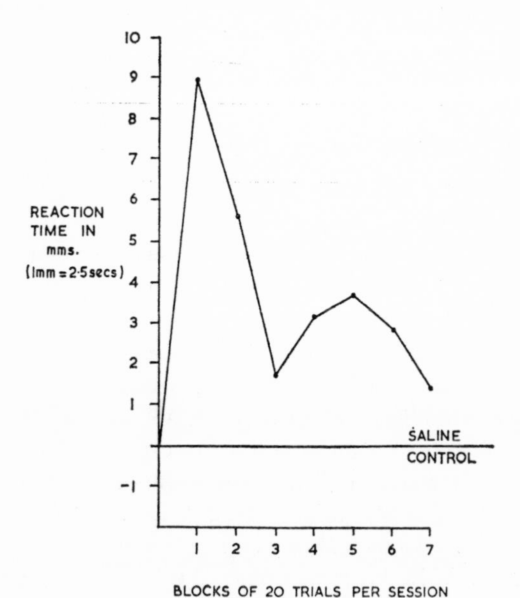

FIG. 6. The effect of dimethoxyphenylethylamine (d.m.p.e.) on RT: 50 mg/kg ($n = 8$).

possibly be d.m.p.e. (tied loosely to the globulin). At any rate, this working hypothesis suggests experiments to confirm or refute it. D.m.p.e. on this test was about one-half as active as mescaline in inhibiting the CAR, a result obtained in previous work (Smythies and Levy, 1960). A dose of 12·5 mg/kg had no observable effect, neither excitatory nor inhibitory.

We investigated N,N-dimethylmescaline to explore the idea that increasing methylation increases behaviour-disrupting potency, and keeping the strongly hallucinogenic effects of N,N-dimethyl derivatives of tryptamine and 4- and 5-

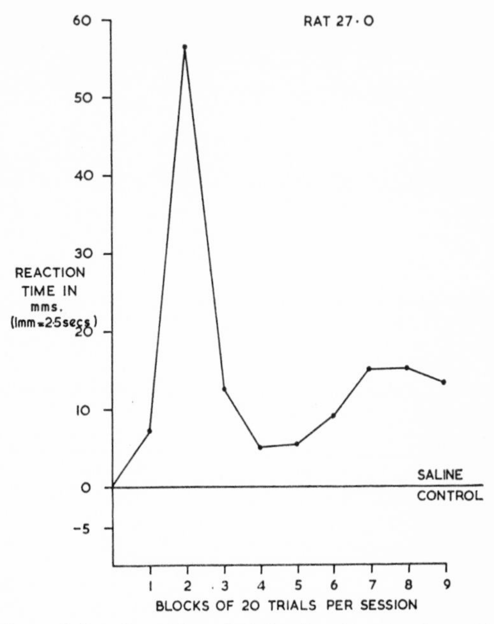

FIG. 7. The effect of dimethoxyphenylethylamine (d.m.p.e.) on RT: 100 mg/kg ($n = 1$).

hydroxytryptamine in mind. Figs. 10–12 show the result at 25, 50 and 100 mg/kg. These results indicate that this compound has a strong "excitatory" (amphetamine-like) effect on rat behaviour, decreasing the RT, but it has none of mescaline's inhibitory effect on the CAR even at 100 mg/kg.

Our next experiments were directed towards estimating the degree of cross-tolerance between mescaline and these two compounds as measured by this test. Our procedure here was to give drug *X* alone to a group of animals. Two weeks later 25 mg/kg mescaline was given every day for 7 days, followed by a second dose of *X*. In this period marked tolerance develops to mescaline (Figs. 13, 14). The primary inhibition in the CAR is abolished or greatly attenuated (depending on the initial sensibility of the rat), whereas the second "excitatory phase" becomes more prominent or unmarked. This differential effect of tolerance on the two actions of mescaline is itself of interest.

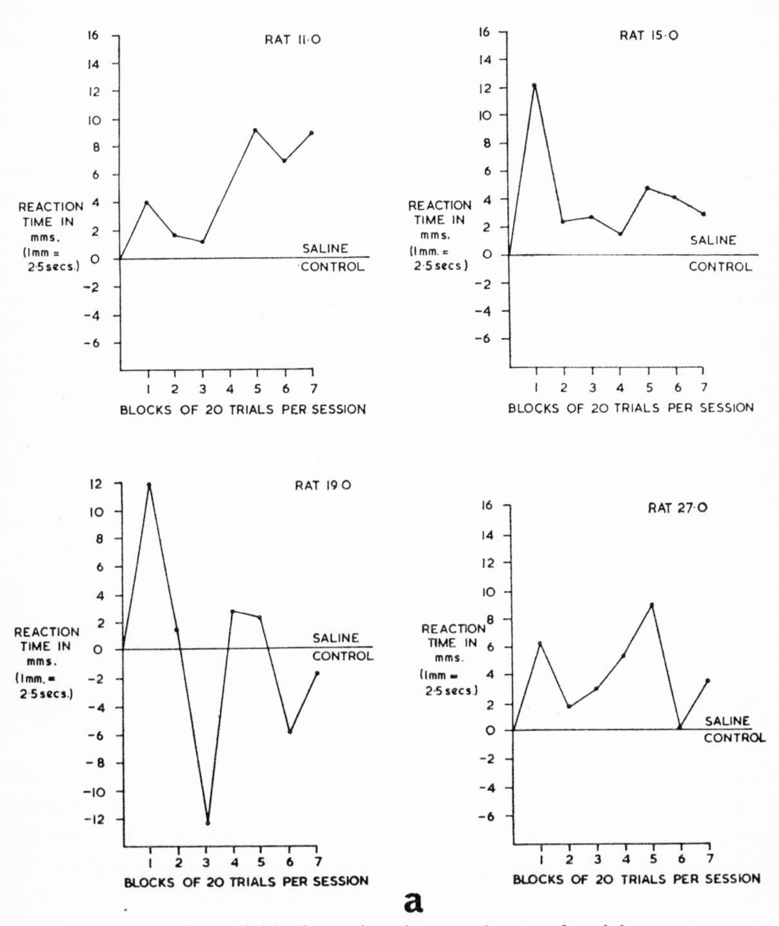

FIG. 8 (a, b). Individual reaction times to d.m.p.e. for eight rats.

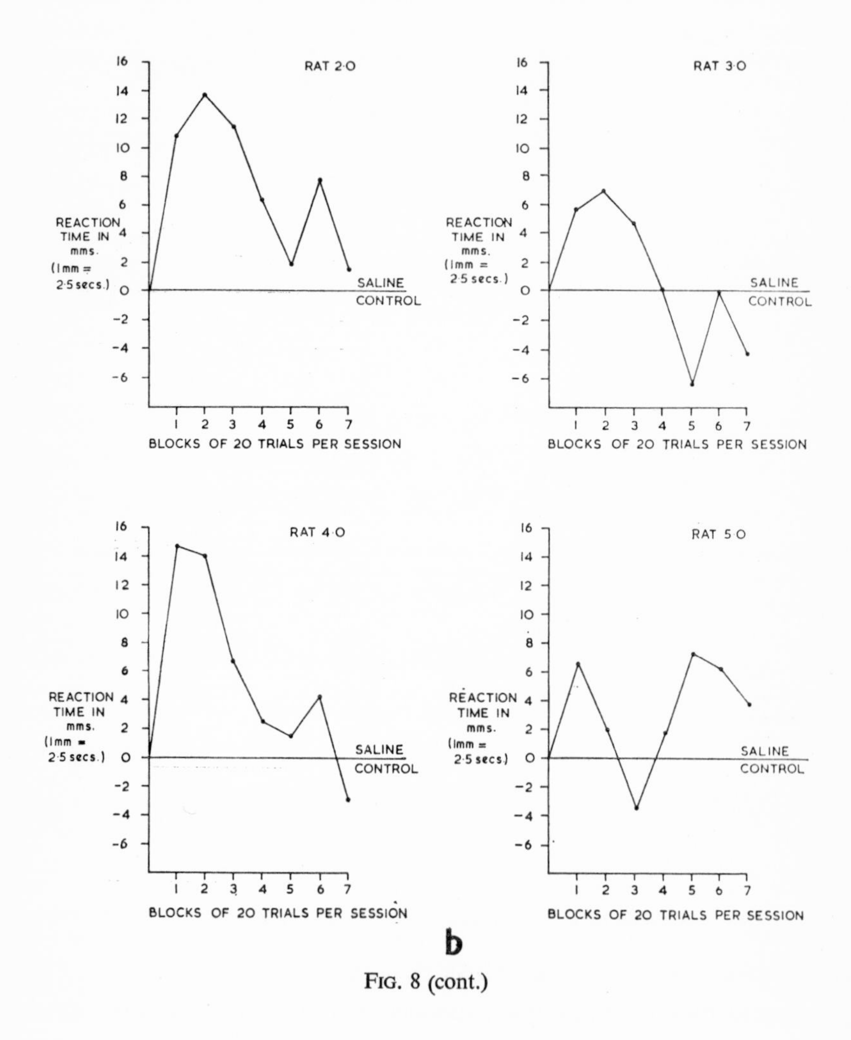
RAT 2·O
RAT 3·O
RAT 4·O
RAT 5·O
REACTION TIME IN mms. (1mm = 2·5 secs.)
SALINE CONTROL
BLOCKS OF 20 TRIALS PER SESSION
16
14
12
10
8
6
4
2
0
−2
−4
−6
1 2 3 4 5 6 7
b

FIG. 8 (cont.)

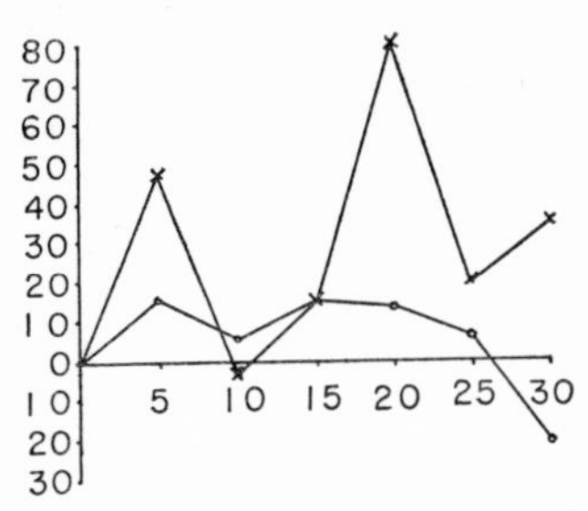

FIG. 9. Mean change in climbing time per set of twenty mice, expressed as schizophrenic score minus control score. ×–×–× : using plasma protein fractions shown to be most active by Bergen; ○–○–○: using fractions chosen at random (from *Archives of Neurology*, **2,** 146–50, 1960).

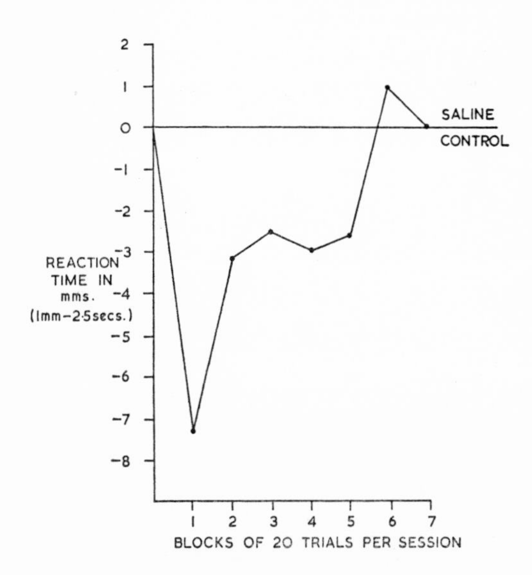

FIG. 10. The effect of N,N-dimethylmescaline (DMM) on RT: 25 mg/kg (n = 4).

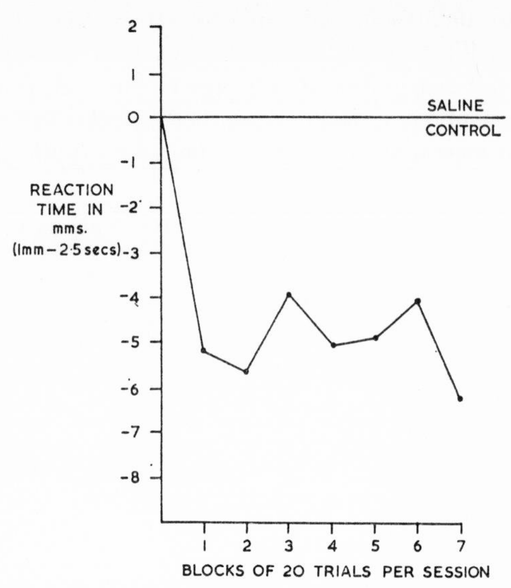

FIG. 11. The effect of N,N-dimethylmescaline (DMM) on RT: 50 mg/kg ($n = 4$).

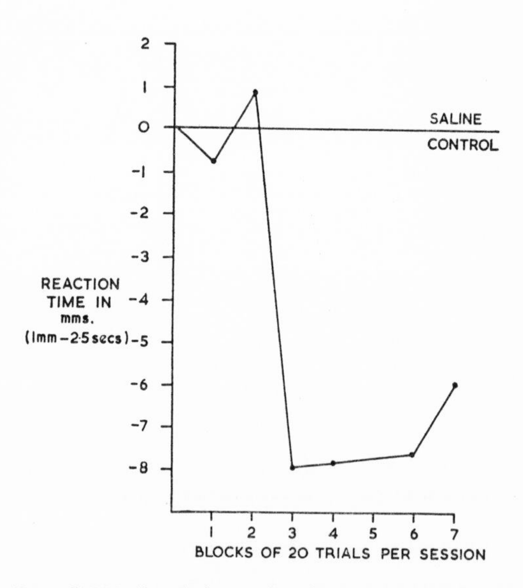

FIG. 12. The effect of N,N-dimethylmescaline (DMM) on RT: 100 mg/kg ($n = 4$).

Figure 15 gives the results for cross-tolerance between mescaline and d.m.p.e. The total RT increase is not changed to a statistically significant extent. The bimodal distribution is still present but each peak is delayed in time by 1 block (i.e. about 13 min). Thus, there appears to be no clear cross-tolerance between mescaline and d.m.p.e., but some subtle effect is possibly

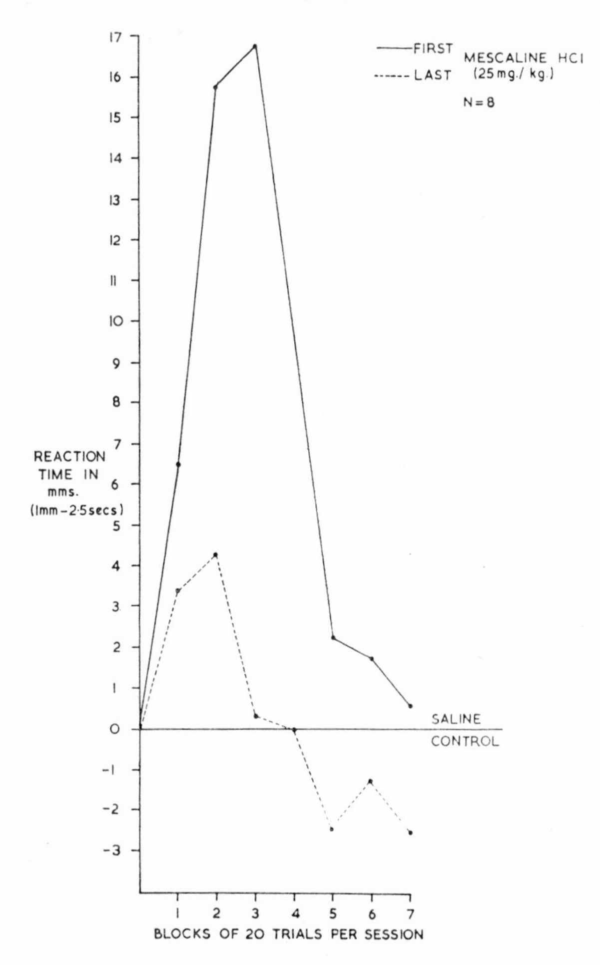

FIG. 13. The development of mescaline tolerance (25 mg/kg) showing effect on RT of first and last of eight successive doses (DMPE groups) ($n = 8$).

suggested by this shift in the peak time. Figure 16 gives the results for cross-tolerance between mescaline and N,N-dimethylmescaline (DMM). This gives a figure of some 40% cross-tolerance. Studies on the reverse tolerance between these compounds and mescaline are proceeding.

From previous work (Peretz *et al.*, 1955; Smythies and Levy, 1960) one can say that α-methyl substitution doubles activity. The 4-methoxy group is necessary for activity as substitution by an hydroxyl abolishes activity, whereas a larger benzyloxy group here increases activity.

Our current programme is (i) to determine to what extent the biphasic mode of action of mescaline in this test is specific—e.g. is it shared by other similar

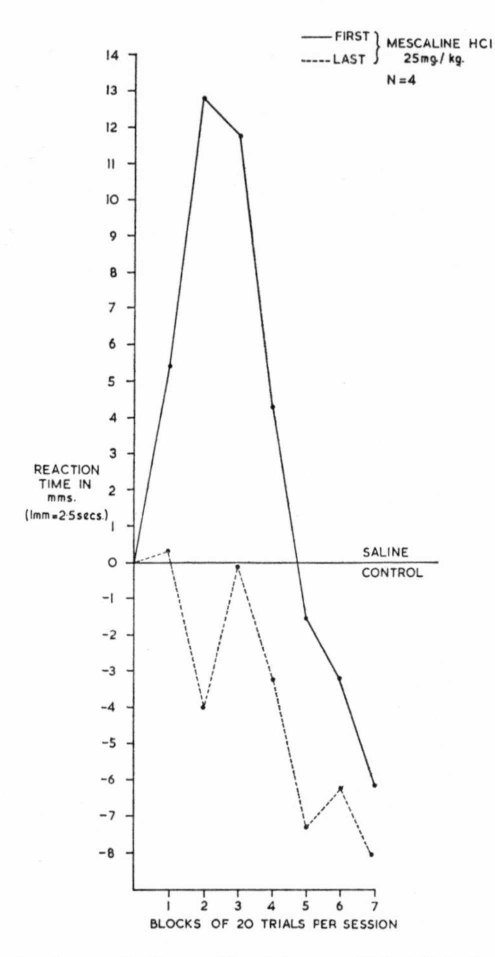

FIG. 14. The development of mescaline tolerance (25 mg/kg) showing effect on RT of first and last of eight successive doses (DMM group) (n = 4).

hallucinogens such as LSD, psilocybin and trimethoxyamphetamine, or is it shared by any non-hallucinogenic compounds?—(ii) to attempt to increase the potency of action of mescaline-like compounds by increasing their liquid solubility (e.g. 3,4,5-trifluophenylethylamine), (iii) by widening our biological testing methods to include ethological and other techniques.

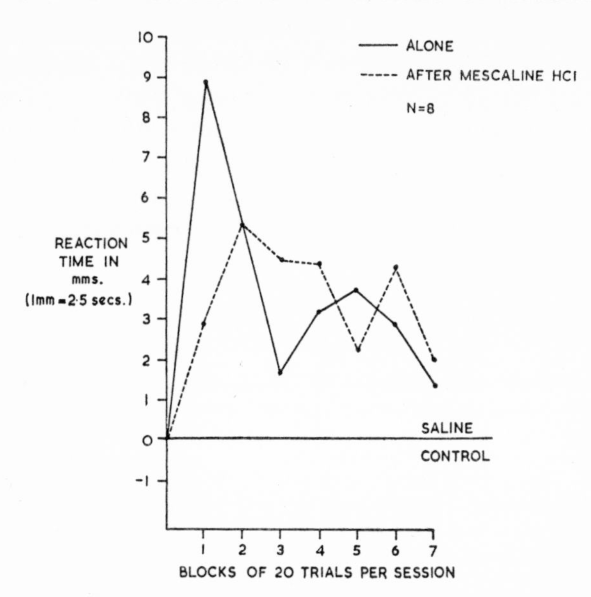

FIG. 15. Cross-tolerance study between mescaline and d.m.p.e. The effect of d.m.p.e. (50 mg/kg) on RT: (i) alone, (ii) after development of the degree of mescaline tolerance shown in Fig. 13.

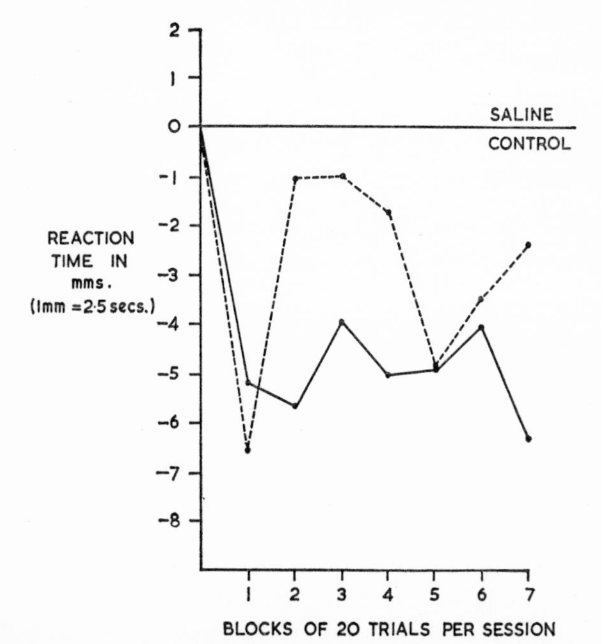

FIG. 16. Cross-tolerance study between mescaline and DMM. The effect of DMM (50 mg/kg) on RT: (i) alone, (ii) after development of the degree of mescaline tolerance shown in Fig. 14.

ACKNOWLEDGMENT

This work was carried out with the aid of grants from the Advisory Committee on Medical Research, the Medical Research Council and the Smith, Kline and French Foundation. We are also grateful to Roche Products Ltd., in particular to Dr. J. Marks and Dr. Cohen, for the kind gift of the compounds tested and to Professor G. M. Carstairs for his encouragement and support of this research programme.

REFERENCES

BERGEN, J. R., PENNELL, R. B., FREEMAN, H., HOAGLAND, H. and SMYTHIES, J. R. (1960) Rat behavior changes in response to a blood factor from normal and psychotic persons, *Archives Neurology*, **2,** 146–50.

BLASCHKO, H. (1965) personal communication.

CHOROVER, S. L. (1960) The effects of mescaline on several behavior patterns in the rat, a psychopharmacological study. Unpublished Ph.D. thesis, New York University.

COOK, L. and WEIDLEY, E. (1957) Behavioral effects of some pharmacological agents, *Annals of the New York Academy of Sciences*, **66,** 740–56.

PERETZ, D., SMYTHIES, J. R. and GIBSON, W. C. (1955) A new hallucinogen: 3·4·5-trimethoxyphenylisopropylamine, *Journal of Mental Science*, **101,** 317–29.

SMYTHIES, J. R. and LEVY, C. K. (1960) The comparative pyschopharmacology of some mescaline analogues, *Journal of Mental Science*, **106,** 531–6.

NEW DEVELOPMENTS IN THE INVESTIGATION OF THE RELATIONSHIP OF 3,4-DIMETHOXYPHENYLETHYLAMINE TO SCHIZOPHRENIA[1]

ARNOLD J. FRIEDHOFF and ELNORA VAN WINKLE

Center for the Study of Acute Psychotic Disorders, Department of Psychiatry and Neurology, New York University School of Medicine, N.Y.C.

FOR A number of years we have been investigating the metabolism of dopamine because of the possible relationship of this compound to the function of the nervous system. The finding that dopamine was concentrated in the brain in structures relating to the extrapyramidal system (Bertler, 1961) led to several investigations of the possible role of this compound in extrapyramidal function (Ehringer and Hornykiewicz, 1960; Friedhoff *et al.*, 1963). Subsequently, the widely made observation that all effective antipsychotic drugs regardless of their chemical structure were capable of producing disturbances in extrapyramidal function stimulated further interest in the possible involvement of dopamine in the genesis of psychotic disorders.

With these findings in mind, we decided to undertake, in 1961, a study of urine obtained from schizophrenic patients and normal controls in order to look for possible differences in the excretion of metabolites of dopamine and other catecholamines. In our first group of nineteen schizophrenic patients and fourteen normal controls we found that a compound which we subsequently identified as 3,4-dimethoxyphenylethylamine (DMPEA) was present in urine of fifteen schizophrenic patients and in none of the normal controls (Friedhoff and Van Winkle, 1962a, b). Since our original studies we have identified DMPEA in more than 250 urine samples obtained from schizophrenic patients. A number of these determinations were made on samples obtained from the same patients on different days. It has not been possible to obtain completely quantitative data from the paper chromatographic methods used, but the day-to-day variations in the same patients were small. Of the schizophrenic patients studied, all demonstrated classical symptoms of acute schizophrenia and approximately 70% of this group of patients was found to excrete DMPEA.

Since we originally discovered DMPEA in urine from schizophrenic

[1] This research was supported by U.S.P.H. Research Career Development Award No. MSF–14024 to Dr. Friedhoff; N.I.M.H. Grant No. MH–08618, and a grant from the Schweppe Foundation.

patients we have confirmed its identity by a number of means. The urinary compound has been shown to co-chromatograph with authentic DMPEA in six solvent systems. A large number of color reactions were used which were identical in result for both the unknown and authentic compound. In addition, a specific test for phenylethylamines was developed (Friedhoff and Van Winkle, 1963a) which reacted only with beta phenylethylamines or beta phenylethylamino acids substituted only on the ring. The specificity of this reaction was studied against forty closely related compounds. We have further characterized DMPEA by means of thin layer chromatography, gas chromatography and the preparation of derivatives. By the extraction of multiple 24-hr urine specimens obtained from schizophrenic patients, we were able to isolate and purify by extraction and paper chromatography enough DMPEA to obtain a melting point on micro amounts of this compound (as the hydrochloride, m.p. 152–157°C, 153–155°C; authentic compound, 152–156°C).

Since our original report investigators in several other laboratories have confirmed our findings that DMPEA is present in the urine of schizophrenics (Takesada *et al.*, 1963; Kuehl *et al.*, 1964; Sen and McGeer, 1964) although there is disagreement as to whether it is also excreted by normals or other types of patients.

Recently we have demonstrated that dopamine infused into the schizophrenic patients can be converted to 3,4-dimethoxyphenylacetic acid (Friedhoff and Van Winkle, 1963b). We have subsequently demonstrated that DMPEA administered to schizophrenic patients is rapidly converted to 3,4-dimethoxyphenylacetic acid (Friedhoff and Hollister, 1965). It has also been possible to obtain preliminary evidence that dopamine can be converted to 3,4-dimethoxyphenylacetic acid using liver obtained by biopsy from schizophrenic patients as a source of enzyme (Friedhoff and Van Winkle, 1963b). Similar findings with liver obtained from autopsy have been made and details of these experiments will be published. These results suggest that a previously undescribed transmethylation reaction can occur that results in the formation of a di-O-methylated derivative of dopamine.

Other studies have been carried out recently that may demonstrate a relationship between methylation and schizophrenia. Pollin *et al.*, 1961 and Brune and Himwich, 1962, have demonstrated that the ingestion of methionine results in an exacerbation of symptoms of schizophrenic patients. It is of considerable interest that methionine is the precursor of the methyl-donor in the methylations that we have described although it is not known that feeding excess methionine can in fact increase the rate of formation of DMPEA. In addition, DMPEA has been shown to have marked effects on the central nervous system of animals. These effects are similar to those occasioned by mescaline administration and include the production of so-called catatonia in cats and mice (Noteboom, 1934; Michaux and Verly, 1963).

In order to investigate the possibility that DMPEA found in urine from schizophrenic patients was not, in fact, related to schizophrenia, we considered factors such as diet, activity, intestinal flora, drug ingestion, toothpaste and smoking. However, it is apparent that endless possibilities exist for an artefactual relationship between DMPEA and schizophrenia. It was clear that adequate studies of all possible sources of DMPEA could be carried out only with great difficulty. For this reason we decided to explore further the pathways for the formation of the methylated compounds that we have described.

The illness, schizophrenia, is undoubtedly a complex resultant of endogenous and exogenous factors. Crash programs designed to answer the question, "Does DMPEA cause schizophrenia?" are not likely to unravel these relationships. It seems to us that the nature of schizophrenia will be delineated only by the orderly and systematic development of metabolic and biochemical aspects of this disorder and their interaction with psychological phenomena.

REFERENCES

BERTLER, A. (1961) Occurrence and localization of catechol amines in human brain, *Acta. Physiol. Scand.* **51,** 97–107.

BRUNE, G. G. and HIMWICH, H. E. (1962) Effects of methione loading on the behavior of schizophrenic patients, *J. Nerv. and Ment. Dis.* **134,** 447–50.

EHRINGER, H. and HORNYKIEWICZ, O. (1960) Distribution of noradrenaline and dopamine in human brain and its relation to diseases of extrapyramidal system, *Klin. Wschr.* **38,** 1236–9.

FRIEDHOFF, A. J., HEKIMIAN, L., ALPERT, M. and TOBACH, E. (1963) Dihydroxyphenylalanine in extrapyramidal disease, *J.A.M.A.* **184,** 285–6.

FRIEDHOFF, A. J. and HOLLISTER, L. (1965) unpublished data.

FRIEDHOFF, A. J. and VAN WINKLE, E. (1962a) Isolation and characterization of a compound from the urine of schizophrenics, *Nature,* **194,** 897–8.

FRIEDHOFF, A. J. and VAN WINKLE, E. (1962b) The characteristics of an amine found in the urine of schizophrenic patients, *J. Nerv. and Ment. Dis.* **135,** 550–5.

FRIEDHOFF, A. J. and VAN WINKLE, E. (1963a) A method for the detection of β-phenylethylamines and β-phenylethylamino acids, *J. Chromatog.* **11,** 272–4.

FRIEDHOFF, A. J. and VAN WINKLE, E. (1963b) Conversion of dopamine to 3,4-dimethoxyphenylacetic acid in schizophrenic patients, *Nature,* **199,** 1271–2.

KUEHL, F. A., HICHENS, M., ORMOND, R. E., MEISINGER, M. A. P., GALE, P. H., CIRILLO, V. J. and BRINK, N. G. (1964) Para O-methylation of dopamine in schizophrenic and normal individuals, *Nature,* **203,** 154.

MICHAUX, R. and VERLY, W. G. (1963) Action catalepsigne des ethers methyliques des mono- et polyphenolamines, *Life Sciences,* No. 3, 175–83.

NOTEBOOM, L. (1934) Experimental catatonia by means of derivatives of mescaline and adrenaline, *Proc. Acad. Sci. Amsterdam,* **37,** 562–74.

POLLIN, W., CARDON, P. V. and KETY, S. S. (1961) Effects of amino acid feedings in schizophrenic patients treated with iproniazid, *Science,* **133,** 104.

SEN, N. P. and MCGEER, P. L. (1964) 4-Methoxyphenylethylamine and 3,4-dimethoxyphenylethylamine in human urine, *Biochem. and Biophys. Res. Comm.* **14,** 227–32.

TAKESADA, M., KAKIMOTO, Y., SANO, I. and KANEKO, Z. (1963) 3,4-Dimethoxyphenylethylamine and other amines in the urine of schizophrenic patients, *Nature,* **199,** 203–4.

PARA-O-METHYLATION OF DOPAMINE IN SCHIZOPHRENIC AND NORMAL INDIVIDUALS

FREDERICK A. KUEHL, JR.

Merck Sharp & Dohme Research Laboratories, Rahway, N.J.

DERANGEMENTS of amino-acid metabolism have been implicated in a variety of mental disorders (Sourkes, 1962). In particular, recent investigations have drawn our attention to a possible aberrant para-O-methylation of 3,4-dihydroxyphenethylamine (dopamine) in schizophrenia. Friedhoff and Van Winkle (1962) reported that 3,4-dimethoxyphenethylamine is present in urines of schizophrenic patients, but is not excreted by normal subjects. Ernst (1962) found that the 4-O-methyl and 3,4-di-O-methyl derivatives of dopamine provoked a catatonic effect in cats, whereas 3,5-dimethoxy-4-hydroxyphenethylamine was without effect. Michaux and Verley (1963) found 3,4-dimethoxyphenethylamine to be a more potent catatonic agent in mice than 3-methoxy-4-hydroxyphenethylamine. Recently Carlini *et al.* (1965) presented evidence suggesting that experimental catatonia induced by agents possessing the 4-methoxyphenethylamine moiety and the catatonic state observed in human schizophrenics are related to a disturbance of histamine catabolism induced by these compounds in the brain.

Since no satisfactory technique was available for the separation of both di-O-methyl and the isomeric mono-O-methyl ethers of dopamine, a method was developed for this purpose. I will describe the details of the method and studies that this technique permitted, on the para- and meta-O-methylation of dopamine *in vitro* and *in vivo* in normal and schizophrenic individuals.

In our early work with urine samples, neither the chloroform extraction technique and paper-strip chromatographic systems described by Friedhoff and Van Winkle (1962) nor the two-dimensional chromatographic method employed by Takesada *et al.* (1963) were satisfactory. With the former procedure we experienced difficulties with resolution, and could not obtain unequivocal evidence for the presence of 3,4-dimethoxyphenethylamine in the schizophrenic urines. Furthermore, the method was not applicable to the mono-methyl ethers of dopamine since they are not well extracted by chloroform. Using the two-dimensional paper-strip technique of Takesada, we observed diffuse zones and tyramine was not well separated from 3,4-dimethoxyphenethylamine. Our final procedure (Kuehl *et al.*, 1966) for urine specimens involved the ion-exchange resin step of Kakimoto and Armstrong (1962) for the isolation of basic compounds, followed by extraction of the catecholamines with the isoamyl alcohol- toluene mixture employed by Senoh *et al.* (1959). Two-dimensional thin-layer chromatography on silica gel, first employing an acid and then an alkaline solvent system, effected an excellent separation of all three derivatives of dopamine, a direct separation not previously possible in the case of the mono-methyl isomers. With this technique it was possible to detect less than 0·2 μg of 3,4-dimethoxyphenethylamine with ninhydrin, but detection with the Ehrlich-ninhydrin method of Friedhoff and Van Winkle (1963) was less sensitive (1 μg limit), due to highly colored backgrounds that occur with this reagent on silica gel. In order to strengthen the identification of the compounds, two thin-layer plates were ordinarily used for each sample examined and a known amount of dimethoxy compound was added to one of them.

Using this procedure we were unable to find 3,4-dimethoxyphenethylamine in urine specimens of 10 normal individuals, whereas this amine was detected in urines of 7 of 12 acute[1] and 3 of 11 chronic[2] schizophrenics. In the chronic series, excretion was not consistent with individuals on different days. Analysis of urines of chronic schizophrenics treated with monoamine oxidase inhibitors showed a much higher content of catecholamines than the non-treated, but no dimethoxyphenethylamine was found to be present in the limited number examined.

In these studies we could find no evidence for the presence of para-O-methyl derivatives[3] of epinephrine, norepinephrine or dopamine, although the normal meta-O-methyl catabolite of the latter compound, 4-hydroxy-3-methoxyphenethylamine, was readily detected in all cases. We did observe a compound isographic with 3-hydroxy-4-methoxyphenethylamine, and which reacted similarly with dichloroquinone-chlorimide and ninhydrin. However, by eluting this area from the thin-layer plate and rechromatographing in methanol-1-butanol-benzene-water (2:1:1:1) on Whatman 3MM paper pretreated with 2·5% sodium carbonate, it was shown that our tentative identification was incorrect. The compound was not identified further nor was it peculiar to schizophrenic urines.

The results of our examination of urines by this new method are in agreement with the original findings by Friedhoff and Van Winkle (1962) that 3,4-dimethoxyphenethylamine is a metabolic product unique to schizophrenic

[1] We are indebted to Dr. Arnold J. Friedhoff of the New York University School of Medicine for these specimens.

[2] We are indebted to Dr. Nathan Kline of the Rockland State Hospital for these specimens.

[3] We are indebted to Dr. Marvin D. Armstrong of Fels Research Institute and Dr. S. Archer of Sterling-Winthrop Institute for the sample of paranephrine and norparanephrine.

urines. We also confirmed Dr. Friedhoff's statement that the incidence of occurrence of the amine is probably higher in acute cases of schizophrenia than in chronic ones (Friedhoff, 1963). In all cases, however, the amount of amine measured was low, 3–10 μg/day, compared to the 20–50 μg value reported by Friedhoff. The detection of this metabolite by Takesada *et al.* (1963) in both normal and schizophrenic individuals, may be attributable to non-selective methodology, since we found the spot on the paper corresponding to 3,4-dimethoxyphenethylamine in their isolation scheme to contain several components, chiefly tyramine, when eluted and subjected to thin-layer chromatography. Subsequent to these studies, Sen and McGeer (1964) detected this amine in eleven of twenty-two schizophrenics, using a combine paper strip-gas chromatographic technique. They also detected a compound indistinguishable from *p*-methoxyphenethylamine. No examination of normal urines was reported. Recently, Perry *et al.* (1964) reported on their failure to detect the amine in either normal or schizophrenic urines and therefore suggested the possibility that 3,4-dimethoxyphenethylamine may be of dietary origin. The question of dietary origin appears to have been settled, however, by Friedhoff and Van Winkle (1963) who found that di-O-methylation of dopamine occurred *in vitro* when the substrate was incubated with a liver biopsy homogenate obtained from a schizophrenic patient known to excrete 3,4-dimethoxyphenethylamine and further that di-O-methylation of administered labeled dopamine could be demonstrated *in vivo*.

In order to determine whether catechol-O-methyl transferase is capable of di-O-methylating dopamine as well as forming the mono-O-methyl derivatives, the rat liver enzyme system of Axelrod and Tomachick (1959) was studied using dopamine and S-adenosylmethionine-methyl-C^{14} as co-substrates. Aliqots were removed from the reaction mixture at intervals and the methylated products separated by thin-layer chromatography. The results are summarized in Table 1.

In this system, 3-methoxy-4-hydroxyphenethylamine and 3-hydroxy-4-methoxyphenethylamine were formed from dopamine in the ratio of approximately 4 to 1, in good agreement with the *in vitro* values for these compounds reported by Senoh *et al.* (1959). Similar results were obtained with rat-brain enzyme. The relative rates of formation of the two isomeric monomethyl compounds *in vitro* did not change with time during the course of the reaction, and were the same whether a crude or a purified COMT preparation was used. Hence it seems likely that one enzyme is responsible for formation of both isomers. In no case could we find any evidence for the formation of 3,4-dimethoxyphenethylamine with dopamine or its isomeric monomethyl ethers as substrates. Of particular interest was the observation that incorporation of radioactivity occurred when 3-hydroxy-4-methoxy or 4-hydroxy-3-methoxyphenethylamine was incubated with the enzyme and labeled S-adenosyl methionine, more in the case of the former substrate. In each case partial conversion to the isomer occurred. Ordinarily de-O-methylation is associated with a TPNH-dependent cytochrome C reductase, but in our enzyme preparation, purified by ammonium sulfate precipitation and adsorption by calcium phosphate followed by dialysis, no TPNH was added or should have been present. Since thin-layer chromatography of the substrate 3-hydroxy-4-methoxyphenethylamine demonstrated the absence of dopamine, which if present could have accounted for the apparent interconversion, we must conclude that demethylation by a novel mechanism occurs.

In order to more closely approximate *in vivo* conditions, liver and brain specimens from normal and schizophrenic individuals were examined

TABLE 1. MONOMETHYLATION OF DOPAMINE *in vitro*†

Time (min)	Radioactivity of isolated derivatives (c.p.m.)		Ratio
	3-O-methyl derivative	4-O-methyl derivative	
5	1740	431	4·0
10	3177	854	3·7
15	5161	1270	4·1
20	5383	1368	3·9
60	9905	2174	4·6

† A solution of 5 μm dopamine-HCl, 1·0 μm (1·0 μc) S-adenosyl-L-methionine-methyl-^{14}C, 35 μm $MgCl_2$, 0·65 mg rat liver enzyme protein (0·14 units/mg) and 175 μm phosphate buffer in a total volume of 3·6 ml at pH 7·8 was incubated at 37°. The figures given present the radioactive counts of aliquot portions.

(Wagner *et al.*, 1964) for the di-O-methylating enzyme. All autopsy material was immediately frozen in dry ice and stored until used. Tissue was homogenized in isotonic potassium chloride and the 8000 × *g* supernatant was used as the enzyme source. Incubations were carried out as with the rat enzyme except that Catron (α-methylphenethylhydrazine) was added to minimize monoamine oxidase activity. The incubation mixture was extracted with iso-amyl alcohol-toluene, this with dilute alkali to remove the bulk of the phenols, and finally with dilute hydrochloric acid to remove any 3,4-dimethoxy-phenethylamine formed. After subjecting the residue of the acid extract to thin-layer chromatography in the butanol-ethyl acetate-ammonia system previously described, appropriate spots were eluted and subjected to liquid scintillation counting.

From these studies no evidence was obtained for the *in vitro* formation of 3,4-dimethoxyphenethylamine from homogenates[4] of six schizophrenic

[4] We are indebted to Dr. W. Strutton of Rockland State Hospital, Orangeburg, N.Y., Dr. H. E. Himwich of Galesburg State Research Hospital, Galesburg, Ill., and Dr. S. Merlis of Central Islip State Hospital, Islip, N.Y., for the liver specimens; we are also indebted to Dr. J. V. Auditore of Meharry Medical College in Nashville, Tennessee, for the brain specimens, and to Mr. P. Wittreich for the sample of 3,4-dimethoxyphenethylamine-1-^{14}C used to evaluate the methodology.

and three normal liver specimens or from those of four schizophrenic and one normal brain specimens. Normal COMT activity was observed, however, in all cases in varying degrees as indicated in Tables 2 and 3 suggesting, as with the rat *in vitro* studies, that the di-O-methylating enzyme present in schizophrenic liver is distinct from normal COMT.

TABLE 2. RESULTS OF HUMAN LIVER STUDIES

Specimen	Diagnosis	Age (yr)	Sex	Postmortem autopsy interval	Mono-O-methyl dopamine ext. (c.p.m.)	Relative† COMT activity	Di-O-methyl dopamine (c.p.m.)
1	N	2		5 hr	1,057,820	1·00	844
2	N	26	F	4 hr	504,167	0·48	498
3	N			3 hr	957,956	0·91	81
1	S				4,859	0·005	41
2	S				3,269	0·003	0
3	S	77	F	40 hr	411,732	0·39	38
4	S	78	F	8·5 hr	50,273	0·05	36
5	S	75	M	6 days	11,819	0·01	7
6	S	89	F	3 days	262,232	0·25	21

† COMT activity relative to normal liver no. 1 which mono-O-methylated 32·0% of the dopamine substrate.

TABLE 3. RESULTS OF HUMAN BRAIN STUDIES†

Specimen	Diagnosis	Age (yr)	Sex	Postmortem autopsy interval	Mono-O-methyl dopamine ext. (c.p.m.)	Relative COMT activity	Di-O-methyl dopamine (c.p.m.)
3	S	34	M	6–8 hr	32,595	2·06	24
4	N	72	M	6–8 hr	15,751	1·00	11
5	S	74	M	6–8 hr	3,025	0·19	8
6	S		M	6–8 hr	47,572	3·02	36
7	S	48	M	6–8 hr	7,930	0·50	17

† Since the brain enzyme preparations contained twice the amount of tissue used in the liver enzyme preparations, the data in columns 6 and 8 were halved to make them equivalent to the data in Table 1.

COMT activity relative to normal brain no. 4.

Limited studies (Porter, 1964) were undertaken to determine the absorption and distribution of 3,4-dimethoxyphenethylamine in rats.

Male albino rats, weighing about 100 g each, were given single oral doses (6·7 mg/kg) of C^{14}-labeled amine. The animals were maintained in metabolism cages for 24 hr. Urine, feces, gastrointestinal tract contents, carcasses and expired CO_2 were counted. Results are shown in Table 4 indicating that the compound is well absorbed orally.

In a subsequent study rats were given single i.v. doses (50 mg/kg) of the labeled amine. One-half, 1, 2 and 4 hr later, counts were made on blood and brains, with results as shown in Table 5.

Since the brain contained as high a count concentration as the blood, ½ and 1 hr after drug administration, it is clear that the material freely entered

TABLE 4

Fraction	Radioactivity in fraction (% of dose)			
	No. 1	No. 2	No. 3	Average
CO_2	0·03	0·25	0·34	0·21
Urine	92·84	85·39	101·92	93·38
Carcass	0·14	0·26	0·16	0·19
Feces	0·25	0·29	0·10	0·21
GI tract	0·09	0·15	0·10	0·11
Total	93·35	86·34	102·62	94·10

TABLE 5

Time (hr)	Radioactivity in brain/in blood ±s.d.†
½	0·95±0·11
1	0·99±0·31
2	0·63±0·17
4	0·47±0·05

† Three animals per time.

TABLE 6

	Group A (4 rats)	Group B (4 rats)†
Radioactivity present in brain, dpm/g mean±s.d.	3155±96	6604±1250
Radioactivity extracted from acid solution with 1 volume of ethylacetate, mean ±s.d.‡	2073±37	1327±5

† Pre-dosed (17 hr) with 8 mg/kg α-methylphenethylhydrazine.
‡ About 4% of dimethoxyphenethylamine C^{14} extracted from brain tissue under these conditions.

the brain. The question as to whether the major portion of the amine was deaminated was unanswered by these experiments, however. To determine this point rats were treated intravenously with dimethoxyphenethylamine-C^{14} at 50 mg/kg. The results of Table 6 clearly show that most of the counts in the brain (66%) are attributable to deaminated metabolites and that the use of a monoamine oxidase inhibitor appreciably increases the brain concentration of amine. The deaminated label was identified by thin-layer chromatography as 3,4-dimethoxyphenylacetic acid in a single rat experiment (Ormond, 1965).

In view of the rapid deamination of 3,4-dimethoxyphenethylamine that occurs *in vivo*, it was felt that the determination of the corresponding phenylacetic acid would represent a more accurate measurement of the amine present in the body since the acids would be expected to be more abundantly available in the urine. A method was therefore developed which permitted the determination of the acids and amines in the same sample (Kuehl *et al.*, 1966).

In brief, the acidic effluent of the Dowex column used to adsorb the amines was extracted with ethyl acetate, or in cases where no determination of the basic metabolites was to be made, the acid hydrolyzed urine was extracted directly with this solvent. Acidic material was separated from neutral contaminants by extracting into 0·1 normal alkali. After reacidification the metabolites were re-extracted into ethylene dichloride. Unidimensional thin-layer chromatography of this material on silica gel using butanol–benzene–water (3:2:1) separated the dimethoxyphenylacetic acid from the monomethyl derivatives and other impurities. Visualization was accomplished by ultraviolet absorption and by spraying known marker compounds at the edge with alkaline permanganate. After elution of the appropriate areas with chloroform, the acids were esterified by short treatment with diazomethane in ether. Studies with known compounds revealed that no methylation of phenolic groups occurred under these conditions. Gas chromatography, using a column of neopental glycol succinate adsorbed on gas chrom P, afforded an excellent resolution of 3,4-dimethoxy as well as the isomeric mono-O-methyl dihydroxyphenylacetic acids. By addition of 3,4-dimethoxyphenylacetic acid to urine, it was possible to detect less than 1 μg per gram creatinine output.

Using this method, we were able to detect 3,4-dimethoxyphenylacetic acid in several of the normal urines studied. In all cases 3-methoxy-4-hydroxyphenylacetic acid could be determined. 3-Hydroxy-4-methoxyphenylacetic acid was found to be too unstable to oxidation to survive the isolation process; hence its detection was not possible.

We presently plan to apply this process to the urine specimens from human subjects in order to obtain a quantitative measurement of acids reflecting the amounts of 3,4-dimethoxyphenethylamine present in various diseased states.

REFERENCES

AXELROD, J. and TOMACHICK, R. (1959) *Journal of Biological Chemistry*, **233,** 702.
CARLINI, E. A., SANTOS, M. and SAMPAIO, M. R. P. (1965) *Experientia*, **21,** 72.
ERNST, A. M. (1962) *Nature*, **193,** 178.

FRIEDHOFF, A. J. and VAN WINKLE, E. (1962) *Nature*, **194,** 874.
FRIEDHOFF, A. J. (1963) private communication.
FRIEDHOFF, A. J. and VAN WINKLE, E. (1963) *Journal of Chromatography*, **11,** 272.
FRIEDHOFF, A. J. and VAN WINKLE, E. (1963) *Nature*, **199,** 1271.
GOLDSTEIN, M., FRIEDHOFF, A. J. and SIMMONS, C. (1959) *Biochimica et Biophysica Acta*, **33,** 572.
KAKIMOTO, Y. and ARMSTRONG, M. D. (1962) *Journal of Biological Chemistry*, **237,** 208.
KUEHL, F. A., Jr., HICHENS, M. ORMOND, R. E., MEISINGER, M. A. P., GALE, P. H., CIRILLO, V. J. and BRINK, N. G. (1964) *Nature*, **203,** 154.
KUEHL, F. A. Jr., VANDENHEUVEL, W. J. A., and ORMOND, R. E. (1966) to be published.
MICHAUX, R. and VERLY, W. G. (1963) *Life Sciences*, p. 175.
ORMOND, R. E., MANDEL, L. R. and KUEHL, F. A., Jr. (1965) unpublished observations.
PERRY, T. L., HANSEN, S. and MACINTYRE, L. (1964) *Nature*, **202,** 519.
PORTER, C. C. (1964) unpublished results.
SEN, N. P. and MCGEER, P. L. (1964) *Biochemical and Biophysical Research Communications*, **14,** 227.
SENOH, S., DALY, J., AXELROD, J. and WITKOP, B. (1959) *Journal of the American Chemical Society*, **81,** 6240.
SOURKES, T. L. (1962) *Biochemistry of Mental Disease*, New York, Harper & Rowe.
TAKESADA, M., KAKIMOTO, Y., SANO, I. and KANEKO, Z. (1963) *Nature*, **199,** 203.
WAGNER, A. F., CIRILLO, V. J., MEISINGER, M. A. P. and BRINK, N. G. (1964) unpublished results.

STUDIES OF AMINES IN NORMAL AND SCHIZOPHRENIC SUBJECTS[1]

THOMAS L. PERRY, SHIRLEY HANSEN, LYNNE MACDOUGALL and CONRAD J. SCHWARZ

Department of Pharmacology, The University of British Columbia, Vancouver, Canada

WE HAVE for several years been investigating the urinary excretion of biogenic amines by normal and psychotic children and adults in an effort to detect metabolic abnormalities which might be causally related to various psychoses. The presence of certain amines such as norepinephrine, dopamine, and serotonin in brain, and the possibility that one or more of them plays a role in the synaptic transmission of nerve impulses in the central nervous system, suggests that disturbances in the production or destruction of amines might underlie some psychoses. The psychotomimetic properties of other amines such as bufotenin, psilocin, N,N-dimethyltryptamine, and mescaline, lend attractiveness to the theory that one or more toxic amines might cause certain cases of schizophrenia. The marked alterations in behavior noted in schizophrenic patients on monoamine oxidase blockade after oral loads of L-methionine and of L-tryptophan (Pollin *et al.*, 1961) have also added interest to speculation that certain indole amines, methylated either on the side chain amino group or on a ring hydroxyl group, might produce the profound mental disturbance characteristic of schizophrenia.

We believe it likely that there are multiple causes of psychoses, including, but by no means limited to, genetically determined metabolic errors. Just as a wide variety of causative biochemical errors are now being demonstrated in different forms of mental deficiency, so it would seem reasonable to expect that errors in the metabolism of amino acids, amines, proteins, carbohydrates, lipids, and other groups of chemical compounds might in time be demonstrated to produce different kinds of psychoses. In concentrating on studies of the urinary excretion of amines in schizophrenia, we have been aware from the beginning of two major problems in this experimental approach. Firstly, we are probably carrying out biochemical investigations on patients having a number of different diseases which, in our present state of ignorance, we lump together under the name schizophrenia; and secondly, we may not be studying the right chemical group of metabolites.

[1] Supported by grants from the Medical Research Council of Canada, and the Multiple Sclerosis Society of Canada.

The great variety of biogenic amines occurring in human urine, and their very low concentration as compared to urinary amino acids, has made the search for differences between urinary amines in normal and psychotic persons more complicated than was anticipated initially. We have detected more than seventy different bases, most of them presumably amines, in various human urines, and have been able to identify only about thirty of these. Approximately forty different amines can usually be detected at any one time in the urine of a normal subject. This complexity of amine excretion in man has made it necessary to devote considerable effort to the development of suitable techniques for concentrating and separating mixtures of urinary amines. In addition, we have had to direct our attention to the investigation of exogenous sources of urinary amines in normal and psychotic subjects, and to the elimination of these sources where possible.

METHODS USED

We are currently employing two different methods for the preliminary concentration of urinary amines, and for their separation from the acidic and neutral constituents of urine. In one procedure (Perry, Shaw, Walker, and Redlich, 1962), amines and other bases present in urine are adsorbed on to the carboxylic acid cation exchange resin, Amberlite CG–50, in the hydrogen form, and the resin is washed in a column with water to remove acidic and neutral urinary compounds. The bases are then eluted from the resin with 4 N acetic acid, and the eluate is lyophilized. After removal of salt and most of the basic amino acids by extraction with ethanol and acetone, the amine concentrate is ready for chromatographic analysis. In the other procedure (Kakimoto and Armstrong, 1962), amines are adsorbed on to the sulfonic acid cation exchange resin, Dowex 50Wx2, in the hydrogen form, and the resin is washed with 0·1 N sodium acetate and water, and the adsorbed bases are then eluted with 1 N ammonium hydroxide in 65% ethanol. The alcoholic ammonia eluate is taken to dryness on a rotary evaporator, and after desalting by ethanol extraction is subjected to chromatography. In each of these procedures, both the free urinary amines are studied, as well as those conjugated amines not originally adsorbed on to the resin, which are freed by subsequent acid hydrolysis and then adsorbed on to fresh resin.

Amine concentrates prepared by either of these methods are first surveyed by two-dimensional paper chromatography, using the solvent systems and developing spray reagents described by Perry, Shaw, Walker and Redlich (1962). We have found that amines having hydroxyl groups on the benzene ring or on an aliphatic side chain are recovered more completely following preliminary adsorption on to Dowex 50 than on to Amberlite CG–50. Thus the method of Kakimoto and Armstrong (1962) gives better recoveries of *p*-tyramine, *m*-tyramine, octopamine, normetanephrine and serotonin than does the method of Perry *et al.* (1962). The latter method must be used, however, for recovery of volatile aliphatic monoamines, as well as for several other unidentified urinary bases which are not bound to Dowex 50. Neither method is satisfactory for the recovery of small amounts of the catecholamines from urine.

Many urinary amines can be adequately separated by two-dimensional paper chromatography, and can be identified by their characteristic R_fs, and by the colors they give with various spray reagents. On the other hand, a number of amines cannot be positively identified by paper chromatography alone, and not infrequently compounds of potential interest are completely hidden on chromatograms by larger amounts of other compounds migrating to the same loci. We have found that ion-exchange chromatography of urinary amine concentrates on columns of Amberlite CG–50 or Amberlite CG–120 (Perry and Schroeder, 1963) effects separation of a complex mixture of amines into effluent zones containing one or at the most two or three amines, which can then easily be identified by paper chromatography. When ion-exchange resin columns are operated at constant temperatures, and are developed with buffers of the proper molarity and pH, each amine is eluted at a characteristic effluent volume. The elution volumes of amines known or suspected to occur in urine can be determined by column chromatography of authentic compounds. Subsequently, elution of a naturally occurring urinary amine from the column at a given effluent volume can be used as one reliable criterion for its identification. This method is particularly valuable if one wishes to determine whether a certain amine is present in urine in very low concentration. A large volume of urinary amine concentrate, 10 to 100 times the amount which could be spotted on a single paper chromatogram, can be applied to the ion-exchange column and subjected to chromatography. The entire effluent zone characteristic for the amine in question is then reduced to a small volume on a rotary evaporator, or by lyophilization, and is then chromatographed on paper. Trace amounts of amines are usually readily detected after separation from all other interfering substances in this manner.

EXOGENOUS URINARY AMINES

Many of the amines encountered in the urine of both normal persons and of patients with mental disease are of exogenous origin. A variety of drugs, among them the phenothiazine tranquilizers, are known to be metabolized to basic compounds which can be found on chromatograms of urinary amines. In our studies on psychotic patients, we have attempted to avoid these drug metabolites, as well as to eliminate drug effects on endogenous amines, by withdrawing tranquilizers, and where possible all other medications, for periods of 1 to 6 weeks prior to urine collections.

We have found that many phenolic and indole amines present in urine are derived from plant items in the diet. In one experiment (Perry *et al.*, 1965a), two normal subjects were maintained on plant-free diets, and their urinary amines were surveyed. These subjects were then fed, one at a time, large amounts of several common fruits, beverages and flavoring agents. Fifteen exogenous phenolic and indole amines were isolated from urine after these plant foods were given. Three of these, synephrine, *p*-hydroxybenzylamine and 3-methoxy-4-hydroxybenzylamine, were found to follow ingestion of orange, mustard and vanilla extract respectively. Twelve other exogenous amines have not yet been identified, but their chromatographic characteristics on paper and ion-exchange column chromatograms have been determined, as well as their color reactions with various spray reagents. Coffee and orange juice were found to be particularly important common dietary sources of exogenous urinary amines.

Some fruits contain amines themselves, such as serotonin (Udenfriend *et al.*, 1959; West, 1958; Bruce, 1960; Kirberger and Braun, 1961), norepinephrine and dopamine (Udenfriend *et al.*, 1959), and synephrine (Gjessing and Armstrong, 1963). Phenolic aldehydes occur widely in plant glycosides, and conversion of these aldehydes to amines in the body by transamination reactions may account for many other urinary phenolic amines. Many other exogenous amines of plant origin probably occur in human urine in addition to the fifteen we encountered. Some of the unidentified ninhydrin-reactive bases found in urine may well be non-phenolic, non-indole amines of plant origin.

Plant foods are not the only dietary sources of amines in human urine. It has recently been found that certain types of cheese may contain large amounts of *p*-tyramine and tryptamine (Asatoor *et al.*, 1963), and consumption of cheese during monoamine oxidase blockade might well lead to increased urinary excretion of these two amines.

Other amines commonly found in urine are either largely or entirely of intestinal bacterial origin. We have carried out experiments in which normal subjects were maintained on plant-free diets, and the urinary excretion of several different amines was measured before and during alteration of the intestinal flora by orally administered succinylsulfathiazole, with or without neomycin. The urinary excretion of piperidine was markedly reduced when the flora of the large intestine was altered, and the urinary excretion of N-acetylhistamine (after an oral dose of histamine diphosphate in a gelatin capsule) was reduced to as little as 8% of the value found before chemotherapy. It is likely that urinary N-acetylhistamine results from the bacterial acetylation of histamine present in meat in the diet, and that the piperidine found in urine is derived at least in part from the decarboxylation of lysine by intestinal bacteria, and subsequent cyclization of cadaverine to piperidine. In our experiments, "sterilization" of the gut by succinylsulfathiazole resulted in a considerable increase in the urinary excretion of tryptamine and *p*-tyramine. This may have been due to a marked alteration in, rather than an eradication of, the intestinal flora. Reduction in coliform organisms in the large intestine may have resulted in an overgrowth of *Streptococcus fecalis*, an organism not affected by succinylsulfathiazole, and one which has been used as a laboratory source of tyrosine decarboxylase. It has been shown that mammalian liver and kidney preparations contain enzymes which decarboxylate dihydroxyphenylalanine, 5-hydroxytryptophan, *o*-tyrosine, and *m*-tyrosine *in vitro*, but which fail to decarboxylate tryptophan, *p*-tyrosine, and phenylalanine (Awapara *et al.*, 1962; Awapara *et al.*, 1964). Thus it is possible that the *p*-tyramine and tryptamine which are routinely found in human urine are solely of intestinal bacterial or dietary origin.

We have carried out our investigations of urinary amines in schizophrenics and other psychotics while these patients were maintained on a so-called "plant-free" diet. This diet excludes all fresh, canned, or dried vegetables, fruits, fruit juices, jams and jellies, candy, spices and flavoring agents, and all beverages other than water and milk. The diet also excludes cheeses. This has been done primarily to eliminate a number of amines of exogenous origin which complicate the chromatographic separation of urinary amines. It seemed important first to search for the possible presence of unusual endogenous amines in the urine of schizophrenics, or to try to demonstrate the possible absence of amines routinely found in the urine of normal persons, rather than to risk an unnecessary expenditure of time in the investigation of an unusual amine which would eventually prove to be of dietary origin. We have made no special efforts so far to control the possible effect on urinary amines of constipation or of an intestinal flora peculiar to long residence in a mental hospital.

It is conceivable that some mental diseases may be caused by enzymatic errors in the body which lead to the production of toxic products derived from normally harmless items in the diet, or to the failure to detoxify such toxic substances. It is also possible that bacterial amines adsorbed from the large intestine might in some persons fail to be detoxified and cause deranged mental function. The fact that marked alterations in diet do not produce clear-cut changes in the mental condition of schizophrenics, and the failure of chemotherapy designed to alter the intestinal flora to effect clinical improvement in schizophrenia (Dohan *et al.*, 1963) do not lend support to the theory that exogenous amines of dietary or bacterial origin play a part in the etiology of schizophrenia. It seems more likely that those mental and neurological diseases which have a biochemical basis are produced by genetically controlled enzyme deficiencies involving fundamental metabolic processes and that these metabolic errors are not dependent upon diet or intestinal bacteria.

STUDIES ON ACUTE SCHIZOPHRENICS

We have reported elsewhere (Perry *et al.*, 1964b) a study of ten acutely psychotic schizophrenic patients who were studied within the first week or two of an admission to a mental hospital. These patients were receiving no tranquilizing drugs, and were on plant-free diets for at least 5 days before a 48-hr collection of urine was made. Urinary amines were surveyed, with special attention being paid to a search of bufotenin and 3,4-dimethoxyphenylethylamine.

The psychotomimetic amine, bufotenin, has been reported to occur in the urine of most schizophrenics, but not in urine of normal persons and patients with other diseases (Fischer *et al.*, 1961a; Fischer *et al.*, 1961b). Friedhoff and Van Winkle (1962a, 1962b) have reported that the majority of patients with schizophrenia, in contrast to normal individuals, excrete 3,4-dimethoxyphenylethylamine in their urine. The excretion of 3,4-dimethoxyphenylethylamine by schizophrenics assumes special interest because this compound is known to have a marked effect on the central nervous system when administered to experimental animals (Epstein *et al.*, 1932; Ernst, 1962). This amine has also been reported to occur in the urine of schizophrenics by two other groups of workers (Takesada *et al.*, 1963; Sen and McGeer, 1964), although the Japanese investigators also found the amine present in the urine of many normal subjects. They concluded that the amine probably originated from dietary sources, or was a product formed by intestinal bacteria.

We were unable to detect bufotenin or 3,4-dimethoxyphenylethylamine in the urine of any of the small group of schizophrenic patients studied during acute exacerbations of their psychoses. Although many unidentified amines were observed on chromatograms, we could find no obvious difference in the pattern of amines excreted by these patients and normal subjects. It seemed important to pursue further our failure to detect bufotenin and 3,4-dimethoxyphenylethylamine, and to use as controls for schizophrenic patients other psychotics living under the same environmental conditions, whose mental disturbance was clearly due to some disease other than schizophrenia.

STUDIES ON CHRONICALLY HOSPITALIZED MENTAL PATIENTS

Twelve male patients were selected from a group of schizophrenics who had been hospitalized for long periods in a mental hospital. Their symptoms and the clinical courses of their illnesses were felt by competent psychiatrists to be characteristic of schizophrenia. An additional seven male mental patients, who also had been institutionalized for long periods, were selected from the same wards as controls. These seven patients had mental disease which was clearly not schizophrenic. Their diagnoses included Huntington's chorea, multiple sclerosis, carbon monoxide poisoning, massive subdural hematoma, and central nervous system syphilis.

The nineteen patients were taken off all tranquilizing and other drugs for a period of 6 weeks, and for the last 2 weeks of the experiment were fed a "plant-free" and cheese-free diet. After 7 days on the special diet, a 48-hr collection of urine was obtained from each patient. Patients were then given a monoamine oxidase inhibitor, phenelzine, in a daily dosage of 90 mg for a further 7 days. At the end of this period, when it was estimated that maximal monamine oxidase blockade should have been reached, a second 48-hr collection of urine was obtained from each patient. No untoward effects were observed in these nineteen patients as a result of withdrawal of phenothiazine tranquilizers, even though most of them had received these drugs for years. Neither were any harmful or significantly beneficial effects observed from the 2 weeks on a restricted diet, or the 1 week on a high dosage of phenelzine.

The laboratory work-up of the urine specimens of these patients has been time-consuming, and is not yet complete. At this time, we wish to report results obtained from eight of the twelve schizophrenics, and from five of the seven control mental patients. Urinary amines have been surveyed in each patient both before and during monoamine oxidase blockade. In order to obtain maximal recovery of amines, and to survey a wide variety of compounds, urinary bases have been concentrated both by the method of Perry *et al.* (1962), and by the method of Kakimoto and Armstrong (1962). Amine concentrates have been examined by paper chromatography, and in many instances by ion-exchange column chromatography as well.

In the urines of the thirteen patients examined so far, we have found no apparent differences between the amines excreted by chronic schizophrenics and by non-schizophrenic mental patients living under the same environmental conditions. Each patient investigated so far has shown during monoamine oxidase blockade a marked increase in the urinary excretion of the following amines: normetanephrine, metanephrine, 3-methyldopamine, octopamine, *p*-tryamine, *m*-tyramine, serotonin and tryptamine.

No trace of bufotenin has been detected in the urine of any of the thirteen patients, either before or during monoamine oxidase blockade. The sensitivity of the detection methods used, and the completeness of recovery of authentic bufotenin added to urine, is such that this compound should have been found had patients excreted as little as 2 μg of bufotenin per day. No other *N*-methylated derivatives of serotonin or tryptamine have been detected in the urines of any of the patients studied to date.

3,4-Dimethoxyphenylethylamine has not been detected in the urines of any of the eight schizophrenics or five control patients examined, either before or during monoamine oxidase blockade. We felt that if this amine were the product of intestinal bacteria, we might expect to find it excreted by schizophrenics who were chronically hospitalized, and who were physically inactive and probably subject to constipation. Since the amine is believed to be oxidized by monoamine oxidase to 3,4-dimethoxyphenylacetic acid (Friedhoff and Van Winkle, 1963), it also seemed likely that chances of detecting the amine in urine should be improved by inhibition of that enzyme. We have found that when authentic 3,4-dimethoxyphenylethylamine is added in very small amounts to raw urine, 96% of the compound can be recovered when the urine is treated with Dowex 50 by the method of Kakimoto and Armstrong (1962), and when the resulting amine concentrate is then subjected to ion-exchange column chromatography by the method of Perry and Schroeder (1963). Ion-exchange column chromatography of amine concentrates of schizophrenic urines, and subsequent paper chromatography of the elution zone for 3,4-dimethoxyphenylethylamine, have in all cases failed to detect this amine. We calculate that if as little as 10 to 15 μg of this amine had been excreted per day by schizophrenics and contol patients during monoamine oxidase blockade, we should have found it with the techniques employed.

In an earlier study, one of us (Perry, 1963) reported that N-methylmetanephrine was excreted by three of eighteen juvenile psychotics. N-methylmetanephrine is a metabolite of N-methylepinephrine, and it was not clear at the time whether this latter tertiary amine might play a causative role in some forms of psychosis, or was merely a secondary result of mental dysfunction. Since then, careful examination of the urines of normal adults has shown that some healthy persons excrete very small amounts of N-methylmetanephrine. Small amounts of this amine have also been found in the urines of most of the chronic schizophrenics and control patients examined so far. Since non-schizophrenic mental patients and some normal subjects excrete this amine, it now seems unlikely that it bears any causal relation to schizophrenia.

The only unusual observation in our survey of the urinary amines of chronic psychotics to date is a group of four unidentified ninhydrin-positive bases, presumably amines, which have been present in most of the urines of both the schizophrenic and control mental patients. These unidentified bases do not react with sprays for phenolic or indole amines. They appear to be increased in concentration in urine during monoamine oxidase inhibition. Their R_fs on paper chromatograms, and their color reactions with ninhydrin, suggested at first that they might represent 3,4-dimethoxyphenylethylamine, or any of several other di- and tri-methoxylated phenylethylamines. When they were subjected to ion-exchange column chromatography, however, it was found that each of these four unidentified amines was eluted from the resin column much earlier than any of the ring-methoxylated phenylethylamines tested. We do not believe these unidentified amines have any etiological significance in schizophrenia, and suspect that they, like *p*-tyramine and tryptamine, are probably products of bacterial enzymatic activity in the large intestine. They are not usually detected in the urines of normal subjects; but we have found them present in the urines of most institutionalized mentally retarded chidren.

BRAIN AMINES

In studying the possible relationship of abnormalities in amine metabolism to schizophrenia and other forms of mental disease, it is only natural that most investigators commence with the examination of urine. Urine is easy to obtain and to work with, and amines are relatively highly concentrated in it. But it is a long way from the brain to the bladder. It is entirely conceivable that an excess or a deficiency of a physiologically active amine might occur in the central nervous system, might lead to gross derangement of mental function and yet might result in no detectable alteration in the concentration of urinary metabolites. We believe that more direct approaches must be made to the brain in the careful search for biochemical causes of mental disease.

In our laboratory, we first attempted to measure the amine content of cerebrospinal fluid, using the same techniques which have been applied to urine. We found that the concentration of amines in CSF is very low indeed; in a pool of 320 ml of CSF from normal subjects, only ethanolamine and piperidine could be detected (Perry *et al.*, 1964a). The prospect of detecting differences between individual schizophrenic patients and individual normal subjects through measurement of CSF amine content is not encouraging.

More recently we have applied combined ion-exchange column and paper chromatographic techniques to a survey of the amines present in whole cat brain (Perry *et al.*, 1965b). The variety of amines found was greater than anticipated, and suggested the desirability of extending these studies to human brain.

Thus far we have examined only two whole human brains, that of an elderly man, and that of a new-born premature infant. The specimens were obtained from two individuals who died suddenly without antecedent illness, and the brains were frozen on dry ice within a few hours of death. Brain was then homogenized and deproteinized with trichloroacetic acid, and amines were adsorbed on to both Amberlite CG–50 and Dowex 50. Subsequent separation and identification of amines was made with the same ion-exchange column chromatographic and paper chromatographic techniques used on studies of urinary amines. Certain brain amines have been measured semi-quantitatively by applying different amounts of brain amine extracts and appropriate amounts of authentic amines to paper chromatograms, and comparing the color intensities of spots visually. Although the examination of a variety of brain amines in this manner can be very time-consuming, it has distinct advantages over the more commonly employed spectrophotofluorometric or biological assay techniques for measurement of brain amines. One can be positive that a certain amine is present in brain when it is separated from all other compounds and visualized on a paper chromatogram. With spectrophotofluorometric and biological assays, the possibility always exists that one is unwittingly measuring two or more compounds simultaneously.

In our preliminary examination of human whole brain we have detected the following amines: ethanolamine, methylamine, pyrrolidine, piperidine, putrescine, spermidine, spermine, histamine, 1-methylhistamine, normetanephrine and serotonin. The amounts of histamine and serotonin present are far lower than has been reported for other mammalian brain examined by spectrophotofluorometric methods. In the infant's brain, no serotonin could be found, and in the elderly man's brain only about 0·4 μg was detected per 100 g of whole brain. No tryptamine could be detected in the two human brains examined, nor could we find it in cat brain. The techniques employed were not suitable for the study of norepinephrine or dopamine in brain. An interesting finding has been the presence in human brain of at least six unidentified amines.

We plan to extend these studies to a larger series of whole human brains, covering different ages, and including the brains of persons who have died slowly of infectious or wasting diseases. We hope also in time to compare the amine content of various areas of human brain. When the normal distribution of human brain amines has been ascertained, it will then be possible to examine the brains of persons dying with schizophrenia and other psychoses with a view to searching for possible differences in brain amine content which might have a bearing on disordered mentation.

We believe there is every reason for continuing to search for biochemical abnormalities which may cause schizophrenia, using the most rigorous techniques, and taking great care to avoid artifacts due to drugs, diet, intestinal flora and physiological state. Continued examination of urine for unusual amines is certainly worth while, but other physiological fluids and particularly brain should be examined as well. It also must be remembered that schizophrenia is likely to be a group of different diseases with different etiologies, and that amines are by no means the only class of chemical compounds which might produce psychotic illnesses.

REFERENCES

ASATOOR, A. M., LEVI, A. J. and MILNE, M. D. (1963) Tranylcypromine and cheese, *Lancet*, **2,** 733–4.

AWAPARA, J., SANDMAN, R. P. and HANLY, C. (1962) Activation of DOPA decarboxylase by pyridoxal phosphate, *Archives of Biochemistry and Biophysics*, **98,** 520–5.

AWAPARA, J., PERRY, T. L., HANLY, C. and PECK, E. (1964) Substrate specificity of DOPA decarboxylase, *Clinica Chimica Acta*, **10,** 286–9.

BRUCE, D. W. (1960) Serotonin in pineapple, *Nature*, **188,** 147.

DOHAN, F. C., DURKIN, J., KULICK, A., ROSENBLUM, M. P., BACHRACH, D. L., GRASBERGER, J., LYNCH, F. B. and SPRINCE, H. (1963) Ineffective neomycin therapy of schizophrenia, *Archives of General Psychiatry*, **9,** 520–3.

EPSTEIN, D., GUNN, J. A. and VIRDEN, C. J. (1932) The action of some amines related to adrenaline. I. Methoxy-phenylethylamines, *Journal of Physiology*, **76,** 224–46.

ERNST, A. M. (1962) Phenomena of the hypokinetic rigid type caused by O-methylation of dopamine in the para-position, *Nature*, **193,** 193–4.

FISCHER, E., VÁZQUEZ, A. J., FERNÁNDEZ LAGRAVERE, T. A. and LISKOWSKI, L. (1961a) Bufotenin in human urine, *Lancet*, **1,** 890–1.

FISCHER, E., FERNÁNDEZ LAGRAVERE, T. A., VÁZQUEZ, A. J. and DISTEFANO, A. O. (1961b) A bufotenin-like substance in the urine of schizophrenics, *Journal of Nervous and Mental Disease*, **133,** 441–4.

FRIEDHOFF, A. J. and VAN WINKLE, E. (1962a) Isolation and characterization of a compound from the urine of schizophrenics, *Nature*, **194,** 867–8.

FRIEDHOFF, A. J. and VAN WINKLE, E. (1962b) The characteristics of an amine found in the urine of schizophrenic patients, *Journal of Nervous and Mental Disease*, **135,** 550–5.

FRIEDHOFF, A. J. and VAN WINKLE, E. (1963) Conversion of dopamine to 3,4-dimethoxyphenylacetic acid in schizophrenic patients, *Nature*, **199,** 1271–2.

GJESSING, L. and ARMSTRONG, M. D. (1963) Occurrence of (−)-sympatol in oranges, *Proceedings of the Society for Experimental Biology and Medicine*, **114,** 226–9.

KAKIMOTO, Y. and ARMSTRONG, M. D. (1962) The phenolic amines of human urine, *Journal of Biological Chemistry*, **237,** 208–14.

KIRBERGER, E. and BRAUN, L. (1961) On the presence of 5-hydroxytryptamine in the walnut, *Biochimica et Biophysica Acta*, **49,** 391.

PERRY, T. L., SHAW, K. N. F., WALKER, D. and REDLICH, D. (1962) Urinary excretion of amines in normal children, *Pediatrics*, **30,** 576–84.

PERRY, T. L. (1963) N-methylmetanephrine: excretion by juvenile psychotics, *Science*, **139,** 587–9.

PERRY, T. L. and SCHROEDER, W. A. (1963) The occurrence of amines in human urine: determination by combined ion exchange and paper chromatography, *Journal of Chromatography*, **12,** 358–73.

PERRY, T. L., HANSEN, S. and JENKINS, L. C. (1964a) Amine content of normal human cerebrospinal fluid, *Journal of Neurochemistry*, **11,** 49–53.

PERRY, T. L., HANSEN, S. and MACINTYRE, L. (1964b) Failure to detect 3,4-dimethoxyphenylethylamine in the urine of schizophrenics, *Nature*, **202,** 519–20.

PERRY, T. L., HANSEN, S., HESTRIN, M. and MACINTYRE, L. (1965a) Exogenous urinary amines of plant origin, *Clinica Chimica Acta*, **11,** 24–34.

PERRY, T. L., HANSEN, S., FOULKS, J. G. and LING, G. M. (1965b) Aliphatic and aromatic amines of cat brain, *Journal of Neurochemistry*, **12,** 397–405.

POLLIN, W., CARDON, P. V. and KETY, S. S. (1961) Effects of amino acid feedings in schizophrenic patients treated with iproniazid, *Science*, **133,** 104–5.

SEN, N. P. and MCGEER, P. L. (1964) 4-Methoxyphenylethylamine and 3,4-dimethoxyphenylethylamine in human urine, *Biochemical and Biophysical Research Communications*, **14,** 227–32.

TAKESADA, M., KAKIMOTO, Y., SANO, I. and KANEKO, Z. (1963) 3,4-Dimethoxyphenylethylamine and other amines in the urine of schizophrenic patients, *Nature*, **199,** 203–4.

UDENFRIEND, S., LOVENBERG, W. and SJOERDSMA, A. (1959) Physiologically active amines in common fruits and vegetables, *Archives of Biochemistry and Biophysics*, **85,** 487–90.

WEST, G. B. (1958) Tryptamines in edible fruits, *Journal of Pharmacy and Pharmacology*, **10,** 589–90.

3,4-DIMETHOXYPHENYLETHYLAMINE IN SCHIZOPHRENIA?

R. E. BOURDILLON and A. PAULINE RIDGES

Nuffield Unit of Medical Genetics, Department of Medicine, University of Liverpool

SCHIZOPHRENIA was first defined by Bleuler in 1911; he was of the opinion that it might be a metabolic disease. However, since then, in spite of a vast amount of research, little progress has been made in associating the disease with a specific biochemical abnormality.

Until Osmond and Smythies (1952) suggested a possible biochemical basis for the aetiology of schizophrenia there had been no hypothesis on which to base investigations and although various attempts to associate abnormal metabolites with the suggested aetiology have failed, the hypothesis has in no way been invalidated. Current research is still directed, as they suggested, towards detecting a compound in the urine of schizophrenics which has the hallucinogenic properties of mescaline and which could conceivably arise from an abnormality of adrenaline metabolism. Harley-Mason in his development of Osmond and Smythies' hypothesis commented that it was possible that a pathological disturbance of the transmethylating mechanism occurring in the final stage of the biogenesis of adrenaline might result in the production of such a substance. He predicted that 3,4-dimethoxyphenylethylamine would be an interesting compound to investigate.

Although dimethoxyphenylethylamine had been found by Noteboom (1934) to produce catatonia in experimental animals, it was only following the report by Friedhoff and Van Winkle (1962) of its occurrence in the urine of fifteen out of nineteen schizophrenics tested that it has been seriously investigated. Its present in the urine of schizophrenics has been confirmed by Takesada *et al.* (1963), by Sen and McGeer (1964) and by Kuehl *et al.* (1964), but its significance is uncertain, for Takesada *et al.* also found it to occur in 46% of the samples of urine from normal individuals whom they investigated; whilst Friedhoff and Van Winkle failed to detect it in fourteen normals and Perry (1964) has failed to detect this compound in the six samples of schizophrenic urine which he has examined.

PRESENT INVESTIGATION

Our investigation has been done to see whether there is an association between schizophrenia and the excretion of 3,4-dimethoxyphenylethylamine ("the pink spot") and whether there is a genetic factor governing the excretion of this compound.

During the course of the investigation the urine of nearly 800 individuals has been examined and we are reporting the incidence of "pink spot"[1] in the urine of:

(i) 370 mentally normal individuals including—
   250 apparently healthy volunteers,
   120 mentally normal hospital in-patients;
(ii) 101 psychiatric in-patients taken from the acute and chronic wards of three mental hospitals and examined as possible schizophrenics;
(iii) 296 psychiatric in-patients studied as a planned blind trial;
(iv) the close relatives of three schizophrenic patients who have been found to excrete "pink spot".

MATERIALS AND METHODS

In most instances either a 20-hr or a 16-hr overnight sample of urine has been tested.

Dimethoxyphenylethylamine has been detected in the urine by the method of Friedhoff and Van Winkle. In addition a method has been developed which employs dichloroethane as an extraction agent. This enabled the extract to be examined by UV spectroscopy before chromatographic separation was carried out as described by Friedhoff and Van Winkle. There is no statistical difference between the two methods.

Derivatives of dimethoxyphenylethylamine have not been prepared but the "pink spot" and authentic 3,4-dimethoxyphenylethylamine were always compared by using mixed spots of DMPE and the unknown extracts on chromatograms.

EXPERIMENT I

Survey of Mentally Normal Individuals

The urine of 370 mentally normal individuals has been tested. Two hundred and fifty were apparently healthy volunteers and were mostly university students or hosptal nurses between the ages of 18 and 25 years. About twice as many men as women were tested.

Fifty mentally normal hospital in-patients were tested immediately prior

[1] In this survey the results are expressed in terms of the presence or absence of "pink spot" rather than dimethoxyphenylethylamine, because although it has not proved possible to differentiate the "pink spot" substance from authentic DMPE it is evident that further criteria would need to be fulfilled to confirm the identity.

TABLE 1. RESULTS OF EXAMINATION OF URINE EXTRACTS FOR "PINK SPOT"

Experiment I	Present	Absent	Impossible to assess	Total
Apparently healthy volunteers	1	249	—	250
Mentally normal hospital in-patients	—	120	—	120
Total	1	369	—	370

to operation and twenty shortly following operation. Ten cases of liver disease were studied and also twenty patients suffering from a variety of medical conditions. In addition to these, twenty patients were examined who were suffering from chronic neurological disorders. Of the entire group only one individual, a 54-year-old women suffering from periodic migraine, was "pink spot" positive. There was no history of mental disease in either herself or her family. The results are given in Table 1.

EXPERIMENT II

Incidence of "Pink Spot" in "Possible" Schizophrenics

Acute and chronic cases of schizophrenia have been included in this survey. Acute admissions were referred from the observation wards with a provisional diagnosis of schizophrenia; the chronic cases were referred as "probable schizophrenics". Each individual was subsequently reassessed and some of the diagnoses modified. In order to provide uniformity of diagnostic criteria one psychiatrist (S. L.) has seen all the patients in this series. The chemical analysis and clinical assessments were done independently and compared later. All the urine samples were tested by the method of Friedhoff and Van Winkle, and forty of them by both methods. Drug therapy but not the diagnosis was known at the time of analysis.

It was not possible to control the dietary intake of these patients, but schizophrenics and non-schizophrenics were tested who were taken from the same wards and who had been in hospital for similar lengths of time and receiving similar food.

Patients were examined who had never received drugs, who had been off drugs for periods of up to 2 months or who were still on drug therapy at the time of testing.

The possibility that "pink spot" is produced by bacteria in the gut has been considered. Six patients were found to be "pink spot" positive before and after a 5-day course of neomycin.

The results of Experiment II are shown in Table 2.

The results have also been analysed in relation to drug therapy as is shown in Table 3. "Pink spots" were found in patients on and off treatment but a higher proportion were present in the patients not receiving treatment.

TABLE 2. RESULTS OF EXAMINATION OF URINE FOR "PINK SPOT" IN EXPERIMENT II

	Pink spot present	Pink spot absent	Pink spot impossible to assess	Total
(a) Schizophrenics excluding (b)	44	12	11	67
(b) Paranoid schizophrenics†	2	15	—	17
(c) Non-schizophrenics	—	16	1	17
Total	46	43	12	101

† These have also been categorized as suggested by Fish (1962) but this classification has not been used in this paper.

TABLE 3. RESULTS OF EXPERIMENT II SHOWING INCIDENCE OF "PINK SPOT" IN RELATION TO DRUG THERAPY

	No treatment or no treatment for more than 1 month	Off treatment for more than 1 week but less than 1 month	Off treatment for 48–72 hr	On treatment	Impossible to assess	Total
(a) Schizophrenics excluding (b)	16/20	6/7	12/13	10/16	11	44/67
(b) Paranoid schizophrenics	1/3	1/5	0/2	0/7	—	2/17
(c) Non-schizophrenics	0/7	—	—	0/9	1	0/17
Total	17/30	7/12	12/15	10/32	12	46/101

EXPERIMENT III

The Planned Blind Trial

This series was studied to test whether the "pink spot" was a significant finding in schizophrenia.

Every urine sample was tested using the dichloroethane extraction method and forty of them by both methods.

The patients were selected by a different psychiatrist (P. H.) and were classified according to their case sheet diagnosis into—

(i) Schizophrenics—Paranoid
Non-paranoid;

(ii) Schizophreniform syndromes—where it was uncertain whether schizophrenia was the primary diagnosis;

(iii) Non-schizophrenics.

During the course of this experiment the investigators knew only that they were dealing with mentally abnormal patients and were ignorant of both diagnosis and drug therapy. The code was broken when all the cases had been assessed.

The results are shown in Table 4.

TABLE 4. RESULTS OF EXAMINATION OF URINE FOR "PINK SPOT" IN EXPERIMENT III

	Present	Absent	Impossible to assess	Total
(a) Schizophrenics excluding (b)	20	30	19	69
(b) Paranoid schizophrenics	2	54	6	62
(c) Schizophreniform syndromes	5	58	25	88
(d) Non-schizophrenics	1	68	8	77
Total	28	210	58	296

TABLE 5. RESULTS OF EXPERIMENT III SHOWING INCIDENCE OF "PINK SPOT" IN RELATION TO DRUG THERAPY

	Off drugs at time of examination	On drugs	Impossible to assess	Total
(a) Schizophrenia excluding (b)	7/14	13/36	19	20/69
(b) Paranoid schizophrenia	0/19	2/37	6	2/62
Total	7/33	15/73	25	131

In this experiment fewer patients had been off drug therapy for prolonged periods than in Experiment II. The results in relation to drug therapy are shown in Table 5.

EXPERIMENT IV

Survey of Close Relatives of Three Schizophrenic Patients

An, at present, very limited study has been made of the close relatives of three "pink spot" positive schizophrenics. None of the nineteen non-schizophrenics tested gave a positive result. Eleven of the samples tested came from the same family and the pedigree is shown in Fig. 1. The one "pink spot" positive sample was from a diagnosed schizophrenic.

DISCUSSION

It is clearly evident that within both these series there is an association between schizophrenia and the "pink spot" and within the group of schizophrenics the correlation is highest in "non-paranoid" schizophrenics.

As things stand at present it appears that "pink spot" is a product of a metabolic abnormality connected with the disease process and that certain types of schizophrenics are more likely to show the phenomenon than others

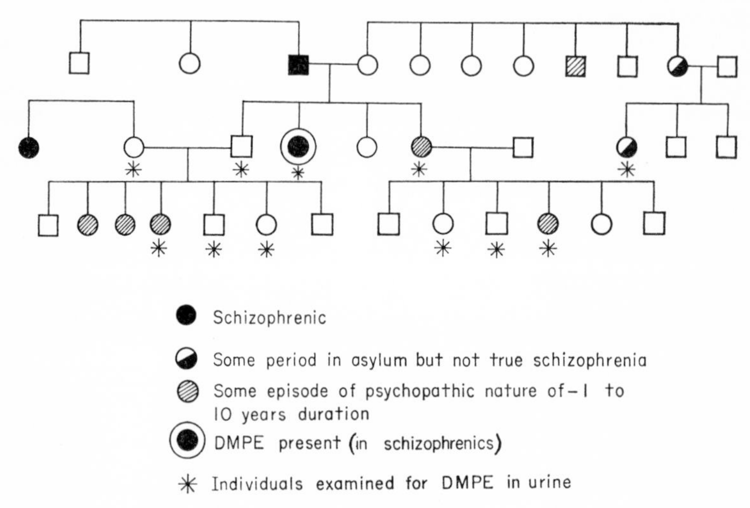

FIG. 1. Family study.

There is no evidence to support a dietary cause and it is not related to the length of hospital stay. The small family survey suggests that using these methods the presence of "pink spot" is of no use as a genetic marker.

ACKNOWLEDGMENTS

We should like to thank Professor C. A. Clarke who instigated this investigation and has given constant encouragement and helpful criticism. We are greatly indebted to Professor F. Fish and his department and to Drs. P. Harper and Shirley Leslie who carried out the psychiatric assessments and selection of patients and without whose collaboration the work would not have been possible.

We are grateful to the consultants who provided cases for inclusion in these experiments from the following hospitals in the Liverpool area—Rainhill, Winwick, Sefton General, Royal Southern, Broadgreen and the Liverpool Royal Infirmary.

REFERENCES

BLEULER, E. (1911) *Dementia Praecox or the Group of Schizophrenias*. Translated by Joseph Zinkin, 1950, International Universities Press.

FISH, F. J. (1962) *Scizophrenia*, John Wright & Sons, Ltd., Bristol.

FRIEDHOFF, A. J. and VAN WINKLE, E. (1962) Isolation and characterization of a compound from the urine of schizophrenics, *Nature* (*London*), **194,** 897–8.

KUEHL, F. A., HICHENS, M., ORMOND, R. E., MEISINGER, M. A. P., GALE, P. H., CIRILLO, V. J. and BRINK, N. G. (1964) *Para*-O-methylation of dopamine in schizophrenic and normal individuals, *Nature* (*London*), **203,** 154–5.

NOTEBOOM, L. (1934) Experimental catatonia by means of derivatives of mescaline and adrenaline, *Proceedings of the Amsterdam Academy of Science* (Science Section), **37,** 562–74.

OSMOND, H. and SMYTHIES, J. (1952) Schizophrenia—a new approach, *Journal of Mental Science*, **98,** 309–15.

PERRY, T. L., HANSEN, S. and MACINTYRE, L. (1964) Failure to detect 3,4-dimethoxyphenylethylamine in the urine of schizophrenics, *Nature* (*London*), **202,** 519–20.

SEN, N. P. and MCGEER, P. L. (1964) 4-Methoxyphenylethylamine and 3,4-dimethoxyphenylethylamine in human urine, *Biochemical and Biophysical Research Communications*, **14,** 227–32.

TAKESADA, M., KAKIMOTO, Y., SANO, I. and KANEKO, Z. (1963) 3,4-Dimethoxyphenylethylamine and other amines in the urine of schizophrenic patients, *Nature* (*London*), **199,** 203–4.

GENERAL DISCUSSION

Discussion after Dr. Smythies' Paper

KETY: Thank you, Dr. Smythies. I am glad that in his introductory remarks Dr. Smythies had occasion to review the very interesting hypothesis he was instrumental in formulating. The transmethylation hypothesis which will receive a great deal of discussion and examination today is attributable to an early paper by Dr. Smythies, Dr. Osmond and Harley-Mason in which this interesting and imaginative hypothesis was first put forth. I find it especially gratifying that Dr. Smythies is attacking the problem of behavioral effects of such methylated compounds and in an effective and quantitative manner. This paper is open for discussion.

HIMWICH: You have emphasized both the O-methoxy and N-dimethyl or N-diethyl components of mescaline. Could you give your opinion as to the specific contributions they make to the psychotomimetic activity of that substance?

SMYTHIES: I think this is a task for the chemists.

HIMWICH: I mean biologically, what actions do they bring out?

SMYTHIES: The N-methylation substitution turns mescaline into an amphetamine-like compound which is rather unexpected because the N-methyl derivatives of tryptamine are all hallucinogens. Of course, one cannot say from animal experimentation whether our compounds are hallucinogenic—one needs further human experiments, which are not easy to carry out. There are all sorts of difficulties in the way. What one has to do is proceed more subtly and make a working hypothesis that the biphasic mode of distribution is specific for hallucinogenic compounds. This can then be tested. I would mention here the work which Dr. Costa was doing when he was in your laboratory, Dr. Himwich, on the effect of hallucinogenic drugs and the effect of epinephrine on the nicitating membrane of the cat. They have a similar biphasic mode. At a low dose they had one effect; in larger doses they had the opposite effect. We also found this effect when we examined the effect of mescaline on topic and evoked potentials in the rat, and Purpura found this with LSD.

It would be most interesting to speculate on why N-methylation of mescaline should entirely change its properties and why an OH group in the 4-position abolishes all activity, but this is out of my field. If you have this compound (Fig. 4, Smythies) with the 4-position carrying hydroxyl groups this is quite inactive. If you put a heavy benzene ring on in this position this increases activity about twofold.

EFRON: I would like to mention only that there are data in the literature showing that the 3,4-dimethoxyphenylethylamine is much more potent in experiments using catalepsy as tests. Some authors say that the essential position for the methoxy group is the 4-position The optimal number of methoxy groups is two; by increasing the number to three, one loses a little activity as measured by the cataleptic tests (Ernst, A. M., *Psychopharmacologia*, **7**, 383, 1965). I would like to ask how soon after the administration of mescaline you have conducted your experiment.

SMYTHIES: When the experiment is run the animal is put in the box and the first two runs of 8 min are discarded. In these first runs, before the injection, the animal put into the box has to readapt to the situation each time. At the end of the second run mescaline is given and the experiment carried on, so one gets the results about 2 min after the injection for 2 hr.

SZARA: I would like to comment on the biphasic action you have found in your experiments using the conditioned avoidance response. We have seen a similar biphasic response in mice in the activity cage test using N,N-dimethyl and N,N-diethyl tryptamines. We found first a decrease in the spontaneous exploratory activity of the animals and later an increase

[1] This discussion refers to the papers of Drs. Smythies, Friedhoff, Kuehl, Perry and Bourdillon.

when compared to a control test. If we gave the same drugs to rats in another test, the Sidman type conditioned avoidance test, the animals respond not biphasically but one-phasically with a temporary deterioration of the avoidance response. It is interesting that in different situations you can get different responses.

PSCHEIDT: It may not be valid to make a direct comparison of free amino group N-methylation between indoles and catechol amines in evaluating their effect on the hallucinogenicity of the compounds, because the amino group of the catecholamines could possibly be sterically equivalent to the ring nitrogen of the indoles.

FRIEDHOFF: Dr. Smythies, do your rats develop tolerance to 3,4-dimethoxyphenylethylamine as they do to mescaline?

SMYTHIES: This I cannot answer. The experiments are going on in our lab. at this moment.

RICHTER: I wonder if you could say anything more about the relation between mescaline intoxication and schizophrenic psychosis? There are probably quite a number of people here who have taken mescaline at one time or another and who have personal experience of its effects.

SMYTHIES: It depends very much upon the exact circumstances under which mescaline is given. If you give mescaline to the same person three different times under three different situations, you may get entirely different effects. All I could say is that these drugs produce the closest known analogy to schizophrenia, but of course there are differences.

DISCUSSION AFTER DR. FRIEDHOFF'S PAPER

BALDESSARINI: Dr. Friedhoff, I understand that you have now about 250 schizophrenic patients with about 70% positive results. How frequently is the "methylated amine" chromatographic spot found in control urines?

FRIEDHOFF: We have studied about 300 urines but some are duplicates from the same patients so I would say we have about 150 different patients in the group, about 70% positive. We have studied about 50 normal controls without finding this compound in any.

HORWITT: I have a general comment. We were able to take advantage of the fact that we have had a group of patients on a very precisely controlled low-protein diet for 10 years to see if we could confirm these tests. Here we again came up with a negative result for presence of 3,4-dimethoxyphenylethylamine. I felt that perhaps we were being a little unfair since these were truly not acute schizophrenics. Accordingly we did what we had done before—went out into the wards at Elgin State Hospital and picked out some of the most active schizophrenic patients. They were so active that we had to let them have some kind of tranquilizers to keep them on the research ward. While we had no success in finding Friedhoff's compound in the schizophrenics who were not acute, we did very definitely find a reasonable amount on the four patients we took out of the Diagnostic Center. Remember now, these were not controlled when they came to us. Therefore we felt it was wise to take advantage of the facilities in our control diet kitchen and put the four acute patients on a low-protein diet for 3 days. I did not want it to be for more than 3 days because if we put them on too low a protein diet they would go into negative nitrogen balance and start excreting some other unknowns. Using the various tests that have been reported in the literature with some modifications of our own with bi-dimensional thin-layer chromatography we were able to study the compound in question. In the patient who previously had excreted 5–10 gamma/24 hr (Patient 1) none was detectable after 3 days on the low protein diet. Patient 2 who also started with 5–10 gamma/24 hr gave very questionable low results after the low-protein diet. We could not be sure whether any was present. Patient 3 did not have any before or after the low-protein diet. Patient 4 went from a high 10–20 gamma/24 hr down to 2–5 gamma/24 hr. I offer these abbreviated data to indicate the number of variables involved in this are no different than they were 25 years ago when I started controlling the diets of schizophrenic patients.

SPRINCE: Is there any possibility that this compound (3,4-dimethoxyphenylethylamine) could come from intestinal bacteria?

FRIEDHOFF: This is one of the other things that we considered and it is a difficult thing to evaluate. We took patients who were not in our hospital, most of our patients are there for only a short time anyway so it is unlikely that they have uniform flora. We took some who were not in there—we also gave antibiotics to a couple of patients. I do not know whether this is really any good in controlling intestinal bacteria or not but it did not affect the excretion. Dr. Horwitt, your findings are interesting and I think Dr. Perry has some words to say about this too, that diet may have some effects on excretion of this compound. There are two precautions I think we have to keep in mind about the significance of this kind of finding. One is that the turnover of this compound to the acid is enormously fast, much more so than for mescaline so that the amine we are determining in urine represents only a very small fraction of material that is either ingested or has been synthesized from whichever source this compound is coming. It is conceivable to me that there may be precursors in diet which increase the output of this material and therefore when the diet is restricted this may increase to some degree the excretions of dimethoxyphenylethylamine. But I do not think we know that this means that this compound is in fact being ingested as 3,4-dimethoxyphenylethylamine or whether it is being synthesized from a precursor. The second thing that I think we have to keep in mind is that if we demonstrated that patients were eating mescaline this would be a fact of some considerable interest. Since this compound has many mescaline-like properties in animals, it is important to bear in mind that even if it is of dietary origin it has still some role in the genesis of mental symptoms. There are other cases where ingested compounds are not adequately metabolized and produce all sorts of symptoms.

BERLET: I would like to ask two questions. First, did you try to establish any relationship between stress and the excretion of 3,4-dimethoxyphenylethylamine in your patients? I wonder especially about the controls in whom you found this compound.

FRIEDHOFF: We have not carried out extensive experimental controls of the various clinical responsibilities, mainly because we have our eggs in another basket at the present time, but we did attempt to look at our data to see if they were related to the activity of patients, and we did not find that they were. That is, we found it in some patients who were hyperactive and in some who were hypoactive, so it did not appear to be related to activity. As to stress, it is a difficult thing to define.

BERLETT: My other question concerns a report by Sen and McGeer (Sen, N. P. and McGeer, P. L., *Biochem. Biophys. Res. Commun.* **14,** 227, 1964) on the presence of 4-methoxyphenylethylamine in the urine of agitated schizophrenic patients. Did you have an opportunity to look for this compound during your studies?

FRIEDHOFF: Yes, we had found in a number of cases a compound which could be 4-methoxyphenylethylamine. We have not identified it more than by chromatography so that I do not know, but we have found in some patients a compound which might be there, the same compound they talk about.

SMYTHIES: I wish to emphasize that whether this compound arises, in part, from dietary sources may be in a sense irrelevant. The important fact to consider is whether it is there or not and whether it is present in schizophrenics in substantial amounts and is not present in the urine of normal patients. DMPEA may well be a normal dietary constituent which the normal can metabolize completely, whereas the schizophrenic cannot. The example of phenylketonuria will jump to mind here. In addition, there may be an abnormal endogenous source as well in the schizophrenic, or again this may be a normal stage in endogenous metabolism which the normal can metabolize further and the schizophrenic cannot.

KUEHL: As for the question of the possible bacterial origin of the compound, I am not sure that an enzyme of bacterial origin is known to be capable of methylating dopamine. We did study the obvious one from the intestinal flora, namely *E. coli*, and found that it was not able to convert dopamine to 3,4-dimethoxyphenylthylamine in the presence of S-adenosylmethionine. With respect to Dr. Berlet's question, we looked for 4-methoxyphenethylamine in urines of chronic schizophrenics and were not able to detect the compound by thin-layer chromatography. This was probably not a very definitive experiment though since the urine specimens were not from acute patients with a demonstrated ability to excrete 3,4-dimethoxyphenethylamine.

SNYDER: Have you made any attempts to quantitate the amounts of dimethoxyphenylethylamine?

FRIEDHOFF: Although the quantities of amine vary from patient to patient, 3 to 10 μg per 24-hr period, it is very difficult to obtain truly quantitative data because of the low amounts present. On the basis of *in vivo* experiments in rats with 3,4-dimethoxyphenylethylamine, where by far the major portion of the amine is converted to 3,4-dimethoxyphenylacetic acid, we feel that a study of this acid would be a much more accurate yardstick of the quantities of amine present. With this objective in mind we are developing a method for quantitatively determining the acid.

SNYDER: You might be able to quantitate it by a tracer technique such as adding tritiated acetic anhydride and a tracer of C^{14} 3,4-dimethoxydopamine and then dating the doubly labelled acetylated d. methoxydopamine. The H^3/C^{14} ratio would indicate the amount of endogenous 3,4-dimethoxydopamine present.

FRIEDHOFF: We have tried acetylation, but with little success—there are so many other impurities that also are acetylated.

SNYDER: Have you tried administering monoamine oxidase inhibitors which should markedly increase the urinary levels of 3,4-dimethoxydopamine?

FRIEDHOFF: We have done this *in vivo* in rats. There is no doubt that monoamine oxidase inhibitors increase the amounts of the amine in brain and liver. We have not examined urines though.

AVERAGE DAILY EXCRETION OF URINARY CONSTITUENTS (±SD) OBSERVED OVER NINE 5-DAY COLLECTION PERIODS IN 9 SCHIZOPHRENIC PATIENTS

COLLECTION PERIODS	1	2	3	4	5	6	7	8	9
DIET	CONTROL		LOW		TRYPTOPHAN-METHIONINE			CONTROL	
Norepinephrine μg/day	28 ± 19	40 ± 18	29 ± 15	38 ± 18	30 ± 18	31 ± 11	37 ± 13	34 ± 15	34 ± 9
Epinephrine μg/day	8 ± 7	21 ± 17	8 ± 5	8 ± 5	11 ± 5	13 ± 8	19 ± 7	10 ± 6	8 ± 6
Dopamine μg/day	155 ± 90	270 ± 100	200 ± 80	320 ± 60	690 ± 390*	460 ± 130*	590 ± 310*	360 ± 160	430 ± 250
Vanilmandelic Acid mg/day	4·6 ± 1·1	4·5 ± 1·1	4·7 ± 1·2	4·9 ± 1·3	4·9 ± 1·4	4·9 ± 1·3	4·5 ± 1·2	4·3 ± 1·2	5·1 ± 1·1

* Difference from second control period, significant p < ·01 level.

FIG. 1

SNYDER: This is what we are attempting in *in vitro* studies, I mean in people.

FRIEDHOFF: We have not done it.

RODNIGHT: In stress and anxiety states, catecholamine excretion may increase and I wonder whether you have looked at the excretion of this substance in other mental hospital patients suffering from anxiety and agitated depressions, for instance.

FRIEDHOFF: We have not done it, but according to Dr. Bourdillon's abstract he has, and I am eager to hear what he found.

HIMWICH: Our observations of urinary indoles as well as catechols and steroids reveal that the latter two groups are associated with increased motor activity or motor restlessness as well as elevations in tension and anxiety. In contrast, rises of urinary indoles are accompanied by intensifications of hallucinatory and delusional experiences and frequently mounting hostility. When both constellations of symptoms occur together, all three classes of urinary products are significantly elevated in the urine.

The results of our longitudinal study concern observations of four catechols during a period when the patients were comparatively free of exacerbations of psychotic symptoms at a time when they are on a low tryptophan, low methionine diet (Pscheidt, G. R. and Himwich, H. E., *Biochem. Parmacol.* **12**, 65, 1963). You will observe (Fig. 1) that there were no significant changes in norepinephrine, epinephrine or in VMA. On the other hand, during periods 5 and 6 there were significant increases in dopamine. In view of the fact that these changes in dopamine were associated neither with psychotic activation nor motor activity and anxiety, it would seem that the increases in dopamine accompany the nosological classification of schizophrenia and are not necessarily associated with any group of symptoms. But the point I am trying to make now is that this rise of dopamine may be of interest in view of the work of Drs. Friedhoff and Van Winkle on the precursor role played by dopamine in the formation of DMPEA in the body (Friedhoff, A. and Van Winkle, E., *Nature*, **199,** 1271, 1963).

————: Is that free dopamine?

HIMWICH: Yes.

SPRINCE: It might be worth while to try a methionine load test to determine whether increased methionine will effect an increased excretion of Dr. Friedhoff's compound. In this connection, Dr. Kety, if the urines obtained by Pollin, Cardon and Kety (*Science*, **133,** 104, 1961) are still available, it might be worth while to look for an increased excretion of this compound in the urine of those patients receiving a load dose of iproniazid and methionine.

KETY: We do still have those urines and we are interested in just that thing but have been waiting for a more quantitative assay.

RICHTER: I wonder to what extent esterification competes with methylation in the production of the compounds which have been gotten *in vivo* and also in your *in vitro* studies? Regarding the fairly low yield of methylated products I was wondering if that could be because esterification competes in their formation?

FRIEDHOFF: I cannot answer you. I think there is a possibility.

BRUNE: Dr. Friedhoff, did you investigate with your method patients with extrapyramidal syndromes? This would be of interest in view of the work of Barbeau and Sourkes and others who observed alterations of dopamine metabolism in these patients.

FRIEDHOFF: No, we have not. There are, of course, a number of very interesting clinical experiments that I think should be carried out.

BOURDILLON: We have tried Dr. Friedhoff's method in several patients suffering from Parkinsonism and also in other neurological disorders, but have never demonstrated any abnormal findings.

DISCUSSION AFTER DR. KUEHL'S PAPER

BERLET: I am very interested in your chromatographic approach. Since I missed some of the technical details during your presentation I wonder if any of these methods that you used in this study have been published elsewhere.

KUEHL: The details of the method for separating the amine have been published. I will be glad to give you a reprint. The gas chromatographic method for separating the acid is presently in the developmental stage.

BERLET: I was particularly interested in the solvent systems for the thin-layer chromatography.

KUEHL: We used silica gel G as an adsorbent for the thin-layer chromatography. The amines were run first in n-butanol–acetic acid–water 4:1:1 and then at right angles to this in n-butanol–ammonia–ethyl acetate (3:1:1). This method separates the 3,4-dimethoxyphenylethylamine from the mono-O-methyl derivatives of dopamine.

BERLET: The column packing used for gas chromatography was neopentyl glycol succinate. I wonder what percentage of coating proved to be the best in your experiments.

KUEHL: I am sorry, these results were obtained only a few days ago and I do not recall all the details.

BERLET: Did you convert the catecholamines to their derivatives?

KUEHL: No, we have not separated the amines by gas chromatography. The acids were converted to the methyl esters prior to gas chromatography.

FRIEDHOFF: In the liver experiments that you carried out, what in general were the ages?

KUEHL: The ages of the liver specimens prior to autopsy varied widely—from 3 to 40 hr. Although we could find no evidence for the formation of 3,4-dimethoxyphenylethylamine from dopamine using these livers as the enzyme source, in almost every case substantial conversion to 3-O-methyl dopamine by COMT was observed.

FRIEDHOFF: What was the specific activity of the dopamine?

KUEHL: I do not recall the specific activity of the dopamine. In a typical experiment we observed one million counts in the mono-O-methyl dopamine area. With but 800 counts in dimethoxyphenylethylamine area, we considered this negative.

FRIEDHOFF: These are amines or acids?

KUEHL: Amines.

SNYDER: What were the diagnoses of the schizophrenics and from what source were the urine samples obtained?

KUEHL: The urine specimens from acute schizophrenics were supplied by Dr. Friedhoff. Those from chronic cases were supplied by Dr. Nathan Kline.

SYNDER: The acute schizophrenics then were Dr. Friedhoff's patients. From what source were control urines obtained?

KUEHL: The controls were chemists from the laboratory. As far as the gas chromatography of the acid is concerned, to date we have examined one urine specimen from a chronic schizophrenic. This was negative as were urines from a number of normals. We have not yet examined urines of acute schizophrenics with a demonstrated ability to excrete 3,4-dimethoxyphenylethylamine for the corresponding acid.

LEONARD: This is a question which might be answered either by Dr. Friedhoff or Dr. Kuehl. Have you already observed schizophrenics through the active course of disease into a period of remission for the appearance of the metabolite? It would be an interesting thing if the metabolite disappeared during the period of remission.

FRIEDHOFF: Over the last six months we have collected several. It is difficult to predict in advance who is going to recover but we have taken a number of patients we thought might recover and collected urine from them and a couple of them have in fact recovered and we have those urines and are now in the process of analyzing them.

KUEHL: We have not attempted to correlate the exacerbation of symptoms of schizophrenia with the urinary output of 3,4-dimethoxyphenylethylamine. We did examine urines of some chronic schizophrenics collected at different dates though sometimes they were positive and other times negative with respect to the excretion of the amine.

SPRINCE: In his abstract, Dr. Kuehl states that 3,4-dimethoxyphenylethylamine cannot be formed by COMT obtained from rat liver. I wonder if this has any special significance especially with respect to species specificity.

KUEHL: The only significance that we can attach to those experiments is that rat COMT will not convert dopamine to 3,4-dimethoxyphenylethylamine. Our studies with autopsied human liver specimens also suggest that in man the enzyme that di-O-methylates dopamine is not COMT.

SPRINCE: What I really meant to ask is could the *in vivo* metabolism of the rat be used as a model system to study the nature of the formation of 3,4-dimethoxyphenylethylamine and 3,4-dimethoxyphenylacetic acid?

DISCUSSION AFTER DR. PERRY'S PAPER

KETY: I am sure there will be others in addition to Dr. Perry who will comment on the discrepancies in the biochemical studies but one expects discrepancies in such a new science as biochemistry. However, in the more precise science of psychiatry, I think that we probably can agree on one comment which you made relevant to the concept that schizophrenia is a unitary disease. I do not think there are many people in the room who hold that concept, and of course I am sure most of us would agree with you that schizophrenia is a phenomenological syndrome which may have many etiologies. None the less, the most useful way to examine the various etiologies which may be operating in schizophrenia may be to study patients who are schizophrenics, and I think this is probably the rationale that most people would use. I want to reinforce your words of caution and I am sure that we all agree that it is important to keep a very level head in this area. One wants all of the critical comment and an awareness of all the pitfalls.

SMYTHIES: In the case of the patients in whose urine you failed to detect DMPEA while they were on a plant-free diet, did you then put them on a diet containing fruit and vegetables and see if you could detect DMPEA in the urine?

PERRY: I think it would be done. Whether or not I shall plan to I do not know because I find the work quite complicated enough as it is now. I think it certainly should be done. In some ways we find it difficult because surprisingly we have in Canada psychiatrists who are very much opposed to anybody looking for biochemical causes for mental illness, just as one has them here in the United States. It is no easy thing to persuade psychiatrists in institutions of this sort to take patients off drugs and to put them on a plant-free diet, then put them back on a normal diet and so forth; but one can certainly do this, and I think people who find 3,4-dimethoxyphenylethylamine in the urine of their patients should do so. I think Dr. Friedhoff, who has been working in the mental hospitals, might find it a bit easier to do than it has been for me.

SMYTHIES: We have had many reports that this compound, whatever it is and whatever its origin, occurs more often in schizophrenic urine than normal urine. You suggest that it is possibly of plant origin. You would have to say that schizophrenics eat more of these plants than other people. This seems to be rather unlikely. How do you correlate your plant-oriented data with Dr. Horwitt's protein-oriented data? We have to explain where this stuff comes from—is it from endogenous metabolism or from food plants or proteins? How do we correlate this information?

PERRY: I cannot do it. All I can tell you is that with my best deliberate efforts to find 3,4-dimethoxyphenylethylamine, I cannot find it. It may well be a failure on my part, but I have never been able to identify any of the compound in any urines of any patients, and quite honestly I am a little bit skeptical that this compound is an important compound in the etiology of schizophrenia. The only person I have talked to who seems to have come up with negative findings like mine is Dr. Leiv Gjessing in Oslo (*J. Psychiat. Res.* **2**, 149, 1964). However, unfortunately he had his patients on an even stricter diet than I did, so he essentially has done his experiment in the same way I have, although with somewhat different techniques for recovering the amine.

SMYTHIES: You claimed at one time that N-methylmetanephrine might have some role in childhood schizophrenia, as you said that they excreted more than normals.

PERRY: I doubt very much that it plays a role in either childhood schizophrenia or in adult schizophrenia. I suppose I fell into the same trap that many of us are likely to. When we find an unusual compound excreted by three patients with a given disease and we do not find it in our controls, we are prone to think "this is it", and of course the stakes are so high that many of us tend to fall into this trap. I now believe that urinary excretion of N-methylmetanephrine is probably nothing more than a result of stress. I tried studying its excretion by normal subjects under emotional stress, for instance university students just prior to Ph.D. oral exams, and I found that some of them excreted as much N-methylmetanephrine as my juvenile schizophrenics did. Later, I found that some normal individuals who appeared to be very relaxed also excreted this compound, while other people under stress did not excrete it at all. One can find some N-methylmetanephrine in the urines of many retarded children such as mongoloids, who do not appear to be under any particular stress. I really do not believe that N-methylmetanephrine, or presumably N-methylepinephrine, its predecessor, plays a part in the etiology of the schizophrenias.

HORWITT: If it is any consolation to Dr. Perry, I think I should report that we biochemists had great trouble for three months finding this particular spot, and I had just about decided that I too could not find it until we changed the technique slightly and used bi-dimensional thin-layer chromatography instead of paper chromatography. All of a sudden the compound showed up. I have a feeling that this particular situation varies with laboratories and we are now convinced that it is there in the places where we see it. The question is now to analyse why it is present in one subject and not in another. The fact that I pointed to diet earlier is part of a long-term crusade to get more people to use more dietary controls. But this does not necessarily mean that this is the most important point, as Dr. Smythies has noted. I would much rather see the focus of attention placed upon the "stress" the individual is under and here we are using a word which is as bad as "schizophrenia". Is emotional stress the same as the stress of a woman having a child or somebody having surgery or something else? It is probably entirely different. You get different reactions from different stresses. We know, for example, that the stressed schizophrenic has an entirely different glucose tolerance curve than when he is not stressed. We know, and this has been demonstrated many times, that the stressed individual will handle benzoic acid differently. There are many other biochemical differences between the so-called stressed individual and the other individuals.

But before we can study this we have to learn more about our base-lines and that is why we are stressing nutrition. I am making a point of this because many people think that those of us who stress the artifacts are complete agnostics in this field and that we do not want to recognize any biochemical difference between schizophrenia and normal subjects. On the contrary, what we are promoting is the development of our techniques to the point where there is some agreement on how to run these tests. I got into the nutritional control of schizophrenics 25 years ago because the nutritional differences were bigger than the other ones I was studying. Therefore, recognizing that one can have exacerbations of symptoms by dietary means and other differences with stress, we should not consider either to be more or less important than the other. It may be that the schizophrenic has some liver dysfunction caused by prolonged stress and that some of the biochemical oddities noted may be secondary to the liver dysfunction. At least this is the basis upon which I have been working for many years. But let us not feel, as I have often pointed out, that because one person does not find a compound and other people do that it is not there. In most cases a compound claimed to be excreted is not to be denied; only the circumstances under which it is excreted needs more probing.

BALDESSARINI: Dr. Perry, have you tried your system with authentic dimethoxyphenylethylamine to see if your method can identify it?

PERRY: We get our best recoveries of authentic 3,4-dimethoxyphenylethylamine added to urine if we use the Kakimoto–Armstrong method. If one has added perhaps as little as 10 gamma of 3,4-dimethoxyphenylethylamine to a 300 or 500 mg creatinine equivalent of raw urine, using the Kakimoto–Armstrong method, and then places the entire amine concentrate on an ion-exchange resin column and separates the zone for 3,4-dimethoxyphenylethylamine, one gets about 96% recovery. The recovery of the authentic compound added to urine is excellent; and I am quite sure we would detect 3,4-dimethoxyphenylethylamine, in the urines of our psychotic patients if it were there.

BERLET: Did you compare the two methods, that is to say Dr. Friedhoff's method and your method, on the same urine? This might have either shown in that these patients did not have it in their urine or that there are some specific differences in the methods.

PERRY: I should have made this point clearer. Actually, in our studies on *acute* schizophrenics, we used both my own method and Dr. Friedhoff's method. If one uses my method, absorbing the amine on to Amberlite CG–50, one gets a less good recovery than with Dr. Friedhoff's method. I find that with the Kakimoto–Armstrong method, one gets an even better recovery than with Dr. Friedhoff's method. I think we got something like an 85% recovery with his chloroform extraction. We got about 50–60% recovery if we used Amberlite CG–50 alone. But if we used the Kakimoto–Armstrong method, we got above 95% recovery. The studies on our *chronic* psychotics I have reported today have been done using all three methods. In all three methods we find no 3,4-dimethoxyphenylethylamine. On those acute psychotics studied earlier, we used Amberlite CG–50 and we used Dr. Friedhoff's chloroform extraction technique, but we did not use the Dowex–50 technique at that time.

STRAUGHAN: Dr. Perry, I should like to ask you several questions in connection with your comment that there was only a little 5-HT in post-mortem specimens of human brain.

1. Did you study the regional distribution of 5-HT in the human brain?
2. How much is a "little" 5-HT?
3. How do your results compare with control specimens taken from animals which had been dead for a similar length of time?

PERRY: I would preface my remarks by saying that I am embarrassed to admit how limited are the examples of human brain studied by our techniques so far. Here is what we have found. We have studied two humain brains. One was from an elderly man whose brain was reduced to −80°C within 2½ hr after he died. The subject had died suddenly and the brain was grossly normal. We found 0·4 gamma of serotonin/100 g of whole brain. In other words, a very small amount. The other human brain studied was at the other end of life. It was that of a premature infant of about 7½ months gestation who died within several hours of birth. The brain in this case was reduced to −80°C about 5 hr after the infant's death. We could detect no serotonin in it at all. We could have just detected serotonin had there been 0·1 gamma/100 g of brain. It is entirely possible that we may be losing some serotonin in the procedure, which is rather complicated, or the serotonin may be disappearing between the time the patient dies and the time we examine the brain. However, I think the latter may not be the case, because we have tried killing a group of rats and in some of them taking brains out immediately, homogenizing them, and measuring serotonin by the spectrophotofluorometric method. The other rats from the same colony and of the same ages after being killed were allowed to sit on the table at room temperature for about 3 hours and were then put in the refrigerator overnight at 4°C. These brains were then homogenized and assayed spectrophotofluorometrically for serotonin the next morning. Thus we tried to mimic the conditions that one would run into with a human autopsy. Surprisingly, the serotonin was higher in the brains of those rats that had been allowed to sit out on the table. I am embarrassed to appear to draw conclusions from experiments on only two subjects, but I think it is possible that there is rather less serotonin in human brain than we have generally considered.

Another interesting thing we have studied in more detail, but again on a whole-brain basis, has been the amines found in cat brain. We have taken cats, perfused the common carotid arteries with saline until the venous return was blood-free, killed the cats rapidly, taken out the brains and immediately homogenized them in trichloroacetic acid, and then gone on and worked up the amines present in the brain by the methods I have described. We have found the concentration of serotonin present in whole cat brain to be in the neighborhood of 0·1 to 0·2 gamma/g brain. There are two other possible indole amines present in cat brain which we have not yet been able to identify, and we wonder whether it is possible that in the spectrophotofluorometric determinations of serotonin in brain one is really measuring several compounds. I think this problem has been noted in spectrophotofluorometric measurements of brain histamine. This is one of the advantages of separating the amines from brain, and finally ending up with a paper chromatogram where you are quite sure that you have identified a given amine correctly. I think it is possible that some of the amines which are claimed to be in brain are not there. For instance, I do not believe there is any tryptamine in brain, although its presence there has been reported by a number of people using spectrophotofluorometric techniques. I think it is important to explore what is the normal pattern of various amines in the whole human brain and particularly the human brain at, say, 6 to 24 hr after death, which is the time most autopsies take place in North America. We should then determine the regional distribution of amines in human brain. Once we have this information at hand, it will be possible to go on and examine the brain of patients who have died with schizophrenia and to see whether or not there are any differences from the brain amine patterns found in non-psychotic persons. This will take a long time to do and I would welcome some company in doing it.

SPRINCE: Very briefly, it is well known that indoleamines and catecholamines are rapidly oxidized in the body to their corresponding acids. It is possible, therefore, that Dr. Perry's failure to find 3,4-dimethoxyphenylethylamine in schizophrenic urine might be due to the fact that in his patients this amine was rapidly oxidized to its corresponding acid (i.e. 3,4-dimethoxyphenylacetic acid). Consequently it might be more profitable to look for the acid rather than the amine. Under these conditions, the differences in findings between Drs. Friedhoff and Perry might be reconciled.

KUEHL: I am not sure that I want to jump over on the Canadian side of the fence, but I must agree with Dr. Perry with respect to our studies on urine specimens from several chronic schizophrenics that had been treated with monoamine oxidase inhibitors. Although other catecholamines in urine appeared to be present in increased amounts, no 3,4-dimethoxyphenylethylamine could be detected.

RODNIGHT: I would like to know what alternative tests of identification Dr. Perry had used on the four spots which behaved like 3,4-dimethoxyphenylethylamine in paper chromatography systems.

HOLMSTEDT: You were asking one important question, Dr. Perry, and that is, do we measure 5-hydroxytryptamine with the spectrophotofluorometric method? We do, but as I will point out in my own presentation, we also measure other indol bases. The only way to differentiate between the 5-substituted indole bases and the other ones is to run the experiments in 3 N hydrochloric acid. By a shift of wavelength the 5-substituted can be differentiated from the others, but there may be other 5-substituted indoles than 5-hydroxytryptamine.

PERRY: I agree with the last comment. About the possibility of 3,4-dimethoxyphenylethylamine having been converted to the corresponding acid, I think that had our chronic schizophrenics been excreting, or forming, or eating, or producing 3,4-dimethoxyphenylethylamine—had they been getting it one way or another, we should certainly have found it is their urine, because they were all on very marked monoamine oxidase blockade. Now it is possible that acute schizophrenics excrete 3,4-dimethoxyphenylethylamine and that chronic schizophrenics do not. Of course it would be better, I think, if one were to take an acute schizophrenic who is violently psychotic and put this individual on a monoamine oxidase inhibitor. This would be a better experiment. This we have not done. All I can say is that we could not find the amine in the urines of acute schizophrenics not on monoamine oxidase inhibitors, not in the urines of chronic schizophrenics before or during monoamine oxidase inhibitors. As to the question about these other four unidentified compounds, the point I want to make is that there are four which in two-dimensional paper chromatographic solvent systems are very difficult to distinguish from 3,4-dimethoxyphenylethylamine. In other words, if you co-chromatograph these compounds with 3,4-dimethoxyphenylethylamine they all move to about the same place. As to what these four amines are, the only thing I can say is that I do not think that they are di- or tri-methoxyphenylethylamines. They are eluted from Amberlite CG-50 column very much earlier than authentic 3,4-dimethoxyphenylethylamine, 3,4-dimethoxyphenylethanolamine, 2,5-dimethoxyphenylethylamine, mescaline, and betahydroxy-mescaline. The only spray I have found these four unidentified amines to respond to is ninhydrin-lutidine. They do not respond to sprays for phenols or imidazols or indoles, and unfortunately they behave exactly like 3,4-dimethoxyphenylethylamine. They give the same color change after ninhydrin when chromatograms are sprayed with the Ehrlich reagent. We have found that there are some other compounds, for instance N-butylamine, which when sprayed with ninhydrin and then counter-sprayed with Ehrlich reagent will give this same color. I do not know what the four unidentified amines are, but I doubt that they are phenylethylamine derivatives.

Discussion after Dr. Bourdillon's Paper

Kety: Dr. Bourdillon, I think in your quiet way you have produced quite a blast with your cogently controlled studies. They have certainly given support to the existence of this substance and its correlation to schizophrenia.

Horwitt: I have a few questions with respect to technique. First of all, I am assuming you used bi-dimensional techniques. In collecting the urine, were these 24-hr samples?

Bourdillon: Bi-dimensional techniques were used in some but not in all the samples tested. The urine was collected for 24 hr in a few instances. In most of the samples examined by Friedhoff and Van Winkle's method a 20-hr urine sample was obtained and in the blind trial (Experiment III) a 16-hr overnight sample was used throughout the series.

Horwitt: Did you attempt to control the differences one gets in the morning collections, say between non-schizophrenics and schizophrenics, because the schizophrenic urine in the morning is very often a negative nitrogen urine.

Bourdillon: No, I cannot say we did. The samples were collected over the same period in both schizophrenics and non-schizophrenics because we did not know what was which at the time of testing.

Horwitt: Unfortunately, it is recognized, but not too often applied, that the morning urine you get in hospitalized schizophrenics is very often obtained from a condition of strong negative nitrogen balance because they often eat nothing for 14 hr. You will get many more amine products in such samples. If you collect just the morning urine and then compare it with a so-called normal subject whose daily cycle might be 3 hr later, different results should be expected.

Bourdillon: No attempt has been made to allow for a possible negative nitrogen balance occurring in the schizophrenic patients, but the results speak for themselves.

Horwitt: At many of our hospitals they stop feeding at 4.30 to 5.00 p.m. and we collect the urine at 7.00 or 8.00 a.m. the next morning after a long starvation period. A word about the problem of drug withdrawal which of course bothers all of us. In our work on depot fats in schizophrenics, it has taken us more than 6 months to clear compounds that get into their depot fats. An interval of 1 or 2 weeks has almost no meaning in clearing chlorpromazine.

Bourdillon: I agree that examination of patients receiving drugs is not satisfactory and we were not satisfied. We have examined some patients who had not received any drugs for 2 months and others who had never received any drug therapy at all.

HORWITT: The last question I have, and I hope I am asking questions that are in the minds of others here, is regarding the size of the samples you used to determine your spots. I had previously indicated that we at first had limited success. After we changed our techniques slightly and increased the size of our sample, we found the spots in question. We find it necessary, in order to quantitize our readings on the so-called "pink spot", to use half the total daily urine excretion. I might say that we were usually not successful using only 100–200 ml of urine.

KETY: I have one question that Dr. Horwitt did not ask. I believe you said, although I am not sure, that the studies in normals and in schizophrenics were done concurrently in the same laboratory at the same time.

BOURDILLON: The studies in the normals and schizophrenics overlapped to a small extent only. We were able to deal with a limited number of samples at any one time and it would not have been practicable to run several large surveys simultaneously.

KETY: Were they randomized or did you examine the control urines in one stage and the urines of schizophrenics in another?

BOURDILLON: The controls were done as a separate study but, as you may see from the results, many non-schizophrenic patients were tested at the same time as the schizophrenics.

KETY: What was the order, especially in the early stages of the work?

BOURDILLON: In the early stages of the work a small pilot survey was carried out in which both schizophrenic patients and mentally normal individuals were examined. Experiment II was next in chronological order and overlapped Experiment I, the survey of mentally normal individuals. Experiment III, the blind trial, was carried out last of the work reported here. The family studies have been done at the same time as the other experiments. I think it is almost impossible to control dietary factors in a busy mental hospital.

KETY: Mrs. Ridges collaborated with Dr. Bourdillon. Would you like to comment?

RIDGES: In our experiments we had no control over the diets of the individuals whose urines we examined, but the evidence we have obtained is against dietary factors being responsible for the production of DMPEA. The diet of the non-schizophrenics included in our experiments was so varied as to make likely that "pink spot" would have been detected had it resulted from a dietary constituent. The point has already been made in the paper that patients who had been in the same hospitals for comparable periods to the schizophrenics were not excreting the "pink spot".

HORWITT: This question of liver dysfunction in state hospital populations is being used more frequently. It may be of interest that we are now finding that one out of five patients will give a high bromsulphalein retention time. If anyone asked me if there was one special "test in schizophrenia", after 25 years of studying many of them I would say that the liver function test is most consistently the one that turns out to give the greatest difference from normals. However, since both prolonged stress and prolonged consumption of pharmacological reagents can both cause changes in liver function, work in this area is different to controls. Obviously, a change in the rate at which the liver can handle metabolites of catecholamines or tryptophan will give you differences in the levels of related compounds in the urine. How much this affects the topics we are discussing cannot be determined without more and better metabolic studies on schizophrenic patients. My last word is that "liver function" is like "stress" and like "schizophrenia". We do not know exactly with what we are dealing.

KETY: Perhaps we may have some general discussion at this time of all the papers dealing with the presence or absence of dimehoxyphenylethylamine in urines of normals or schizophrenics and the implications of these for schizophrenia.

BALDESSARINI: The following table attempts to summarize most of the available reports of finding 3,4-dimethoxyphenylethylamine (DMPEA) in the urine of schizophrenic and normal patients but is complete only through late 1964.

The most striking figures are the totals, which indicate that 63 % of reported cases of schizophrenia had the chromatographic spot in question, while only 31 % of control urines had it. The main questions that come to mind concern the significance of the spot in normal urine and its apparent failure to appear in some cases when the patient has been given a plant-free diet. Furthermore, does the presence of the spot in only some schizophrenic patients' urine suggest a diagnostic subdivision among schizophrenics? In summary, these summarized figures and the very impressive new data presented today cannot but help to leave the impression that the chromatographic spot in question has been found more frequently in the urine of schizophrenic patients than in the urine of controls.

HOLMSTEDT: Mr. Chairman, may I ask you a very rapid question? Isn't it more reasonable to look for the acids corresponding to the amines? This seems to be the conclusion of Dr. Friedhoff after some time, and he has been primarily working with the amines. I will give you a good example of what I mean. In the skin disease *Urticaria pigmentosa* we know that there is a release of histamine. If we measure histamine in urine we do not find any value different from the histamine content of normal urine, but if we measure the corresponding imidazole acids, we get a tremendous increase, almost a hundred times the normal value.

CHROMATOGRAPHIC DETECTION OF URINARY DMPEA (POSITIVE/TOTAL)

Schizophrenics	Controls	Reference
15/17	0/14	Friedhoff (1)
57/62 (on tranquilizers)	21/46	Takesada (2)
13/16 (off tranquilizers)		
0/10 (plant-free diet)	—	Perry (3)
4/22	0/1	Sen (4)
5/12 (Friedoff's patients)	0/10	Kuehl (5)
2/3	2/4	Baldessarini (6)
0/2 (plant-free diet)	—	Gjessing (7)
98/156 63%	23/75 31%	TOTALS

1. FRIEDHOFF, A. J. and VAN WINKLE, E., *J. Nerv. Ment. Dis.* **135,** 550 (1962).
2. TAKESADA, M., KAKIMOTO, Y., SANO, I. and KAMIKO, Z., *Nature*, **199,** 203 (1963).
3. PERRY, T. L., HANSEN, S. and MACINTYRE, L., *Nature*, **202,** 519 (1964).
4. SEN, N. P. and MCGEER, P. L., *Biochem. Biophys. Res. Comm.* **14,** 227 (1964).
5. KUEHL, F. A., HICHENS, M., ORMOND, R. E., MEISINGER, M. A. P., GALE, P. H., CIRILLO, V. J. and BRINK, N. G., *Nature*, **203,** 154 (1964).
6. BALDESSARINI, R. J. and KOPIN, I., unpublished observations (1963).
7. GJESSING, R., personal communication (1964).

This is but one example; I believe there are many. As a matter of fact, Dr. Friedhoff, since the ratio between the acid and amines is so tremendous, and since you are examining the urines now for the acids, could you give us just a little insight as to whether you have enough information yet on schizophrenics as compared to normals with regard to the dimethoxy series.

KETY: As a matter of fact, Dr. Friedhoff, since the ratio between the acid and amine is so tremendous and since you are examining the urines now for the acids, could you give us some insight on whether you have any information yet in schizophrenics or in normals with respect to the dimethoxy acids?

FRIEDHOFF: No, we have just developed a method that is working to our satisfaction for the determination of acids. The reason why we originally looked at the amines—we looked at the acids at the same time—is because the acid faction is very dirty and it is tremendously difficult to separate all the acids, one from the other, while with the amines it is a little easier. So even though there may be more acids, the technical problems are greater I think, so we have now mastered these and I believe Dr. Kuehl has another method.

SCHILDKRAUT: I was wondering if there might be a blood-brain barrier of significance which limited the exit of dimethoxyphenylethylamine from brain. Before leaving the brain might most of the amine be converted to the acid? Has this been studied? What are the relative psychomimetic powers of mescaline and DMPEA?

HIMWICH: As far as can be estimated from the criterion of i.v. injections adequate to evoke EEG alerting, we may say that mescaline is approximately three to four times more potent than DMPEA.

BERLET: I would like to add a word to Dr. Holmstedt's remark. On the urinary excretion of amines, Erspamer and his group (Erspamer, V. and Bertaccini, G., *Arch. Int. Pharmacol. Pharmacodyn.* **137**, 6, 1962; Erspamer, V. and Nobili, N. B., *ibid.* **137**, 24, 1962) have studied the fate of 4-hydroxytryptophan and 5-hydroxytryptophan and their urinary metabolites. On the basis of their experiments they come to the conclusion that only the acids excreted in the urine seem to reflect tissue levels of the precursor amines. For instance, if the 5-HTP or 4-HTP were injected subcutaneously only a small percentage was excreted as serotonin or 4-hydroxytrypamine. If injected intravenously, however, a large portion of 5-HTP and 4-HTP was recovered as the corresponding amine. They concluded therefore that urinary amines may be primarily derived from precursor amino acids in the plasma rather than originating as amines from body tissues directly. If this view is applied to our considerations today we must postulate the presence of both 3,4-dimethoxyphenylethylamine and 4-dimethoxyphenylethylamine in the blood steam.

SMYTHIES: Is there any evidence that these abnormal compounds may be present in cerebrospinal fluid?

————: I might try answering Dr. Smythies's question, but I must say my experimental results in that direction are discouraging. In the first place, some years ago, we tried to examine cerebrospinal fluids of phenylketonurics as compared with mongoloid children while both groups were on monoamine oxidase inhibitors. We were looking for phenylethylamine and orthotyramine as possible substances to explain the mental defect in phenylketonuria. We found nothing in 20 mm of cerebrospinal fluid. More recently, we collected a large amount of pooled lumbar cerebrospinal fluid simply by getting a friendly anesthesiologist to save us 4 or 5 ml every time when he withdrew it just before giving spinal anesthesia. These were frozen immediately and pooled and we worked up 320 ml but were disappointed to find the only amines we could detect were ethanolamine and piperadine—there was quite a bit of piperadine, surprisingly, in cerebrospinal fluid. But we found no serotonin, no tryptamine, none of the others. I should add that our techniques have never been adequate for working with catecholamines, so we obviously did not study them. But we found, for instance, absolutely no serotonin in cerebrospinal fluid and I suspect that when it has been reported that it may well have come from small amounts of platelets subsequent to tiny hemorrhages. We had hoped that we would find enough of these that we could then compare schizophrenics and other psychotics with normals, but taking 320 ml is rather impractical.

KETY: I would like to go back to Dr. Bourdillon, whose results are so compelling that one is driven to think of every possible alternative explanation for this than the one which seems most obvious. Were there any differences in the extent of hospitalization or the place in which the patients lived between the schizophrenics and non-schizophrenic individuals? I raise this question because it is conceivable that a group of individuals living together for a period of time in close proximity and fed from the same kitchen develop a common type of intestinal flora which might not be exhibited by another group. I expect that your schizophrenics and non-schizophrenics were quite randomized throughout the hospital in regard to duration to stays.

BOURDILLON: Yes, for instance some of the chronic cases examined were mental defectives who had been in the hospital for many years and largely in the same wards and under the same conditions as chronic schizophrenic patients who had also been there for about the same period. I can only repeat that we did not apparently show this phenomenon in those cases. These studies were completely blind—we did not know anything and I do not think there is any significant difference between these two groups overall as to length of stay in the hospital and in regard to diet. They were under the same conditions as far as we can gather.

SPRINCE: In the slide shown by Dr. Baldessarini, it was my impression that the Japanese investigators found a relatively high incidence of Dr. Friedhoff's compound in their normal subjects. Could we have that slide again for a moment? This finding again raises the question of dietary differences.

RODNIGHT: Mrs. Ridges did try this Japanese method on a few cases.

RIDGES: Yes, I tried it and I think Dr. Friedhoff has also mentioned having used it.

SPRINCE: See the high incidence of normals (21 out of 46) showing this compound in Dr. Baldessarini's slide.

FRIEDHOFF: If you calculate the percentage of the schizophrenics in which we found dimethoxyphenylethylamine it was about 70%. With the Japanese method it is about 92%, which is higher than that observed by anybody else. In repeating this method we felt that specificity of the Japanese method was rather low and this perhaps accounts for the high incidence in schizophrenia. It may also account for a certain number of false positives in normals. Now whether this accounts for all the positive normals is impossible to say.

RICHTER: May I just comment on the suggestion that one might look for the acids instead of the amines. It seems to me that these show entirely different things. Whereas the acid excretion is reasonably related to the total amount of amines released in the body, the excretion of amines is surely a reflection rather of the efficacy of the monoamine oxidase in removing the last traces of amines or of the transport mechanisms taking the amines to the sites where the enzymes act upon them.

SPRINCE: Just to follow up on that point. In the case of the indoles, it should be remembered that indoleacetic acid can arise not only by way of an amine (tryptamines) but also by way of a keto-acid (indolepyruvic acid). An analogous situation holds true for phenylacetic acid originating from phenylalanine. This point now raises a new area to consider, namely that 3,4-dimethoxyphenylacetic acid could originate from 3,4-dimethoxyphenylalanine via a keto-acid pathway as well as the amine pathway which we have been discussing this morning. It might be of interest, therefore, to look for the increased frequency of occurrence of 3,4-dimethoxyphenylethylamine.

————: The indolepyruvic acid is extremely difficult to isolate. In practically every bi-dimensional solvent system indolepyruvic acid which we ran, we found it breaks down into anywhere from six to eleven different substances, so I wonder whether anyone has genuinely seen it.

SPRINCE: On theoretical grounds, I am just trying to emphasize that if work on 3,4-dimethoxyphenylacetic acid turns out to be promising, then one ought to consider a keto-acid pathway for this acid as well as the amine pathway which currently is commanding so much attention.

KETY: I would like to raise a question which deals with the sociological aspects of science and which may be relevant here. That is, the obvious tendency of scientists to publish positive findings and their reluctance to publish negative results. It may be that many people in this room have, like Dr. Baldessarini, done a very preliminary trial to see if they could find the dimethoxyphenylethylamine and have not published their results because the study was very preliminary, inexact and they were not entirely satisfied with it. But it would still be interesting to know what information there was on the existence of these studies. I wonder if there are people in this room who have tried this and would they tell us about their experiences simply that we get the whole picture rather than a possible biased picture in favor of positive findings.

RICHTER: I would like to mention that Dr. Nishimura told me he had done some work on this problem but was not able to find this amine in the urine.

KETY (*added after conference*): There have been three additional reports of failure to find DMPEA in schizophrenic patients: Faurbye, A. and Pind, K. (*Acta psychiatrica scand.* **40,** 240, 1964) were unable to demonstrate it in chronic schizophrenic patients. Nishimura, T. and Gjessing, L. R. (*Nature,* **206,** 963, 1965) did not find it in the urine of a periodic catatonic patient on a plant-free diet. Studnitz, W. (unpublished) was unable to confirm its presence in the urine of schizophrenics.

RIDGES: I would like to ask Dr. Friedhoff a question concerning the method of Takesada *et al.*, which you say you have tried. Using their method did you in fact get positive results in the mentally normal individuals you investigated?

FRIEDHOFF: I did not mean to suggest that. We have repeated their method though we have not done any studies with it. If I interpret Takesada's report correctly, the final identification of this material is made only with ninhydrin and thereafter he is simply identifying amines. We find a failure to separate dimethoxyphenylethylamine from other amines while using his column system. We have not, however, done studies with his method.

RIDGES: I have investigated a small series of normal individuals using the method of Takesada *et al.* and did not obtain any positive results, as I would have expected if it was simply a question of the different methods employed. This has led me to think that possibly some other factor such as diet or social difference is responsible for their results.

KETY: Although the question of dietary factors has been raised appropriately, I still find myself somewhat dissatisfied with the evidence that we have on this aspect of the question. It would have been more cogent, I think, had Dr. Perry found patients who showed this spot in this laboratory and then found the spot to disappear if he put them on the plant-free diet. It would have been equally worth while if Dr. Friedhoff or those who do find the spot in uncontrolled dietary situations were then to test the same subjects on a plant-free diet. But unfortunately neither group has yet done that so I am left somewhat at a loss to know what conclusive summation one can make in terms of dietary factors. I would agree with Dr. Smythies that merely finding it to be of dietary origin does not force its irrelevance to schizophrenia unless one can explain why the diets of schizophrenics should be so consistently different from that of normals or other patients in psychiatric institutions.

SPRINCE: In attempting to answer this point, it should be remembered (leaving the question of diet aside for the moment) that most of the techniques of measurement of 3,4-dimethoxyphenylethylamine seem to be based on relating this compound to urinary creatinine. This raises a question about the variability of creatinine excretion which Dr. Himwich may want to comment upon. I should also like to raise the question as to whether a sufficient volume of urine is being used by different investigators for the detection and assay of 3,4-dimethoxyphenylethylamine. You say there is no place but the diet to get it from. In other words, the loads would have to depend on the diet. Dr. Horwitt, what I was thinking was this: suppose someone did the experiment which calls for being done; let us say as in Dr. Bourdillon's study which so clearly differentiates schizophrenics from non-schizophrenics. If such studies were carried out now in patients on a plant-free diet using Dr. Perry's technique and then the compound disappeared in all the patients on a plant-free diet, it would still not indicate that this may not be of significance in schizophrenia. Even though the compound may come from plants, it may go through all the pathways before excretion in terms of some factor of which schizophrenia is a variable.

HORWITT: Well, this is the point I unsuccessfully tried to make earlier. Of course, if this meeting had been held four months earlier, I would have been among those very strongly stating that we could not find it. But because it was held today instead of four months earlier, I can say we found it but not by the techniques which were reported. We had to change the technique and use larger amounts of urine. Obviously there are little technical differences which will give large disparities in data from different laboratories because chromatography unfortunately happens to have that particular variable in it—the person doing it. Because of this we felt that it was important to take the protein out of the diet for one group. Now it so happens that we had a large group of patients who happen to be not on plant-free diets and do not show it even by our better technique. Then we have a smaller group of patients who although not on a plant-free diet were fed a low level of protein and on this level, the compound in urine decreased about 75%. So all these variables have to come into this picture when you analyze this protein. Now I would like to agree with what Dr. Smythies had alluded to before, that what you get from the diet might not only be due to the load but also the liver or tissue dysfunction, or differences due to stress that may be taking place, and these factors may be the reason for getting more or less of the compound. I am really surprised by some reports; I do not question them, I am just surprised that we do not get any of the compound in question in some of the normals of so large a group. But that is why we are here.

SMYTHIES: The point I was going to make is this—schizophrenics may be different, not because of their liver dysfunction or other such differences. What you may be seeing, even if there are dietary constitutuents in this phenomenon, is that there may be an underlying disorder of metabolism in the schizophrenic which makes him unable to deal with this added dietary load, whatever it is, 3,4-dimethoxyphenylethylamine or some precursor of this. We have been hearing much about this phenomenon, but I think we ought to link it up with the other evidence that there is disorder of metabolism in the schizophrenic which we will be talking about this afternoon, i.e. about the effects of feeding methionine and betaine and that this all points to the possibility that there may be something wrong with the methylation.

PSCHEIDT: Just to continue briefly with the effect of diet; there is another possibility that what you see may not involve some constituent of the diet. To return to the slide that Dr. Himwich showed, our finding here was that when we put our schizophrenic patients on a low-tryptophan, low-methione diet at around the minimum daily requirement, possibly a little bit less, the urinary dopamine increased. Now in the published paper we speculated that this may represent an inability to methylate dopamine. In other words, that under these conditions we are getting more dopamine and less of the methylated metabolite which again could apply with equal strength to the formation of the dimethoxy compounds so that if there is a defect in the methylation or defect in the absorption or dietary utilization of the available methyl groups in different patients, you will obtain differences in the excretion of methylated products and that would not be due to a contaminant or spurious compound present in the diet. In other words, you would have to take two different types of dietary effects on the excretion of an abnormal compound.

PERRY: I have several odds and ends I want to discuss here. First of all, on the general question of dietary sources of amines or other chemical substances which might produce mental disease, I think we all should recognize that this is a real possibility and that we should look for them. A good example is that in a culture where people do not drink milk there would be no mental deficiency from galactosemia. It might be that amines of plant or animal origin which are ingested in the diet or which are produced by intestinal bacteria are normally detoxified in most of us but cannot be detoxified by psychotics. Certainly one should be looking for these, and I am afraid that I did not emphasize that enough in my talk.

I think the point that has been made about using large amounts of urine to search for an unusual compound is important. I have not used more than a 300 mg creatinine equivalent of the urine of an acute schizophrenic not on monoamine oxidase inhibition not more than about 200–300 mg creatinine equivalent of the urine of a chronic schizophrenic on monoamine oxidase blockade. Perhaps I have not used enough, and I think the point that one might use a whole day's worth of urine is important. I think the point that has been made about collecting urine over a long period of time is important. We have tried at least to do this, so all of our collections are 48-hr urines.

I wanted to say regarding the Japanese workers' technique that it is a good way of recovering 3,4-dimethoxyphenylethylamine from urine but not a very good way of separating it from other urinary amines recovered. The key point is that one simply cannot separate by any two-dimensional paper chromatographic system that I have seen 3,4-dimethoxyphenylethylamine from many other urinary bases which also are going to be recovered. One has to, I think, rely on either an additional column chromatographic method or a gas chromatographic method to separate the complex mixture of amines recovered from urine.

The final thing I want to say is that I think it is most important for us to try to design better experiments and not be so intimidated by psychiatrists. If you will excuse me as a non-psychiatrist for saying so, we tend to say that because most of the psychiatrists do not want us taking their patients off phenothiazine tranquilizers, or because they do not want us doing this or that or the other thing, that therefore we cannot do it. I think that the stakes are very high and that it is most important that we begin finding out what are some of the biochemical cases of schizophrenia and whether we cannot do something about preventing them or treating them. The only way we can do this is to design proper experiments. So it seems to me that perhaps if the mentally ill were hospitalized more in general hospitals and if they did not get so far away from physicians, if they were handled on regular medical wards and were handled by physicians who were closer to biological causes of disease, that we might do better. I think that none of us should be satisfied with *not* getting dietary controls if we want them, and none of us should be satisfied with *not* having patients off phenothiazine tranquilizers for a month or more, if that is what we want. I think we could answer this question as to whether or not 3,4-dimethoxyphenylethylamine is particularly related to the schizophrenias. Anybody who wants to be bold enough to organize the project in chronic patients and study them first on a regular diet and then on a plant-free diet and maybe then on a low-protein diet should find out whether or not 3,4-dimethoxyphenylethylamine is excreted in urine during these various periods. One can either study the urinary excretion of the corresponding acid or one can use monoamine oxidase blockade if one wants to study the amine itself. It seems to me that if we put together the different kinds of experiments we have all been doing, it ought to be possible to get a very solid answer one way or the other.

RODNIGHT: Well, I would say Dr. Perry has made the point that I was going to and that is the importance of collecting urines over a long period of time and to freeze each sample as you get it.

BERLET: I would like to raise a question. Is there any report in the literature in which someone has been able to show the presence of 3,4-dimethoxyphenylethylamine or an enzyme system concerned with its formation, for instance in plants? It is obvious that if plant material is suspected to interfere we should look for this particular amine.

KUEHL: There is an enzyme from a plant called *Nerine boudenii* that para-O-methylates catechols. Although dopamine is a substrate for this enzyme the question as to whether it forms 3,4-dimethoxyphenylethylamine from dopamine remains unanswered.

SPRINCE: Is this compound, 3,4-dimethoxyphenylethylamine, found in the urine, blood or tissues of any laboratory animals? The rat, I take it, does not look promising. But how about other laboratory animals?

HIMWICH: I should perhaps say we have not looked for it yet in our dogs with *Eck fistulas* and various stress circumstances, but I certainly intend to go home and look; I hope I find it.

STUDIES ON THE ASSOCIATION OF URINARY TRYPTAMINE WITH THE EXCRETION OF AMINO ACIDS AND 17-KETOSTEROID HORMONES IN SCHIZOPHRENIC PATIENTS

H. H. BERLET,[1] J. K. SPAIDE, K. MATSUMOTO[2] and H. E. HIMWICH
Thudichum Psychiatric Research Laboratory, Galesburg State Research Hospital, Galesburg, Illinois

INTRODUCTION

URINARY indole compounds and their relation to mental diseases, especially schizophrenia, have been the object of numerous studies. The interest in these investigations has been revived in recent years by the discovery of pharmaceutical agents and their potent psychic effects as well as their structural similarities with tryptophan. The particular object of indole studies was therefore to reveal possible abnormalities of the metabolism of tryptophan leading to the endogenous formation of indole derivatives similar in structure and action to known pharmacological agents. Quantitative variations of urinary indoles in relation to schizophrenic behavior have been studied extensively in our laboratory as one aspect of this problem. Brune and Pscheidt (1961) and Brune and Himwich (1962) have found in their studies that schizophrenic patients periodically eliminate larger amounts of indoles, not primarily in relation to the underlying mental illness but in relation to momentary changes of intensity of certain psychotic symptoms. Increases were reported which involved 3-IAA,* tryptamine and 5-HIAA and it was suggested that elevations of indoles in plasma and possibly in tissue may facilitate the formation of indolalkylamines similar to those found in plant material (Stromberg, 1954; Holmstedt *et al.*, 1964) or prepared by chemical synthesis (Stoll *et al.*, 1955; Heinzelman and Szmuszkovicz, 1963). Even so the implication of an abnormal tryptophan metabolism in schizophrenia

[1] H. H. Berlet, M.D., Neurologische Klinik und Poliklinik, Universitaet Goettingen, Goettingen, Germany.

[2] Kei Matsumoto, M.D., Department of Neuropsychiatry, Osaka City University Medical School, Asahi-Machi, Abeno-ku, Osaka, Japan.

* Abbreviations used: α-amino-acid nitrogen, α-A.A.N.; 5-hydroxyindole-3-acetic acid, 5-HIAA; indole-3-acetic acid, 3-IAA; 17-ketosteroids, 17-KS; 1-methylnicotinamide, 1-MNA.

had to remain but a working hypothesis as long as two main questions were left to be answered. Where do the urinary indoles come from and indole increases linked to other metabolic or endocrine mechanisms?

The first question about the origin of urinary indoles is concerned with the contributions of dietary tryptophan to excretory indole products. More recent studies (Berlet *et al.*, 1964b) in our laboratory in this regard have shown that increases of urinary indoles can occur independently from tryptophan intake provided that a fairly constant amount of tryptophan is contained in the diet and actually consumed by the patients. The same studies have revealed that the excretion rates of tryptamine are significantly correlated to those of creatinine in patients exhibiting variable excretions of both tryptamine and creatinine. This relationship between creatinine and tryptamine was considered an indication that the major part of the urinary tryptamine must come from endogenous sources. Tryptamine was therefore tentatively termed an endogenous factor in schizophrenic behavior (Berlet *et al.*, 1964a).

At the same time the relationship between tryptamine and creatinine provided a clue to the second question concerning the link of rises of urinary indoles to the overall metabolism of the body in schizophrenics. The important point in this connection is whether increases of indoles are a specific phenomenon such as increases of particular amino acids in amino acidopathies or serotonin in the carcinoid syndrome or whether they are part of other metabolic mechanisms. Concomitant releases of creatinine in our studies had already suggested that increases of urinary indoles originate from endogenous sources, possibly from an increased protein breakdown. We consequently reasoned that if there was in fact a general breakdown of protein we should expect rises of other related urinary constituents. We decided therefore to study the excretion of other urinary constituents which are either related to the metabolism of tryptophan or to that of amino acids and proteins in general. We had also an opportunity to study the steroid hormone excretion along with these constituents.

METHODS

Two chronic male schizophrenic patients in good physical health were studied. Their ages were 47 (E. S.) and 53 (J. F.) years respectively. They had been without psychotropic medication for 8 months prior to the beginning of this observation. They displayed active psychotic symptoms like withdrawal, disorganized thinking, hostility to the occasional degree of attempted agression and somatic delusions. J. F.'s behavior pattern changed in a typical way approximately every 10–15 days. First he was usually very withdrawn, lethargic, slow and without any contact with reality. At the end of this quiet period he then began to become more active in pacing and staying up. This was accompanied by gradually progressing intensifications of hyperactivity, hostility, loudness to the degree of bursts of shouting, and delusions about time and location. The other patient, E. S., was not predictable in his behavior. He usually responded with increased delusional somatic complaints and marked hostility towards other patients and ward personnel as soon as he received less attention or another patient received more attention than he did for medical reasons for instance. These outbursts did not last longer than 1 day and in this way his behavioral pattern was most typical for its sudden and unexpected changes.

For comparison three mental defectives with an IQ of 70 and of a comparable age range and in good physical health were submitted to the same evaluation. All patients were maintained on our metabolic ward and received a specially prepared diet. This diet was controlled as previously described (Berlet *et al.*, 1964a) with respect to the content of tryptophan, protein, fat and calories. The actual daily intake was recorded for each patient. The schizophrenic patients received this standard diet 2 months before as well as throughout the observation period. In contrast, the mental defectives, serving as controls, received a "low" protein and tryptophan diet. During the actual observation period their daily calorie intake was reduced from the original amount of 2500 cal/day to 1000 cal/day. This reduction was done in order to cause weight losses and to determine the effect of induced weight losses on urinary excretion patterns.

In addition to tryptamine (Sjoerdsma *et al.*, 1959) we determined the daily excretion of such urinary constituents as total alpha-amino-acid nitrogen Müting and Kaiser, 1963) total urinary nitrogen (Scales and Harrison, 1920), creatinine and 1-methylnicotinamide (Jaffe's alcaline picrate method, in *Practical Physiological Chemistry*, 1949; Pelletier and Campbell, 1962). Determinations were also made for 17-KS (Natelson, 1957) but not for 17-OHCS because the urines had been acidified for preservation during collection. Aliquots of representative urine samples were analyzed for individual amino acids on the Beckman amino-acid analyzer using the methods of Moore *et al.* (1958).[1]

Urine collections for daily determinations were made in the two schizophrenics for periods ranging from 16 to 20 consecutive days and a single collection over a period of 18 consecutive days was made in the control subjects. Urines were acidified with 10 ml 6 N HCl and kept frozen unless analyzed immediately.

RESULTS (PART I)

Figures 1–4 show the daily urinary excretion patterns of the two schizophrenic patients. Figure 1 (patient J. F.) discloses a close relationship of the tryptamine pattern to that of the three other constituents and a repeated coincidence of increased excretory rates of all four categories. The best

[1] We are indebted to Dr. W. A. Himwich and her co-workers for the determinations of urinary amino acids.

correlation as far as high and low excretion rates are concerned appears to exist between creatinine and tryptamine. In Fig. 1, on the 6th and 7th day, however, there is a delay of 1 day between the peaks of creatinine and tryptamine, as well as that of the total amino acids and 1-methylnicotinamide. When the increases of all four constituents on the 6th and 7th day are calculated as increases in per cent of the values of the 5th or 6th day it is

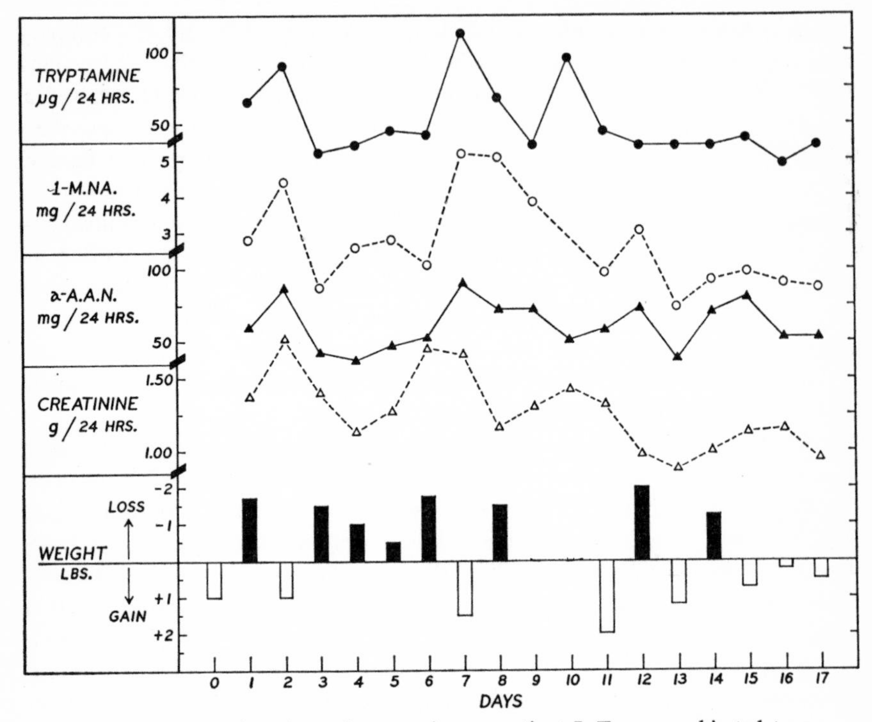

FIG. 1. The excretion data of tryptamine on patient J. F. were subjected to a statistical analysis for their correlation (r) with 1-methyl-nicotinamide (1-MNA), total alpha-amino-acid nitrogen (alpha-A.A.N.) and creatinine (Rosander, 1951). A significant correlation ($p < 0{\cdot}05$) of tryptamine was obtained with creatinine ($r = +0{\cdot}66$), 1-MNA ($r = +0{\cdot}62$) and alpha-A.A.N. ($r = +0{\cdot}55$).

revealed that increases of tryptamine and 1-methylnicotinamide are very similar (approx. 200%) while the increase of amino acids is only 100% and that of creatinine only 50% of the base values. Figure 1 also shows that the excretion values tend to return to a stable base line after temporary increases remaining at the same level in the case of tryptamine, 1-MNA and amino acids and showing only a slight decline in the case of creatinine. With regard to weight fluctuations listed in this figure, we were first inclined to assume that weight losses may account for increases of excretion rates of amino acids and metabolites. A comparison of peak excretions and weight fluctuations, however, fails to reveal a consistent pattern. The net loss over 17 days in this patient was less than 1 kg. Figure 2 tabulates the results of a 21-day collection period in the second schizophrenic patient (E. S.) with daily excretion rates for tryptamine, 1-methylnicotinamide, alpha-amino-acid nitrogen and creatinine. The overall pattern is very similar to that of Fig. 1. When the results are examined for a delay between tryptamine and creatinine one notices on this figure only simultaneous rises of tryptamine and creatinine. However, while creatinine begins to return to the base line, tryptamine con-

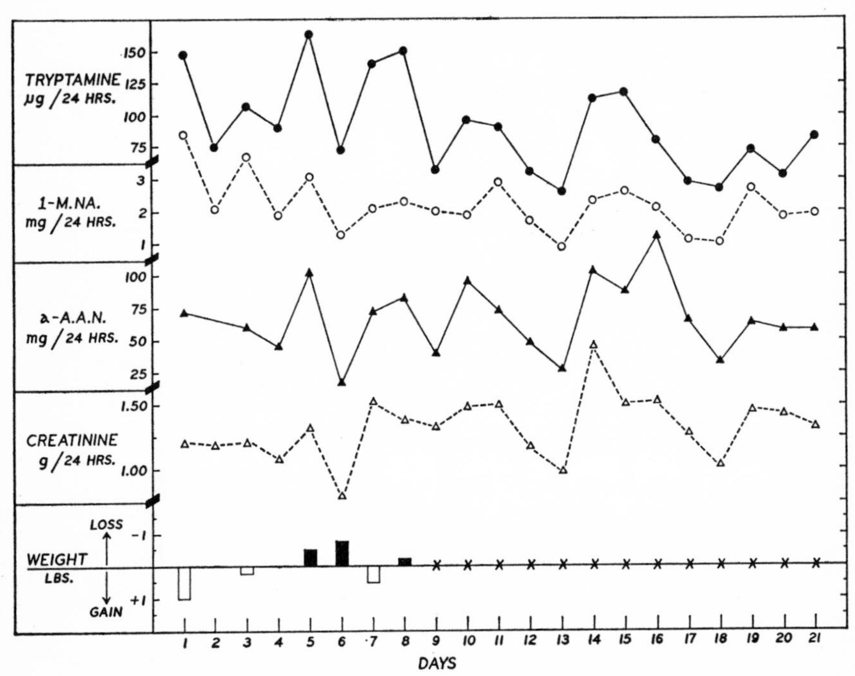

FIG. 2. The correlation of the tryptamine values of patient E. S. is significant with creatinine ($r = +0{\cdot}46$), 1-MNA ($r = +0{\cdot}65$) and alpha-A.A.N. ($r = +0{\cdot}70$). The patient refused to be weighed from day 9 to 21 (X–X).

tinues to rise (e.g. on the 7th and 8th day or on the 14th and 15th day). There also appears to be a slight dissociation between tryptamine and 1-MNA in regard to the quantitative rise over basal values. This dissociation, however, is not found consistently. Comparisons with weight were not possible in this case because the patient refused to be weighed on 15 out of 21 observation days.

Essentially the same observations are given in Figs. 3 and 4 showing the results of the second urine collection in the two schizophrenic patients. It should be mentioned, however, that patient E. S. (Fig. 4) displayed a net gain of approximately 0·2 kg in this period and of approximately 1½ kg in

3 months during which the collections were carried out, while the other patients experienced a net loss of 1·3 kg in this period and an overall loss of 3 kg.

If the data are examined for a possible order in which increases of these constituents occurred one may say that there is an occasional tendency for creatinine to precede rises of tryptamine, 1-methylnicotinamide and total alpha-amino-acid nitrogen.

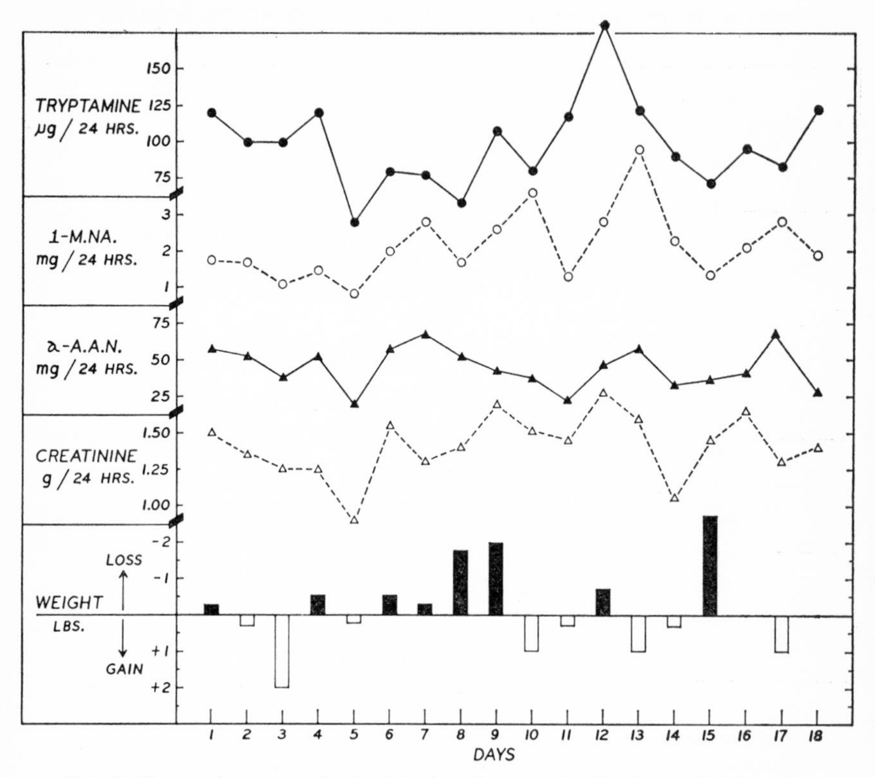

FIG. 3. These values were obtained during the second collection period in J. F. The correlation of tryptamine was significant only with creatinine ($r = +0{\cdot}60$).

Urinary 17-*KS in Relation to Total Urinary Nitrogen and Total Alpha-amino-acid Nitrogen*

In addition to the relationship of tryptamine to the excretion of related metabolic compounds we were interested in the interaction between steroid hormones and amino acids in general. We hoped that a comparison under this aspect would be revealing although the urinary 17-KS are only partially derived from steroids known to be related to the utilization of glucose or to the metabolism of nitrogen.

Figure 5 shows the excretion pattern of steroids, alpha-amino-acid nitrogen and total urinary nitrogen in J. F. The fluctuations of steroid hormones are closely associated with comparable fluctuations of the other two measurements. In addition, increases of 17-KS show a tendency to precede rises of total amino-acid nitrogen or urinary nitrogen and to return to low values ahead of the nitrogen values. This pattern is evident in this patient on the 3rd and 4th day, on the 6th and 7th and on the 15th through 17th day of his collection period.

Figure 6 on the same measurements in the second schizophrenic patient

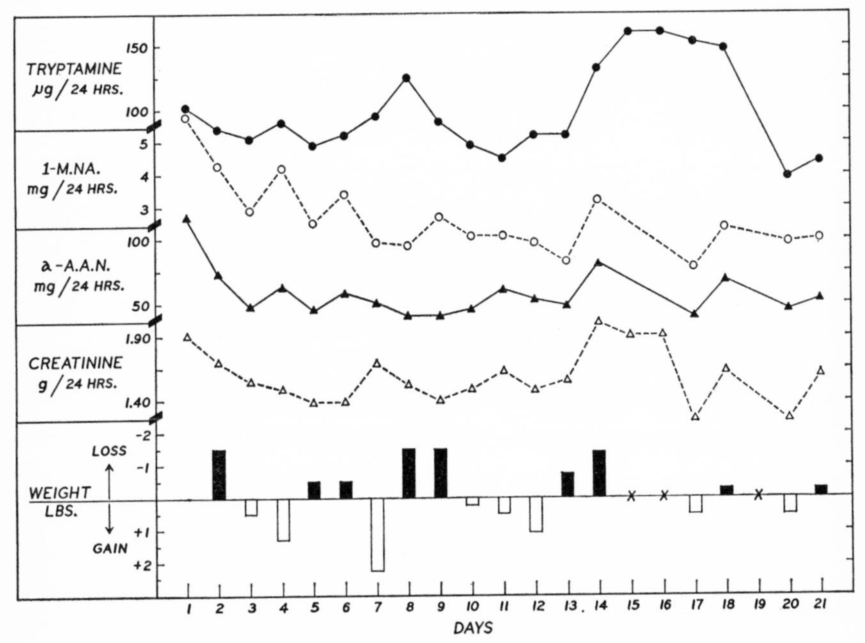

FIG. 4. These values were obtained during the second collection period in E. S. The correlation of tryptamine was only significant with creatinine ($r = +0{\cdot}42$). Assays for 1-MNA and alpha-A.A.N. of the 15th and 16th could not be carried out because the urine samples were lost. On the 15th, 16th and 19th day the patient refused to be weighed.

discloses an almost identical pattern. In addition the excretion rates of 17-KS show a wave-like pattern which was not as clearly evident from the preceding figure. A delay between rises of steroids and those of nitrogen is also evident.

As mentioned in the beginning, we have subjected three control patients to the same type of evaluation as our schizophrenic patients. In addition the controls were maintained on a diet which was designed to induce weight losses or at least weight fluctuations.

Figure 7 contains a composite comparison of the excretion data which were obtained in the three mental defectives. It is striking that correlations between the urinary constituents exist in these subjects similar to those found in the two schizophrenics. However, if weight fluctuations are taken into consideration it becomes apparent that there is a more regular relationship between days of weight losses and rises of excretion rates. Also the weight losses were in all cases higher than in the schizophrenics and ranged from 2½ to 3 kg in 18 days. Thus, it appears that changes of excretion rates in mental defectives were brought about by the externally imposed semi-

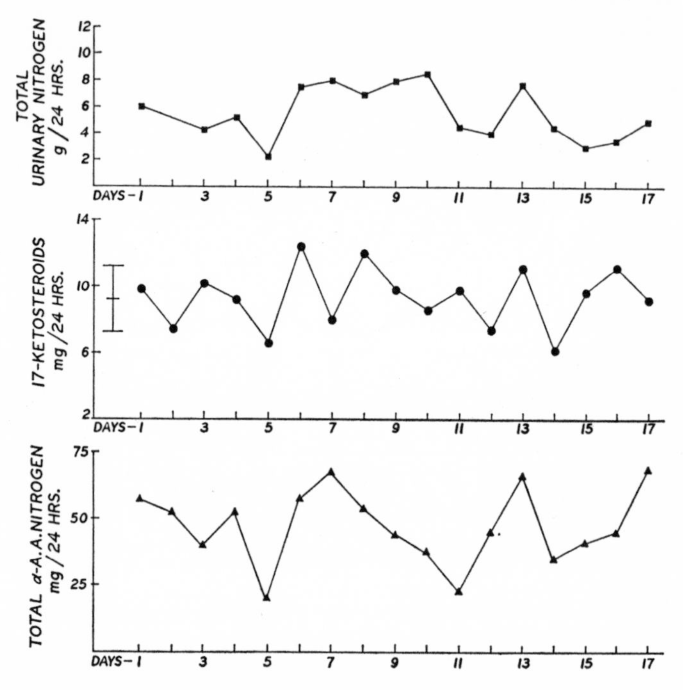

FIG. 5. The correlation of 17-KS excretion rates to total urinary nitrogen was positive (+0·38) but not significant, while the correlation between total urinary nitrogen and alpha-A.A.N. was significant (+0·71).

starvation and the accompanying weight losses, while these changes may have been caused internally, i.e. by central mechanisms, in the schizophrenic patients. In addition, the daily variations of creatinine and steroids were smaller than those of the schizophrenics. Amino acids and tryptamine cannot be compared quantitatively because the diet of the controls contained only half the amount of protein and approximately one-third the amount of tryptophan as compared to our standard diet.

To summarize briefly the results of the first part of this study we found that rises of tryptamine were generally related to concomitant increases of creatinine, amino-acid nitrogen, 1-methylnicotinamide, total urinary nitrogen and steroid hormones. This can be considered good evidence that rises of urinary tryptamine and indoles reflect sudden alterations in the retention or metabolism of amino acids and nitrogen by the body. The concomitant rises of creatinine suggest that a rise of such urinary constituents as measured in this study is due to a breakdown of endogenous protein rather than variations in the excretory function of the kidneys. Changes in eating habits as often seen in schizophrenic patients on the verge of a behavioral worsening may precipitate such a breakdown of body protein and finally lead to the elimination of

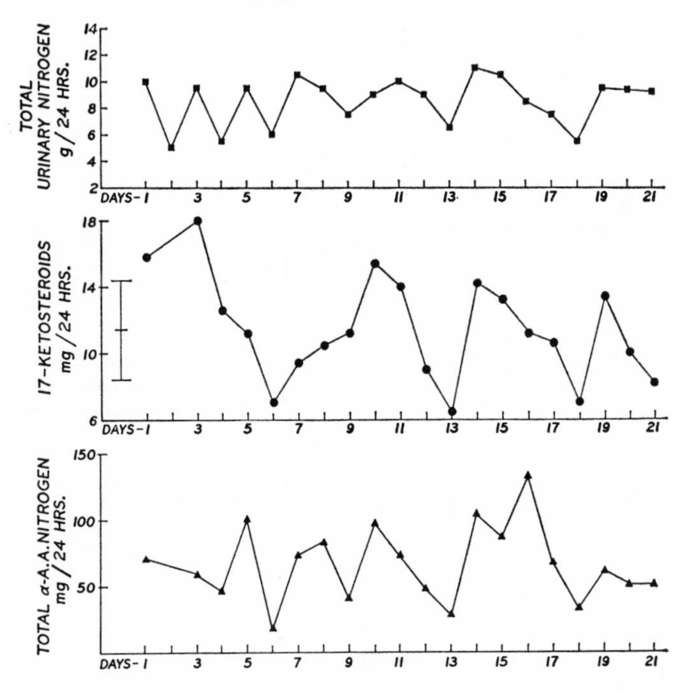

FIG. 6. Total urinary nitrogen was significantly correlated with the excretion values of 17-KS (+0·74) and total alpha-A.A.N. (+0·65). Total urinary nitrogen was also correlated significantly in this instance with creatinine and 1-methylnicotinamide.

larger amounts of metabolites in the urine. This loss, however, appears to be compensated by the schizophrenics rapidly as seen by the subsequent decreases of excretion rates. The net losses of body constituents are therefore small and in one patient, for instance, we even observed an overall increase of weight.

The control experiments have shown that similar alterations can be induced by a reduced food intake. Our data viewed in this light do not reveal a qualitative abnormality in schizophrenic patients but rather a quantitative abnormality in that some of the alterations were more marked in our schizophrenics than in the controls.

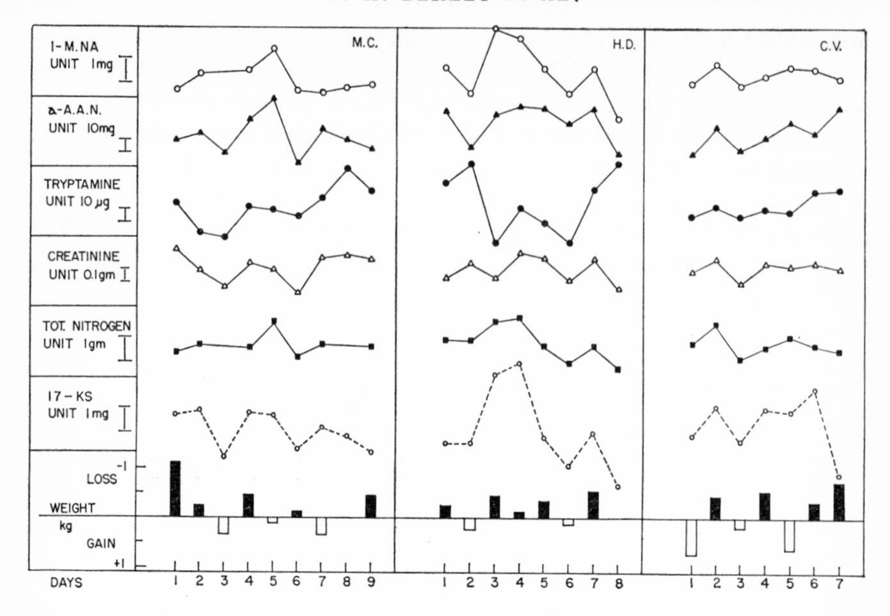

FIG. 7. This figure shows the excretion patterns during a representative number of consecutive days out of the 18-day collection period in the control group. The excretion values are given in units rather than in absolute amounts because the absolute excretion levels were too widely scattered among the three control patients. Significant correlations were found between tryptamine on one hand and creatinine ($r = +0{\cdot}74$), alpha-amino-acid nitrogen ($r = +0{\cdot}58$) and total urinary nitrogen ($r = +0{\cdot}35$) on the other. Total urinary nitrogen in turn was significantly correlated with creatinine ($r = +0{\cdot}77$) total alpha-amino-acid nitrogen ($r = +0{\cdot}71$), 1-methylnicotinamide ($r = +0{\cdot}44$) and 17-KS ($r = +0{\cdot}44$).

PART II

Excretions of Individual Amino Acids

During the second part of our studies we became interested in the variations of individual amino acids in our patients. We considered the possibility that some amino acids (e.g. tryptophan) may rise to a greater extent than others. We therefore subjected several urines of E. S. and J. F. to an analysis for individual amino acids.

In Table 1 we chose three urines, two of which had been previously found to contain large amounts of these constituents and another one containing comparatively low levels. Absolute values for urinary constituents including the individual amino acids are also tabulated. Not all amino acids found during analyses are listed for lack of space and we selected for this table only the ones which are known to be precursors of proteins. H_1 and H_2 designate the two urines of high concentrations. The table shows clear-cut differences between urines of high levels and that of a low level with regard to all amino acids. These differences corresponding to the previously obtained values are reflected in all amino acids. The table also shows the ratios between high and low excretion values in order to facilitate a comparison of individual values. The absolute values tend to be slightly below normal and none of the amino

TABLE 1. INDIVIDUAL URINARY AMINO ACIDS IN RELATION TO OTHER URINARY CONSTITUENTS (E. S.—B)

Compound	Excretion values			Ratios between high and low excretion values (low values = 1)	
	Low	$High_1$	$High_2$	H_1:L	H_2:L
Tryptamine μg/24 hr	49	106	133	2·16	2·7
Pref. creat. g/24 hr*	1·25	1·90	2·00	1·52	1·6
α-A.A.N. mg/24 hr	46	118	80	2·56	1·7
Tot. urin. N. g/24 hr	5·0	10·5	9·6	2·10	1·9
1-Methyl-N′ amide mg/24 hr	1·86	5·88	3·19	3·18	1·7
INDIVIDUAL URINARY AMINO ACIDS (MG/24 HR)					
Alanine	9·4	32·2	23·3	3·21	2·5
Glutamine	37·8	77·4	72·3	1·91	2·1
Glutamic acid	6·6	7·2	9·4	1·42	1·1
Glycine	66·6	139·7	160·5	2·40	2·1
Histidine	49·5	89·9	107·0	2·17	1·8
Isoleucine	2·9	8·7	7·1	3·00	2·5
Leucine	2·9	4·5	5·9	1·62	2·1
Lysine	8·5	15·4	15·5	1·81	1·8
Methionine	7·3	11·9	8·8	1·63	1·2
Ornithine	2·1	5·5	4·1	3·62	2·8
Phenylalanine	4·3	7·8	8·3	1·81	1·9
Tryptophan	4·3	13·7	8·0	3·19	1·9
Tyrosine	10·3	14·5	17·0	1·40	1·7
Creatinine	756	1070	1300	1·42	1·72

* Preformed creatinine.

acids is excreted in excess. Only methionine values are slightly above normal limits in this patient.

A similar pattern was found in the second schizophrenic patient (J. F.). His results on individual amino acids are presented in Table 2. A similar agreement between the ratios of urinary excretion rates of creatinine and individual amino acids was found in the mental defectives used for comparison.

TABLE 2. INDIVIDUAL URINARY AMINO ACIDS IN RELATION TO OTHER URINARY CONSTITUENTS (J. F.—B)

Compound	Excretion values		Ratios between high and low excretion values (low values = 1)
	Low	High	H:L
Tryptamine mg/24 hr	45	119	2·7
Pref. creat. g/24 hr	0·90	1·71	1·9
α-A.A.N. mg/24 hr	20	43	2·2
Tot. urin. N. g/24 hr	2·3	8·1	2·8
1-Methyl-N′ amide mg/24 hr	0·83	2·59	3·1

INDIVIDUAL AMINO ACIDS (MG/24 HR)

Compound	Low	High	H:L
Alanine	5·2	6·3	1·2
Glutamine	10·5	35·0	3·3
Glutamic acid	2·1	3·5	1·7
Glycine	12·1	32·2	2·7
Histidine	1·4	3·5	2·5
Isoleucine	0·8	4·5	5·6
Leucine	1·3	3·7	2·8
Lysine	3·0	13·4	4·5
Methionine	2·0	5·7	2·9
Ornithine	1·1	2·1	1·9
Phenylalanine	0·9	3·1	3·4
Tryptophan	2·5	3·3	1·3
Tyrosine	2·0	6·4	3·2
Creatinine	208·0	836·0	4·0

DISCUSSION

The evaluation of the daily excretion of tryptamine in two schizophrenic patients in relation to other urinary constituents which are involved in the metabolism of amino acids and in the elimination of nitrogen has revealed that tryptamine is involved in a more general metabolic pattern. This involvement is particularly well seen during drastic variations in urinary excretion rates of all the constituents measured and substantiates our recently expressed assumption (Berlet *et al.*, 1964a) that rises of urinary indole metabolites indicate a release of the precursor tryptophan amino acid from endogenous sources. The data on total urinary nitrogen and alpha-amino-acid nitrogen suggest that in addition to tryptophan a number of other amino acids may have been mobilized concomitantly. Conclusive evidence for this assumption was obtained by the analyses for individual amino acids which revealed proportional fluctuations of practically all urinary amino acids. These fluctuations corresponded to those of the other urinary constituents related to the amino-acid metabolism.

We have previously examined the relationship of urinary tryptamine to the daily intake of tryptophan (Berlet *et al.*, 1964b) and found no direct relationship between these two concerning the quantitative excretion values of tryptamine. Since tryptophan in our study can be considered as a measure of the overall protein intake and since the tryptophan content of the diet was kept constant in a certain range a comparably constant amount of protein must have been consumed daily by our patients. Furthermore, the same sources of protein were used for the daily preparation of our diets. This fact, viewed together with the correlations of individual amino acids to creatinine and other excretory products, make dietary variations appear unlikely to have caused the parallel fluctuations of amino acids in our study.

Our control experiments with mental defectives demonstrated that increased excretion rates were often associated with marked weight losses which were induced by a low-calorie diet. No such coincidence could be elaborated in our schizophrenic patients with sufficient consistency. It is interesting to note that the net weight changes in our schizophrenic patients during an entire observation period (e.g. 20 days) result in a net weight loss of only 1 kg in one patient (J. F.). The other patient (E. S.) even gained some weight (0·2 kg) during a similar period. Considerably greater weight losses of 2 to 3 kg in 18 days occurred in the control group. Weight losses, however, indicate primarily a loss of nitrogen, i.e. a negative nitrogen balance in the absence of excessive fat deposits or of water retention due to other medical disorders. In view of the continuous weight losses in the control patients it is obvious that their urinary excretion patterns were reflecting a negative nitrogen balance. In our schizophrenic patients, however, it appears that this negative nitrogen balance was only temporary and losses of nitrogen were quickly compensated for by an increased retention of nitrogen. This is evidenced by extremely low excretion values which followed closely their drastic elevations and may represent a characteristic pattern in some patients. The overall result is a fairly stable nitrogen balance despite great temporary variations of nitrogen excretion.

In addition, the eating habits in our schizophrenic patients, especially of those used in this study, varied considerably from day to day in regard to the consumption of foods which provided the necessary amount of calories even though the more concentrated protein-containing foods were usually eaten entirely every day as indicated by our records. Poor eating habits were especially observed shortly before or during the phase of behavioral worsening at times when tryptamine excretion often reached a maximum (Berlet *et al.*, 1965).

Similar observations on eating habits and weight fluctuations in mental patients were described by Kalinowsky (1948) and Krypsin-Exner (1947). Weight fluctuations were ascribed to a central regulatory disturbance rather than to mere fluctuations of food intake. The effect of the emotional status on the creatinine excretion in normal individuals was described by Schottstaedt *et al.* (1956). Tension and anxiety were associated with higher excretory values for creatinine than periods of emotional relaxation and calmness. It would seem, therefore, that eating habits, weight variations, and behavior in our schizophrenic subjects are all intimately interwoven and together form the basis for the urinary excretion patterns as observed in this study. Our control experiments, in fact, demonstrate that some of the metabolic alterations which we observed in our schizophrenic patients must be of a secondary nature and may represent adaptive reactions to imbalances, perhaps of food intake or perhaps to disturbances of a more central nature.

We observed in our schizophrenic patients a tendency of 17-ketosteroids to rise together with amino acids or to precede these rises by 1 day. We therefore suggest that the release of steroid hormones, at first precipitated by the stressful situation of behavioral intensifications, may have caused the breakdown of protein and release of amino acids or largely potentiated other factors in doing so. The enhancing actions of ACTH and steroids on the elimination of nitrogen are well known and were thoroughly reviewed by Engel (1951) and Sprague (1951). Recent reports have elaborated more extensively the mechanism of this action of steroids on protein and amino-acid metabolism. Kaplan and Shimizu (1963) have found that cortisol increases the levels of free amino acids in the plasma and muscle tissue of rats. It was also observed that steroids were inhibiting the incorporation of labelled glycine into skeletal muscle protein of the rat rather than limiting the transfer from the extracellular to the intracellular space (Shimizu and Kaplan, 1964). The elevated urinary amino acids in our study may therefore very well reflect an increase of plasma amino acids and an impaired retention of amino acids for protein synthesis in the presence of elevated steroid hormones.

It may be furthermore important to consider the diabetogenic and gluconeogenetic effect of steroids especially in view of the poor eating habits in our patients. As a result thereof they undoubtedly were at times in a negative energy balance possibly resulting in a temporary state of hypoglycemia. The presence of a state of hypoglycemia, however, would be a strong stimulus not only for an immediate release of adrenaline but also of ACTH, with a subsequent release of steroid hormones and a restoration of normal blood glucose levels, provided that glycogen is available. Some of the necessary energy, however, may be obtained through a mobilization of amino acids and gluconeogenesis at the expense of body proteins. In addition, a vicious circle may arise from an impaired utilization of glucose in the presence of augmented plasma steroid hormones (Engel, 1951).

Our studies (Berlet *et al.*, 1965) as well as those of other investigators

(Brune and Himwich, 1962) have demonstrated that rises of indoles are related to intensifications of behavior, and a cause-effect relationship between tryptamine and schizophrenic symptoms was considered. The results which were obtained in this study do suggest that rises of tissue levels of indoles can very well occur at one time or another if the behavioral disturbance is severe enough as to cause a severe metabolic alteration involving the breakdown of proteins and liberation of amino acids. On the other hand, it ought to be considered that rises of excretory levels, though reflecting rises of plasma levels, may actually be associated with lower levels in the tissue and with a temporary loss of cell constituents. The lack of behavioral responses in the mental defectives to the same metabolic variations suggests that the actual difference between schizophrenics and controls lies in their response to

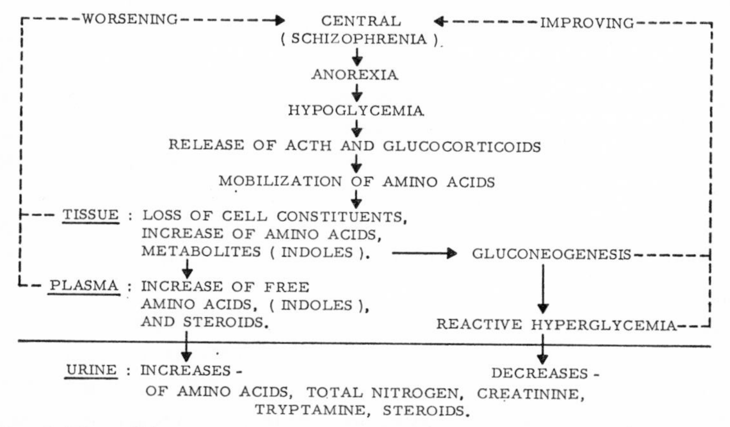

FIG. 8. The solid arrows represent metabolic pathways known to occur under various conditions, especially under stress, to maintain a metabolic equilibrium. The possible feedback through which these metabolic alterations may either intensify or alleviate schizophrenic symptoms is indicated by the broken arrows.

the possible losses of intracellular components or to the sudden liberation of these components and to the necessity to dispose of these compounds. Figure 8 shows an attempt to integrate both clinical and biochemical findings in schizophrenic patients. The patient is viewed as being in a state of equilibrium with regard to his energy metabolism. This equilibrium at times becomes imbalanced in schizophrenic patients due to a central disturbance. Other factors such as a reduced food intake and hyperactivity act as a positive feedback reinforcing the effects of the central disregulation on metabolic alterations. As a mere speculation it is assumed that some of these metabolic alterations either intensify or alleviate psychotic symptoms.

It remains to be seen whether other amino acids than tryptophan or their metabolites contribute to behavioral variations in schizophrenics. The analyses for individual amino acids disclosed that phenylalanine as well as tyrosine, the immediate precursor of dopa, rose along with other amino acids. It is therefore possible that the formation of dopamine and above all of some of the O-methylated dopamine metabolites found in the urine of schizophrenics (Friedhoff and Van Winkle, 1962) is enhanced under these conditions. Sen and McGeer (1964) noted that, for instance, 4-methyoxyphenylethylamine was found especially in agitated schizophrenic patients.

SUMMARY

In this study an attempt was made to relate the daily variations of urinary tryptamine in two schizophrenic patients and three non-psychotic controls (mental defectives) to other excretory products in the urine. The schizophrenic patients were maintained on an adequate, controlled diet whereas the control patients received a low-protein and low-calorie diet in order to induce weight losses in the latter group. The excretion of tryptamine was found to vary in a close relationship with alpha-amino-acid nitrogen, total urinary nitrogen, creatinine, 17-ketosteroids, individual amino acids and, in the majority of instances, with 1-methylnicotinamide. The data indicate that urinary tryptamine reflects to a large extent the metabolism and elimination of tryptophan and other amino acids. An examination of the excretion patterns of the schizophrenic patients for a possible order of events suggested a tendency of 17-KS and creatinine to precede the increases of other excretory products.

Schizophrenic patients and controls did not differ as far as the relationship of tryptamine to variations of other urinary products was concerned. A closer relationship between weight losses and increases of urinary excretion rates was found in the control group than in the two schizophrenic patients. Furthermore, the controls showed marked and continuing weight losses whereas the schizophrenics tended to maintain their overall body weight although marked fluctuations occurred from day to day. Thus weight losses were rapidly compensated by weight gains in the schizophrenic patients.

In conclusion it is suggested that the excretion of tryptamine and its daily variations depend primarily on the availability of the precursor amino acid tryptophan. Tryptophan appears to be mobilized from endogenous sources along with other amino acids and nitrogen-containing urinary products in schizophrenic patients displaying acute psychotic symptoms associated with weight fluctuations and a reduced intake of food. The resulting metabolic alterations seem to be enhanced by the concomitant release of steroid hormones. Finally the data were integrated in an attempt to illustrate the possible metabolic mechanisms involved in variable schizophrenic behavior.

REFERENCES

BERLET, H. H., BULL, C., HIMWICH, H. E., KOHL, H., MATSUMOTO, K., PSCHEIDT, G. R., SPAIDE, J., TOURLENTES, T. T. and VALVERDE, J. M. (1964a) Endogenous metabolic factor in schizophrenic behavior, *Science*, **144**, 311–13.

BERLET, H. H., PSCHEIDT, G. R., SPAIDE, J. K. and HIMWICH, H. E. (1964b) Variations of urinary creatinine and its correlation to tryptamine excretion in schizophrenic patients, *Nature*, **203,** 1198–9.

BERLET, H. H., SPAIDE, J. K., KOHL, H., BULL, C. and HIMWICH, H. E. (1965) Effects of reduction of tryptophan and methionine intake on urinary indole compounds and schizophrenic behavior, *J. Nerv. Ment. Dis.* **140,** 297–304.

BRUNE, G. G. and HIMWICH, H. E. (1962) Indole metabolites in schizophrenic patients, *Archives of General Psychiatry*, **6,** 324–8.

BRUNE, G. G. and PSCHEIDT, G. R. (1961) Correlations between behavior and urinary excretion of indole amines and catecholamines in schizophrenic patients as affected by drugs, *Federation Proceedings*, **20,** 889–93.

ENGEL, F. L. (1951) A consideration of the roles of the adrenal cortex and stress in the regulation of protein metabolism, *Recent Progress in Hormone Research*, **6,** 277–313.

FRIEDHOFF, A. and VAN WINKLE, E. (1962) The characteristics of an amine found in the urine of schizophrenic patients, *J. Nerv. Ment. Dis.*, **135,** 550–5.

HEINZELMAN, R. V. and SZMUSZKOVICZ, J. (1963) Recent studies in the field of indole compounds, *Progress in Drug Research*, E. Jucker (Ed.), Vol. **6,** 74–150.

HOLMSTEDT, B., VANDENHEUVEL, W. J. A., GARDINER, W. L. and HORNING, E. C. (1964) Separation and identification of tryptamine-related indole bases by gas chromatographic methods, *Analytical Biochemistry*, **8,** 151–7.

KAPLAN, S. A. and SHIMIZU, C. S. N. (1963) Effects of cortisol on amino acids in skeletal muscle and plasma, *Endocrinology*, **72,** 267–71.

KALINOWSKY, L. B. (1948) Variations of body weight and menstruation in mental illness, *J. Nerv. Ment. Dis.* **108,** 423–30.

KRYPSIN-EXNER, W. (1947) Course of weight in psychoses, *Wien klin. Wschr.*, **59,** 531–4.

MOORE, S., SPACKMAN, D. H. and STEIN, W. H. (1958) Chromatography of amino acids on sulfonated polystyrene resins, *Analytical Chemistry*, **30,** 1185–90.

MÜTING, D. and KAISER, E. (1963) Zur quantitativen Bestimmung von alpha-Amino-Strickstoff in biologischem Material mittels der Ninhydrin Reaktion, *Hoppe-Seylers Zeitschrift für Biochemie*, **332,** 276–81.

NATELSON, S. (Ed.) (1957) *Microtechniques of Clinical Chemistry of the Routine Laboratory*, Charles Thomas, Springfield, Illinois, 238–41.

PELLETIER, O. and CAMPBELL, J. A. (1962) A rapid method for the determination of N-methylnicotinamide in urine, *Analytical Biochemistry*, **3,** 60–7.

Practical Physiological Chemistry (1949) HAWK, P. B., OSER, B. L., and SUMMERSON, W. H. (Eds.)., Blakiston Co., Philadelphia, Pennsylvania, 840.

ROSANDER, A. C. (1951) *Elementary Principles of Statistics*, D. van Nostrand Company, Inc., New York.

SCALES, F. M. and HARRISON, A. P. (1920) Boric acid modifications of the Kjeldahl method for crop and soil analysis, *J. Ind. Engr. Chem.* **12,** 350.

SCHOTTSTAEDT, W. W., GRACE, W. J. and WOLFF, H. G. (1956) Life situations, behaviour, attidues, emotions, and renal excretion of fluid and electrolytes—V. Variations in excretion of endogenous creatinine, *J. Psycho. Res.* **1,** 292–8.

SEN, M. P. and MCGEER, P. L. (1964) 4-Methoxyphenylethylamine and 3,4-dimethoxyphenylethylamine in human urine, *Biochemical and Biophysical Research Communications*, **14,** 227–32.

SHIMIZU, C. S. N. and KAPLAN, S. A. (1964) Effects of cortisone on *in vitro* incorporation of glycine into protein of rat diaphragm, *Endocrinology*, **74,** 709–13.

SJOERDSMA, A., OATES, J. A., ZALTZMAN, P. and UNDENFRIEND, S. (1959) Identification and assay of urinary tryptamine: Application as an index of monoamine oxidase inhibition in man. *J. Pharmacol. and Exper. Therapeutics*, **126,** 217–22.

SPRAGUE, R. G., MASON, H. L. and MARSCHELLE, H. P. (1951) Physiological effects of cortisone and ACTH in man, *Recent Progress in Hormone Research*, **6,** 315–72.

STOLL, A., TROXLER, F., PETER, J. and HOFMANN, A. (1955) Eine neue Synthese von Bufotenin und verwandten Oxy-tryptaminen, *Helv. Chim. Acta*, **38,** 1452–72.

STROMBERG, V. L. (1954) The isolation of bufotenine from piptadenia peregrina, *J. Amer. Chem. Soc.*, **76,** 1707.

TRYPTOPHAN METABOLISM IN PSYCHOSES

GUENTER G. BRUNE

Neurologische Universitätsklinik, Hamburg 20, Martinistr. 52, Germany

IN CONSIDERING psychoses to represent the clinical expression of certain types of pathological reactions of the brain we would expect that various factors interfering with normal brain function may be involved in psychotic behaviour. The underlying factors of psychoses are still obscure. The fact, however, that psychoses occur in well-defined metabolically determined syndromes suggest that metabolic derangements may play a role in at least some psychotic states.

It is the main purpose of this presentation to review some of the work relevant to the question of a possible role of derangements of tryptophan metabolism in psychotic behaviour.

As indicated in the abbreviated diagram (Fig. 1) there are various pathways of tryptophan metabolism. Tryptophan takes part in the synthesis of proteins and it is released when proteins break down. Two main pathways of tryptophan metabolism are represented by the kynurenine and the indole pathway. The kynurenine pathway leads over various intermediates such as formylkynurenine, kynurenine, 3-hydroxykynurenine, 3-hydroxyanthranilic acid to the formation of nicotinic acid and N-methyl-2-pyridone-5-carboxamide (pyridone) as well as other metabolic products. The main end-products of the indole pathways are represented by indole-3-acetic acid and 5-hydroxyindoleacetic acid. Intermediate products of the indole pathway are represented by 5-hydroxytryptamine and tryptamine. Recently Axelrod[1] showed that the N,N-dimethylated derivatives of tryptamine and 5-hydroxytryptamine can be formed in the mammalian organism.

Neuropsychiatric disorders including psychoses and derangements of tryptophan metabolism have been observed in various clinical syndromes, i.e. in inborn errors of metabolism such as Hartnup disease, Wilson disease and porphyria, as well as in nutritional deficiency states or during treatment with some pharmacologically active agents.

In Hartnup disease the most characteristic and constant biochemical abnormalities were found to be a generalized aminoaciduria. In addition, large quantities of indole-3-acetic acid, indole-3-acetylglutamine and indican were observed in the urine while the kynurenine pathway appeared to be impaired.[2] This was thought to indicate either a deficiency of tryptophan pyrrolase or a reduced amino acid transport.[2, 3] During clinical remission metabolic abnormalities receded.[4]

The predominant biochemical lesions in Wilson disease are represented by disturbances of copper and amino-acid metabolism including constantly high urinary levels of copper and amino acids. In addition, increased urinary levels of 5-hydroxyindoleacetic acid, tryptamine, indole-3-acetic acid and other indole metabolites[5] as well as of adrenaline and dopamine have been reported.[6]

Price *et al.*[7] investigating the kynurenine pathway in porphyria observed abnormalities of tryptophan metabolism in a group of twelve patients with acute, mixed or chronic porphyria after a test load of tryptophan. These

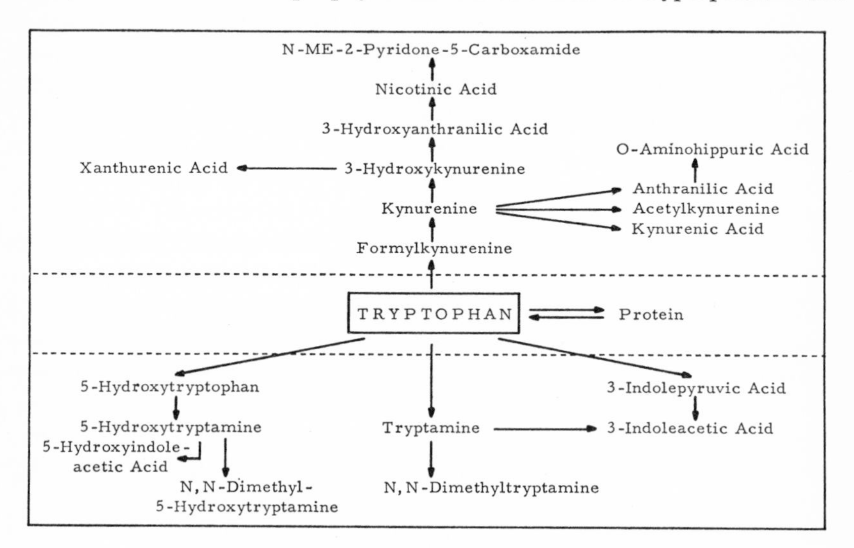

FIG. 1. Abbreviated diagram of tryptophan metabolism.

metabolic abnormalities were characterized by statistically significant increased urinary excretions of 3-hydroxykynurenine, kynurenine, acetylkynurenine, kynurenic acid and occasionally xanthurenic acid. These results were interpreted to suggest a functional pyridoxine deficiency. In a second group of patients with acute porphyria in remission on the other hand the patterns of urinary tryptophan metabolites did not differ significantly from those of the control group except for a lower urinary excretion of pyridoxine after tryptophan loading.

Pellagra represents a nutritional deficiency state of primarily exogenous origin which shows similarities to the genetically determined Hartnup disease. Pellagra has been linked in man to a lack of tryptophan, nicotinic acid and perhaps other vitamins including pyridoxine.[8] Abnormal high urinary excretions of indole metabolites, which have been observed in Hartnup disease are suggested by the work of Sullivan[9] who isolated tryptamine from the urine of pellagrins.

Soon after the introduction of the antituberculous drug isoniazid a variety of neuropsychiatric disorders were observed in patients treated with that drug. Price *et al.*[10] reported that during treatment with isoniazid or deoxypyridoxine and after supplementation with tryptophan abnormally large amounts of 3-hydroxykynurenine and kynurenine were excreted. Less markedly elevated than the latter were xanthurenic acid and acetylkynurenine while there were normal or slightly less than normal urinary excretions of *o*-aminohippuric acid, anthranilic acid, anthranilic acid glucuronide and N-methyl-2-pyridone-5-carboxamide. Pyridoxine administration resulted in a return to normal tryptophan metabolism even when the ingestion of isoniazid or deoxypyridoxine was continued. These metabolic studies point to the conclusion that isoniazid administration may interfere with pyridoxine resulting in an incomplete metabolism of 3-hydroxykynurenine and kynurenine. These investigations may further indicate that urinary pyridone and perhaps other nicotinic acid metabolites may not necessarily reflect an impairment of the kynurenine pathway of tryptophan metabolism.

On the whole the above-mentioned studies point to the conclusion that disturbances of tryptophan metabolism may occur in various syndromes associated with neuropsychiatric disorders whether of endogenous origin as in inborn errors of metabolism or of exogenous origin as exemplified by pellagra and by isoniazid administration. These investigations further show that during clinical remissions as were observed in Hartnup disease and porphyria, tryptophan metabolism tended to normalize. This also appears to be true for the syndromes of exogenous origin. As long as no permanent damage has occurred, the neuropsychiatric disorders tend to disappear after administration of an adequate diet in case of pellagra, and after removal of the drug and/or supplementation with pyridoxine in case of isoniazid.

The fact that all syndromes mentioned may be associated with psychoses sometimes indistinguishable from those occurring in schizophrenic patients[7, 11, 12, 13] makes one wonder whether similar disturbances of tryptophan metabolism may also occur in schizophrenics.

The kynurenine pathway of tryptophan metabolism was studied by Price *et al.*[7] in a total number of nineteen schizophrenic patients. This group of patients excreted significantly less pyridone before or after tryptophan ingestion as compared with controls. Six patients of this group, four of them acutely ill, in addition excreted significantly more 3-hydroxykynurenine, kynurenine, acetylkynurenine, kynurenic acid and *o*-aminohippuric acid after administration of tryptophan than did the controls. The remaining group of thirteen patients, five of them considered acutely ill, excreted significantly less kynurenic acid and *o*-aminohippuric acid before or after tryptophan supplementation and less kynurenine after tryptophan as compared with the controls.

Brown *et al.*[14] found in their group of schizophrenic patients less of a urinary nicotinamide metabolite in comparison with the control group and observed that this difference was abolished after tryptophan supplementation. Oepen[15] reported increased urinary excretions of xanthurenic acid and observed a relationship between the magnitude of urinary excretions of xanthurenic acid and the acuteness of the psychopathological process.

Most of the biochemical work on tryptophan metabolism in schizophrenic patients centred around indole metabolism. From the multitude of observations I wish to refer only to those reports dealing with the urinary excretions of tryptamine, indole-3-acetic acid, and 5-hydroxyindoleactic acid. These investigations have not revealed unique excretion patterns for schizophrenic patients. Rodnight[16] found normal amounts of urinary tryptamine with the exception of a greater variability. Ross in 1913[17, 18] and more recently Sherwood[19] and Masuda *et al.*[20] claimed an abnormally high excretion of indole-3-acetic acid. These observations, however, could not be confirmed by Banerjee and Agrawal,[21] Rodnight and Aves[22] or Weissbach *et al.*[23] Similar contradictory results were also obtained for 5-hydroxyindoleacetic acid. Decreased urinary levels,[24] or an abnormally high output,[20, 21, 25] as well as normal values including a greater variability were observed.[26, 27, 28, 29, 30]

These differences in excretion patterns may in part be due to various factors unrelated or not directly related to the subject of the study such as the amount and composition of ingested food, medications, somatic diseases, metabolism of intestinal bacteria and the function of the intestine itself.

Considering all these factors and excluding them as far as possible, Brune and Himwich,[31] and Brune and Pscheidt[32] determined urinary levels of tryptamine, total indole-3-acetic acid and 5-hydroxyindoleacetic acid in relation to the actual psychopathology in schizophrenic patients. These studies showed that when the psychosis was apparently inactive the average tryptamine excretion was within normal limits while total indole-3-acetic acid was slightly above the normal range. With progressive intensification of the psychoses, however, urinary tryptamine as well as total indole-3-acetic acid significantly rose to abnormally high values. These findings of a correlation between urinary tryptamine and indole-3-acetic acid with the intensity of psychotic activity were confirmed in subsequent studies.[33, 34] Similar results were also obtained for 5-hydroxyindoleactic acid.[32] In interpreting the results we want to emphasize that alterations of the amounts of tryptophan metabolites in urine may be due to many factors thus rendering interpretations difficult. From the presented results, however, it may appear possible that there is a metabolic impairment within the kynurenine pathway in some schizophrenic patients and this may result in a greater formation of indole metabolites. Similar biochemical mechanisms may be operating in Hartnup disease as well as in the other mentioned syndromes.

In order to determine more clearly the nature of possible disturbances of tryptophan metabolism in relation to psychotic behaviour and mental illness, it would be helpful to test as many as possible urinary tryptophan metabolites simultaneously in close association with clinical observations.

In any case, however, investigations of urinary tryptophan metabolites need supplementation by other methodological parameters because even close correlations between urinary levels of tryptophan metabolites with psychotic behaviour alone bear little significance in terms of a cause-and-effect relationship.

A few more methodological parameters relevant to the question of a role of tryptophan metabolism in psychotic behaviour have been tested. Intermediates of the indole pathway such as tryptamine, 5-hydroxytryptamine, as well as their N,N-dimethylated derivatives, have been of current interest in biochemical research of mental illness. It has been observed that 5-hydroxytryptamine is mainly located in those regions of the brain belonging to the limbic system[35, 36, 37] which according to current concepts represents the anatomical substrate of emotions.[38, 39] In addition it was found that the administration of tryptophan, 5-hydroxytryptophan and tryptamine singly or in combination with a monoamine oxidase inhibitor to animals evoked behavioural alterations characterized by sedation and/or excitation.[36, 40, 41, 42] Similar results, including drowsiness and euphoria, were also obtained in healthy human beings.[43, 44] In addition administration of tryptophan and monoamine oxidase inhibitors singly or in the combination of both were observed to be able to evoke recurrences and exacerbations of the psychoses in schizophrenic patients.[45, 46, 47]

On the other hand, neuroleptic drugs such as reserpine and phenothiazines, which either reduce the level of biogenic amines in the brain or block their actions, may induce tranquillization in animal and man. They may also ameliorate psychotic behaviour. An interpretation of these drug effects in biochemical terms should include the consideration that the above-mentioned psychotropic drugs do not only interfere with the metabolism or action of indole amines but also affect catecholamines as well as other biochemical parameters. Although the administration of the immediate precursors of serotonin and tryptamine singly or in combination with a monoamine oxidase inhibitor may induce excitement in mentally healthy human beings and may evoke recurrences and exacerbations of psychoses in schizophrenic patients, there is no evidence that these substances may also induce psychotic behaviour in healthy people. This indicates a different behavioural response of healthy people as compared with schizophrenic patients towards a test load of tryptophan. In contrast N,N-dimethylated tryptamines such as N,N-dimethyltryptamine and N,N-dimethyl-5-hydroxytryptamine may evoke psychotic behaviour in healthy human beings.[48, 49] Thus the question arises as to whether or not there might be a biochemical mechanism in psychotic patients which may facilitate the formation of larger quantities of N,N-dimethylated tryptamines.

To test this hypothesis two methods of investigation were followed. One method was to load healthy as well as schizophrenic patients with methyl donors such as methionine and betaine. When methionine and betaine were combined with a monoamine oxidase inhibitor marked behavioural changes

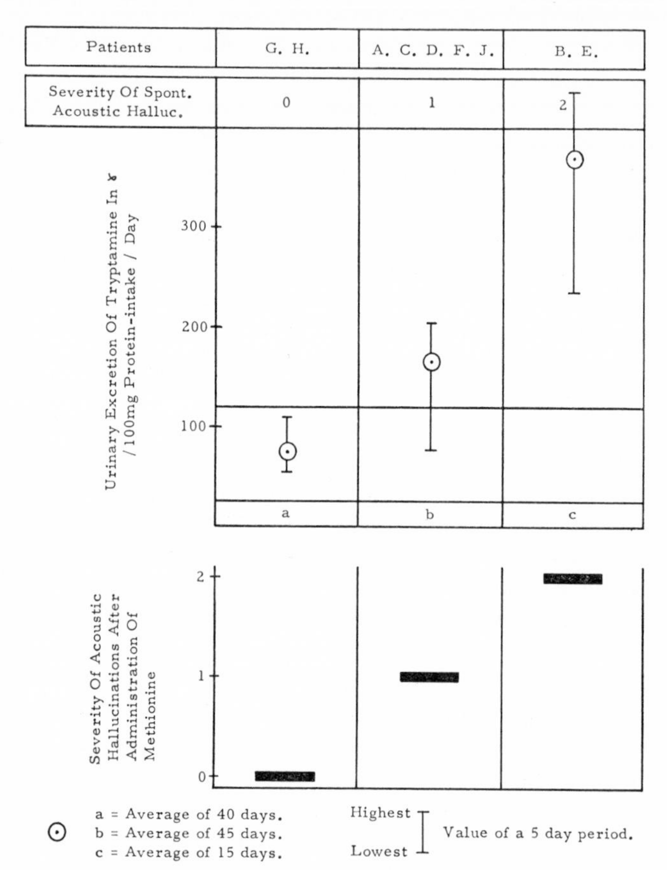

FIG. 2. Acoustic hallucinations as associated with urinary tryptamine and methionine-loading in schizophrenic patients.

including exacerbations and recurrences of individual patterns of psychoses were observed by various investigators.[46, 50, 51] In this connection it is of interest that Pollin, Cardon and Kety[46] reported that besides tryptophan and methionine no other amino acid tested evoked behavioural effects. In our own studies[33, 50] seven out of nine schizophrenic patients showed behavioural changes including exacerbations and recurrences of individual psychotic patterns during two dose levels of methionine in combination with isocarboxazid and these behavioural alterations also occurred in six out of seven patients at two dose levels of betaine in combination with that monoamine oxidase inhibitor.

In addition, we found that behavioural changes exemplified by the intensity of acoustic hallucinations (Fig. 2) were most pronounced after administration of methionine and isocarboxazid in those patients who had experienced marked acoustic hallucinations previously and simultaneously showed a abnormal high level of urinary tryptamine. Sprince *et al.*[52] recently reported that the combination of monoamine oxidase inhibitor plus methionine gave distinctly higher urinary levels of tryptamine and indoleacetamide than did either component alone.

The second avenue of investigation was followed by the study of urinary excretions of methylated indoleamines. Determinations of urinary N,N-dimethylated tryptamines have been attempted in various laboratories. Using paper chromatographic procedures Bumpus and Page[53] reported the occurrence of a bufotenin-like substance in the human urine. Fischer[54] found that substance in twenty-five out of twenty-six hallucinating patients but not in non-psychotic people. Brune, Kohl and Himwich[55] studied five hallucinating schizophrenic patients receiving isocarboxazid in combination with betaine and detected urinary substances with the paper chromatographic characteristics of tryptamine, serotonin and bufotenin. Rodnight[56] Feldstein *et al.*[54] and Sprince *et al.*[32] on the other hand did not find N,N-dimethylated tryptamines. These differences in results may at least partly be due to differences in methods, because those investigators who reported the detection of a bufotenin-like substance generally worked with extracts from large amounts of urine while those authors who did not find this compound have used smaller amounts of urine.

Despite the application of various methodological parameters as presented above, the underlying pathomechanism of psychoses, whether occurring in inborn errors of metabolism or during the treatment with certain drugs, as well as in nutritional deficiency states and in schizophrenics, still remain obscure, and the presented data relevant to the question of a relationship between psychotic behaviour and tryptophan metabolism still leave room for various interpretations.

One interpretation could be that at least in some patients with psychotic reactions there may be one type of defect of tryptophan metabolism due to either endogenous or exogenous causes preventing a normal tryptophan metabolism via the kynurenine pathway and simultaneously facilitating the formation of a larger amount of indole derivatives. This shift may become the basis for a disturbed balance of brain amines and/or a greater formation of highly psychoactive methylated indolamines and this may interfere with normal brain functions. Further investigations are needed to either support or discard this working hypothesis.

REFERENCES

1. Axelrod, J., Enzymatic formation of psychotomimetic metabolites from normally occurring compounds, *Science*, **134**, 343 (1961).
2. Baron, D. N., Dent, C. E., Harris, H., Hart, E. W. and Jepson, J. B., Hereditary pellagra-like skin rash with temporary cerebellar ataxia. Constant renal amino-aciduria and other bizarre biochemical features, *Lancet*, **271**, 421–8 (1956).
3. Nemeth, A. M. and Nachmias, V. T., Changes in tryptophan peroxidase activity in developing liver, *Science*, **128**, 1085–6 (1958).
4. Milne, M. D., Crawford, M. A., Girao, C. B., Loughridge, L. W., The metabolic disorder in Hartnup disease, *Quart. J. Med.* **29**, 407–21 (1960).
5. Sunderman, F. W., Disturbances of indole metabolism in hepatolenticular degeneration, *Am. J. Med. Sci.* **246**, 165–71 (1963).
6. Barbeau, A. and Sourkes, Th. L., Some biochemical aspects of extrapyramidal diseases. *In Extrapyramidal System and Neuroleptics*, J. M. Bordeleau (Ed.), Montreal, pp. 101–7 (1961).
7. Price, J. M., Brown, R. R. and Peters, H. A., Tryptophan metabolism in porphyria, schizophrenia, and a variety of neurologic and psychiatric diseases, *Neurology*, **9**, 456–68 (1959).
8. Bicknell, F. and Prescott, F., *The Vitamins in Medicine*, 3rd edition, W. Heinemann (Ed.), London, p. 352 (1953).
9. Sullivan, M. X., Indolethylamine in the urine of pellagrins, *J. Biol. Chem.* **50**, 39 (1922).
10. Price, J. M., Brown, R. R. and Larson, F. C., Quantitative studies on human urinary metabolities of tryptophan as affected by isoniazid and deoxpyridoxine, *J. Clin. Invest.* **36**, 1600–7 (1957).
11. Hersov, L. A., A case of childhood pellagra with psychosis, *J. Ment. Sci.* **101**, 878–83 (1955).
12. Stucki, A., Uber psychotische Reaktionen bei tuberkalostatischer Behandlung (Cycloserin und INH), *Praxis*, **50**, 592–5 (1961).
13. Stutte, H., *Psychiatrie der Gegenwart. II. Klinische Psychiatrie*, Springer-Verlag, Berlin, Gottingen, Heidelberg, p. 1025 (1960).
14. Brown, F. C., White, J. B., Jr. and Kennedy, J. J., Urinary excretion of tryptophan metabolites by schizophrenic individuals, *Am. J. Psychiat.* **117**, 63–5 (1960).
15. Oepen, H., Uber Xanthurensäure-Bestimmung bei Erkrankungen des Nervensystems, *Arch. Psychiat. u. Zeitschr. f. d. ges. Neurologie*, **202**, 423–39 (1961).
16. Rodnight, R., Body fluid indoles in mental illness. *In International Review of Neurobiology*, C. C. Pfeiffer and J. R. Smythies (Eds.), Academic Press, New York, **3**, 251 (1961).
17. Ross, E. L., A preliminary note on the excretion of indole acetic acid in the urine, *Arch. Intern. Med.* **12**, 112 (1913a).
18. Ross, E. L., The source of urinary indole in two dementia praecox patients, *Arch. Intern. Med.* **12**, 231 (1913b).
19. Sherwood, W. K., Urinary excretion of some tryptophan metabolites in health and certain diseases. *In Biochemistry of Mental Illness*. Biological Sciences, Series No. 4, University of British Columbia Publications, Vancouver, p. 30 (1957).
20. Masuda, M., Stonecker, J. S. and Dorpat, T. L., Urinary aromatic metabolism in schizophrenia, *J. Nerv. Ment. Dis.* **130**, 125 (1960).
21. Banerjee, S. and Agarwal, P. S., Tryptophan-nicotinic acid metabolism in schizophrenia, *Proc. Soc. Exptl. Biol. Med.* **97**, 657 (1958).
22. Rodnight, R. and Aves, E. K., Body fluid indoles of normal and mentally ill subjects. I. Preliminary survey of the occurrence of some urinary indoles, *J. Mental Sci.* **104**, 1149 (1958).
23. Weissbach, H., King, W., Sjoerdsma, A., and Udenfriend, S., Formation of indole-3-acetic acid and tryptamine in animals, *J. Biol. Chem.* **234**, 81 (1959).
24. Leyton, G. B., Indolic compounds in the urine of schizophrenics, *Brit. Med. J.* **2**, 1136 (1958).

25. VILLAR PALASI, V. and SOLDUGA, J., Metabolites de la serotinine et diagnostique differentiel, *Abstracts of Communications, V International Congress of Biochemistry, Moscow, August 10–16*, Pergamon Press, Oxford, p. 360 (1961).
26. BUSCAINO, G. A. and STEFANACHI, L., Urinary excretion of 5-hydroxyindoleacetic acid in psychotic and normal subjects; excretion after parenteral administration of serotonin, *AMA Arch. Neurol. Psychiat.* **80,** 78 (1958).
27. FELDSTEIN, A., HOAGLAND, H. and FREEMAN, H., Blood and urinary serotonin and 5-hydroxyindoleacetic acid levels in schizophrenic patients and normal subjects, *J. Nerv. Ment. Dis.* **129,** 62 (1959).
28. RIEGELHAUPT, L. M., Investigations of the urinary excretion pattern in psychotic patients, *J. Nerv. Ment. Dis.* **127,** 228 (1958)
29. ROBINS, E., LOWE, I. P. and HAVNER, N. M., The urinary excretion of 5-hydroxy-indoleacetic acid (5-HIAA) in patients with schizophrenia and in control subjects, *Clin. Res. Proc.* **4,** 149 (1956).
30. SANO, I., KAKIMOTO, Y., OKAMOTO, T., NAKAJIMA, H. and KUDO, Y., Uber 5-Oxyindo-lessigsaure-Ausscheidung im Urin von Schizophrenen mit Berucksichtigung des Einflusses von Chlorpromazin und Reserpin auf den Serotonin-Stoffwechsel, *Schweiz. med. Wochschr.* **87,** 214 (1957).
31. BRUNE, G. G. and HIMWICH, H. E., Effects of reserpine on urinary tryptamine and indole-3-acetic acid excretion in mental deficiency schizophrenia and phenylpyruvic oligophrenia, *Acta of the International Meeting on the Techniques for the Study of Psychotropic Drugs, Bologna, June 26–27, 1960.*
32. BRUNE, G. G. and PSCHEIDT, G. R., Correlations between behavior and urinary excretion of indole amines and catecholamines in schizophrenic patients as affected by drugs, *Fed. Proc.* **20,** 889 (1961).
33. BRUNE, G. G. and HIMWICH, H. E., Biogenic amines and behavior in schizophrenic patients. *In Recent Advances in Biological Psychiatry*, J. Wortis (Ed.), Plenum Press, New York, **5,** 144–60 (1963).
34. BERLET, H. H., BULL, C., HIMWICH, H. E., KOHL, H., MATSUMOTO, K., PSCHEIDT, G. R., SPAIDE, J., TOURLENTES, T. T. and VALVERDE, J. M., Endogenous metabolic factor in schizophrenic behavior, *Science*, **144,** 311–13 (1964).
35. TWAROG, B. M. and PAGE, I. H., Serotonin content of some mammalian tissues and urine and a method for its determination, *Am. J. Physiol.* **175,** 157 (1953).
36. HIMWICH, W. A. and COSTA, E., Behavioral changes associated with changes in concentrations of brain serotonin, *Fed. Proc.* **19,** S838 (1960).
37. PSCHEIDT, G. R. and HIMWICH, H. E., Reserpine, monoamine oxidase inhibitors and distribution of biogenic amines in monkey brain, *Biochem. Pharmacol.* **12,** 65–71 (1963).
38. PAPEZ, J. W., The visceral brain, its components and connections. *In Reticular Formation of the Brain*, H. H. Jasper, L. D. Proctor, R. S. Knighton, W. C. Noshay and R. T. Costello (Eds.), Little, Brown & Co., Boston, pp. 591–605 (1958).
39. MACLEAN, P. D., Contrasting functions of limbic and neocortical systems of the brain and their relevance to psychophysiological aspects of medicine, *Am. J. Med.* **25,** 611–26 (1958).
40. BOGDANSKI, D. F., WEISSBACH, H. and UDENFRIEND, S., Pharmacological studies with the serotonin precursor, 5-hydroxytryptophan, *J. Pharmacol. Exptl. Therap.* **122,** 182 (1958).
41. BROWN, B. B., CNS drug actions and interactions in mice, *Arch. intern. pharmacodynamie*, **128,** 391 (1960).
42. HIMWICH, W. A., CLAMAN, M. A., PSCHEIDT, G. R., KOHL, H. H. and KNAPP, F. M., The role of the liver in the production of behavioral responses to indole compounds. *In Recent Advances in Biological Psychiatry*, J. Wortis (Ed.), Plenum Press, New York, **6,** 183–9 (1964).
43. SJOERDSMA, A., OATES, J. A., ZALTSMAN, P. and UDENFRIEND, S., Identification and assay of urinary tryptamine: Application as an index of monoamine oxidase inhibition in man, *J. Pharmacol. Exptl. Therap.* **126,** 217 (1959).
44. SMITH, B. and PROCKOP, D. J., Central nervous system effects of ingestion of L-tryptophan by normal subjects, *New Eng. J. Med.* **267,** 1338–41 (1962).

45. Lauer, J. W., Inskip, W. M., Bernsohn, J. and Zeller, E. A., Observations on schizophrenic patients after iproniazid and tryptophan, *AMA Arch. Neurol. Psychiat.* **80,** 122 (1958).
46. Pollin, W., Cardon, W. P. V. and Kety, S. S., Effects of amino acid feedings in schizophrenic patients treated with iproniazid, *Science,* **133,** 104 (1961).
47. Shaw, C. R., Lucas, J. and Rabinovitch, R. D., Metabolic studies in childhood schizophrenia, *Arch. Gen. Psychiat.* **1,** 366 (1959).
48. Fabing, H. D. and Hawkins, J. R., Intravenous bufotenin injection in the human being, *Science,* **123,** 886 (1956).
49. Boszormenyi, Z. and Szara, St., Dimethyltryptamine experiments with psychotics, *J. Ment. Sci.* **104,** 445 (1958).
50. Brune, G. G. and Himwich, H. E., Effects of methionine loading on the behavior of schizophrenic patients, *J. Nerv. Ment. Dis.* **134,** 447 (1962).
51. Alexander, F., Curtis, G. C., Sprince, H. and Crosley, A. P., L-Methionine and L-tryptophan feedings in non-psychotic and schizophrenic patients with and without tranylcypromine, *J. Nerv. Ment. Dis.* **137,** 135–42 (1963).
52. Sprince, H., Parker, C. M., Jameson, D. and Alexander, F., Urinary indoles in schizophrenic and psychoneurotic patients after tranylcypromine (Parnate) and methionine or tryptophan, *J. Nerv. Ment. Dis.* **137,** 246–51 (1963).
53. Bumpus, F. M. and Page, I. H., Serotonin and its methylated derivatives in human urine, *J. Biol. Chem.* **212,** 111 (1955).
54. Fischer, E., Lagravere, T. A. F., Vasquez, A. J. and Di Stefano, A. O., A bufotenin-like substance in the urine of schizophrenics, *J. Nerv. Ment. Dis.* **133,** 441 (1961).
55. Brune, G. G., Kohl, H. H. and Himwich, H. E., Urinary excretion of a bufotenin-like substance in psychotic patients, *J. Neuropsychiat.* **5,** 14–17 (1963).
56. Rodnight, R., Separation and characterization of urinary indoles resembling 5-hydroxytryptamine and tryptamine, *Biochem. J.* **64,** 621–6 (1956).
57. Feldstein, A., Hoagland, H. and Freeman, H., Radioactive serotonin in relation to schizophrenia, *AMA Arch. Gen. Psychiat.* **5,** 246–51 (1961).

METABOLIC INTERRELATIONSHIPS OF TRYPTOPHAN AND METHIONINE IN RELATION TO MENTAL ILLNESS

HERBERT SPRINCE

Veterans Administration Hospital, Coatesville, Pa., and the
Departments of Psychiatry, School of Medicine, and Biochemistry,
Graduate School of Medicine, University of Pennsylvania, Philadelphia, Pennsylvania

IN RECENT years, the amino acids tryptophan and methionine and their respective metabolites have commanded increasing attention in a biochemical approach to mental illness. In the case of tryptophan, behavioral disturbances have been associated with tryptophan itself (Smith and Prockop, 1962); with its indolic metabolites, tryptamine and indoleacetic acid (Brune and Himwich, 1962a) and 6-hydroxyskatole sulfate (Sprince *et al.*, 1960); with its 5-hydroxyindole metabolites, 5-hydroxytryptophan, serotonin and 5-hydroxyindoleacetic acid (Himwich and Costa, 1960; Woolley, 1962; and Olson *et al.*, 1960); and with certain nicotinic acid metabolites which can arise from tryptophan, namely N^1-methylnicotinamide and N-methyl-2-pyridone-5-carboxamide (Heyman and Merlis, 1963). For detailed reviews of these and other aspects of tryptophan metabolism in relation to mental illness, see the publications of Sprince (1961, 1962) and Rodnight (1961).

Methionine and its metabolites have been implicated in disturbances of brain metabolism in a number of ways. Clinically, elevated levels of methionine and/or its metabolites have been reported in hepatic coma (Walsche, 1959; Iber *et al.*, 1957); in cystathioninuria (Harris *et al.*, 1959; Frimpter *et al.*, 1963); and in homocystinuria (Gerritsen *et al.*, 1962; Carson *et al.*, 1963). Mental retardation has been found in association with the latter two amino-acidurias. On a more basic level, the rate of incorporation of S^{35}-methionine into brain protein has been found to be particularly high in the supraoptic and paraventricular nuclei of the hypothalamus, regions which are believed to be rich in "neurosecretory" cells (Gaitonde and Richter, 1957). Decreased incorporation of S^{35}-methionine into rat brain protein has been noted after stress (Shapot, 1957) and after treatment with LSD, brom-LSD and serotonin (Krawczynski, 1961). The convulsant action of methionine sulfoximine ("agenized" flour factor) is well known (Bentley *et al.*, 1950); its control *in vivo* by methionine, glutamine or asparagine has been discussed by Tower (1961).

Increased interest in the possible mental effects of tryptophan and methionine has also developed from studies involving the use of these amino acids in conjunction with various monoamineoxidase (MAO) inhibitors. A number of publications have appeared which document observations of behavioral alterations in mentally ill patients upon oral administration of an MAO inhibitor followed by load doses of L-tryptophan or L-methionine. For tryptophan, this was first reported by Lauer *et al.* (1958) with Iproniazid and confirmed by Oates and Sjoerdsma (1960) with Catron, Pollin *et al.* (1961) with Iproniazid, and Alexander *et al.* (1963) with Parnate. For methionine, this was first reported by Pollin *et al.* (1961) with Iproniazid and confirmed by Brune and Himwich (1962b) with Isocarboxazid, and Alexander *et al.* (1963) with Parnate. A recent paper by Park *et al.* (1965) has further extended confirmation of the methionine effect with Isocarboxazid. In the case of tryptophan, the major clinical changes were mood elevation (euphoria), extroversion, transitory somnolence, and more active deep tendon reflexes. In the case of methionine, there were increased flood of word associations; increased anxiety, tension and motor activity; depression with increased insight; increased hallucinatory activity and intermittent disorientation (Pollin *et al.*, 1961). For methionine effects, the dose level of MAO inhibitor appeared to be less important than the dose level of methionine itself (Pollin *et al.*, 1961; Brune and Himwich, 1962b).

On theoretical grounds, a metabolic explanation for the mental effects observed with tryptophan or methionine load after an MAO inhibitor may be found in certain possible metabolic interrelationships between these two amino acids. Thus, the administration of an MAO inhibitor with either of these two amino acids, particularly methionine (which is necessary for biological transmethylations by way of S-adenosylmethionine), could force the body to produce methylated derivatives of tryptamine and serotonin, both of which are metabolites of tryptophan (Kety, 1961). The N,N-dimethyl derivatives which might be formed under such conditions namely N,N-dimethyl tryptamine and N,N-dimethyl serotonin (bufotenin), have been claimed to be psychotogenic in man (Szara, 1961; Fabing and Hawkins, 1956). Of interest in this regard is the finding of a mammalian enzyme (in rabbit lung) which is capable of converting tryptamine and serotonin to their respective N,N-dimethyl derivatives (Axelrod, 1961). This enzyme, however, has not yet been found in man. Claims have also been made for the occurrence of bufotenin in the urine of schizophrenic patients, but not in normal controls (Fischer *et al.*, 1961). Such reports, however, have yet to be confirmed. For details of these and other possible metabolic interrelationships between tryptophan and methionine, see Fig. 1.

From the above paragraphs, it is apparent that by 1963 a number of investigators had reported behavioral changes in schizophrenic patients after treatment with an MAO inhibitor and tryptophan or methionine. However, none of the publications reporting such findings had to this date presented metabolic data on urinary excretion of indoles, especially N,N-dimethyl indoles in patients so treated. Accordingly, when urine specimens from such test patients were made available to us through the kindness of Dr. F. Alexander

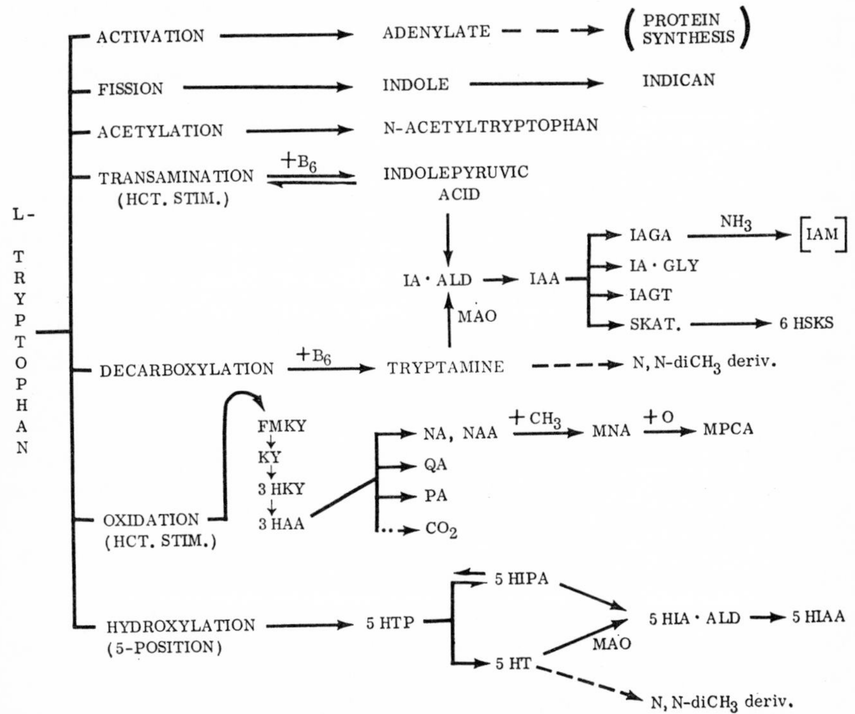

FIG. 1. Metabolic pathways of tryptophan. Key to abbreviations: HCT. STIM. = hydrocortisone stimulated, IA·ALD = indoleacetaldehyde, IAA = indoleacetic acid, IAGA = indoleacetylglucuronide, IAM = indoleacetamide, IA·GLY = indoleacetylglycine, IAGT = indoleacetylglutamine, SKAT. = skatole, 6HSKS = 6-hydroxyskatole sulfate, MAO = monoamineoxidase, FMKY = formyl kynurenine, KY = kynurenine, 3HKY = 3-hydroxykynurenine, 3HAA = 3-hydroxyanthranilic acid, NA = nicotinic acid, NAA = nicotinamide, MNA = N^1-methylnicotinamide, MPCA = N-methyl-2-pyridone-5-carboxamide, QA = quinolinic acid, PA = picolinic acid, CO_2 = carbon dioxide, 5HTP = 5-hydroxytryptophan, 5 HIPA = 5-hydroxyindolepyruvic acid, 5HT = 5-hydroxytryptamine (serotonin), 5HIA·ALD = 5-hydroxyindoleacetaldehyde, and 5-HIAA = 5-hydroxyindoleacetic acid. CH_3 groups for the formation of MNA and N,N-diCH_3 derivatives of tryptamine and 5 HT originate from methionine.

(Alexander *et al.*, 1963), we undertook a survey study of the urinary indole excretion pattern in these patients with special interest focused on the search for N,N-dimethyl derivatives of tryptamine or serotonin. The remainder of this paper will now be devoted to a presentation of: (1) our clinical studies in man with respect to urinary indole excretion under above test conditions, and

(2) our basic studies in rats (still in progress) to evaluate the metabolic effects observed in man.

CLINICAL STUDIES IN MAN

Results of our urinary indole study with Alexander's patients were reported in late 1963 (Sprince *et al.*, 1963). Only a brief description of our methods and results will be presented here. For further details, see the publications from which this review material has been taken (Alexander *et al.*, 1963; Sprince *et al.*, 1963).

Methods. Aliquots of a 24-hr urine sample after each weekly test period were obtained from four chronic schizophrenic and two psychoneurotic patients of Alexander's study. The design of the study was such that a six-by-six randomized Latin square design was used with both the psychiatrist and this laboratory remaining "blind" to the drug combination administered. Six weekly test periods in series were involved with 1 week of rest interspersed between the third and fourth week, making a total of 7 weeks. During each weekly test period, the patient received daily oral doses of test-medication consisting of Parnate (tranylcypromine), L-tryptophan, or L-methionine, each administered alone or in combination in accordance with the Latin square design. Details of this design and amounts of medication administered are given in the legends of Fig. 3 and 4 under Results.

Urine specimens for analysis were treated as follows. Collections were made on the seventh (last) day of each weekly test period and stored under toluene in a deep freeze (−15°C). Creatinine determinations of urines were made by the alkaline picrate method (Folin, 1914). Surveys of urinary indole excretion patterns were made by two-way paper chromatography of ether-butanone extracts obtained under alkaline (pH 10) and acid (pH 3) conditions and equated to urinary creatinine as described in previous publications (Sprince *et al.*, 1962, 1961, 1960). The solvent systems used in such survey studies were as follows: *first*, isopropanol (I)/ammonium hydroxide (A)/water (W) in ratio of 8/1/1; *second*, n-butanol (B)/acetic acid (AA)/water (W) in ratio of 4/1/5. On the other hand, quantitation of two key indole metabolites, tryptamine and indoleacetamide (i.e. indoleacetylglucuronide) was accomplished by a two-way paper chromatographic method utilizing as solvent systems *first*, n-butanol (B)/acetic acid (AA)/water (W) in ratio of 4/1/5 and *second*, 20% (W/V) aqueous KCl solution (Sprince *et al.*, 1963). (Indoleacetamide results from ammonolysis of its parent metabolite indoleacetylglucuronide which is a major conjugate of indoleacetic acid in the urine of man.)

Results. Paper chromatographic surveys of urinary indole patterns revealed that significant changes could be detected in the appearance of tryptamine and in the spot size of indoleacetamide and indoleacetic acid during the Latin square test periods. Despite careful scrutiny, however, no methylated derivatives of tryptamine and serotonin (bufotenin) could be detected in any of the urine extracts under our conditions of test. Urinary excretion of 6-hydroxyskatole sulfate was erratic; no significant change could be discerned. The most well-defined changes observed were with tryptamine and indoleacetamide in the alkaline (pH 10) ether extracts after treatment with Parnate plus methionine (Fig. 2). Results with Parnate plus tryptophan were less clear-cut.

Quantitative results obtained with urines from the four schizophrenic patients and the two psychoneurotic patients for tryptamine and indoleacetamide are shown in Figs. 3 and 4, respectively.

Inspection of the chromatograms of Fig. 2 and the graphical data of Figs. 3 and 4 reveal that a combination of Parnate plus methionine gave definitely

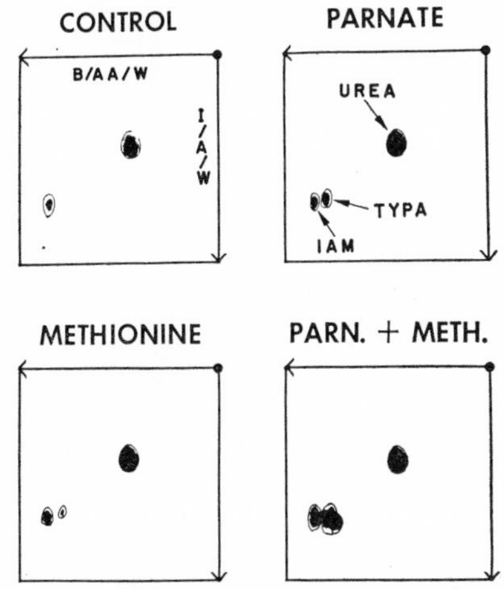

FIG. 2. Paper chromatograms of urines from schizophrenic patient R. U. before treatment (control), after 1 week on Parnate alone, after 1 week on methionine alone, and after 1 week on Parnate plus methionine. For details of dosage see Fig. 3 below. After Parnate plus methionine, note the marked increase in the tryptamine (TYPA) and indoleacetamide (IAM) spots. The TYPA spot is increased to the point where it looks almost like a fusion of several spots; further tests revealed this to be only TYPA.

higher urinary levels of tryptamine and indoleacetamide (i.e. indoleacetylglucuronide) than did either component alone. This effect was consistently observed in three out of four schizophrenics tested and in both psychoneurotic patients, and was found to occur at about the time of onset of one or more of the mental symptoms noted by Alexander *et al.* (1963). Results with Parnate plus tryptophan were inconclusive due to marked variability. The marked increase in urinary indoleacetamide after tryptophan load in the two psychoneurotic but not in the four schizophrenic patients is a finding of interest requiring further confirmation. Care must be taken to rule out carryover effects of medication from preceding test periods. This last point may well explain the aberrant tryptamine and indoleacetamide response of schizophrenic patient (SR) to the combination of Parnate plus methionine.

The above findings with Parnate plus methionine appeared to be of special interest in view of the report of Brune and Himwich (1962a) that urinary tryptamine and indoleacetic acid were elevated in exacerbation of psychotic

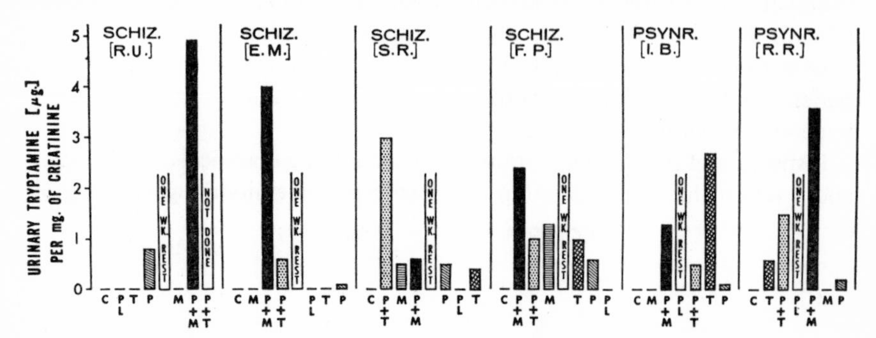

FIG. 3. Urinary tryptamine (TYPA) excretion in micrograms (μg) per milligram (mg) of urinary creatinine (CR). Letters under SCHIZ. (schizophrenic) and PSYNR. (psychoneurotic) are initials of patients. Key to letters on abscissa: C = control before experiment, PL = placebo, P = Parnate (tranylcypromine), M = L-methionine, P+M = Parnate+L-methionine, T = L-tryptophan. P+T = Parnate+L-tryptophan. Dose schedule: P = 30 mg daily (10 mg t.i.d.), M = 20 g daily (6·6 g t.i.d.), and T = 15 g daily (5 g t.i.d.). During the 1-week rest period, the schizophrenics received no treatment; the psychoneurotics received a placebo. The purpose of the 1-week rest period was to prevent a piling up of pharmacologically active substances from the medication tests. Reproduced from Sprince *et al.* (1963) *Journal of Nervous and Mental Disease*, **137**, 246–51.

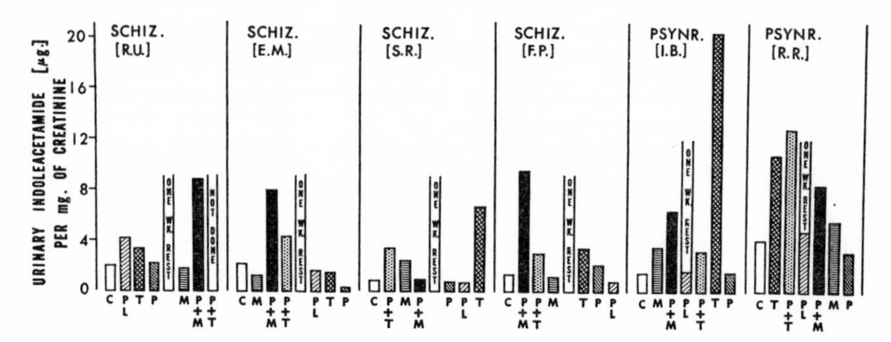

FIG. 4. Urinary indoleacetamide (IAM) excretion in micrograms (μg) per milligram (mg) of urinary creatinine (CR). Other details and abbreviations same as in Fig. 3. Reproduced from Sprince *et al.* (1963) *Journal of Nervous and Mental Disease*, **137**, 246–51.

symptoms and reduced to normal levels with improvement in mental state. Since, in our studies, the psychoactive N-methylated derivatives of tryptamine and serotonin could not be found, no obvious explanation was forthcoming for these mental effects. (Some consideration, however, of larger urine volumes for detection of such dimethyl indole derivatives may be in order.) Equally true was the fact that no obvious explanation could be given for the observation that methionine markedly enhanced the effect of Parnate in increasing urinary indole excretion. This led us to a consideration of animal studies for reasons set forth in the next section.

BASIC STUDIES IN RATS

In order to gain a better understanding of the methionine effect on Parnate in increasing urinary indole output, it is reasonable to inquire into the effect of Parnate *alone* and methionine *alone* on the urinary excretion of indoles. To recapitulate briefly (see Figs. 2, 3 and 4), Parnate *alone* gave detectable increases in urinary tryptamine and indoleacetamide. Methionine *alone* gave variable results. Neither of these compounds *alone*, however, in any instance showed the marked response resulting from a combination of these two compounds. Since the effect of monoamine oxidase inhibitors (such as Parnate) on urinary tryptamine and indoleacetic acid excretion is well known (LaBrosse *et al.*, 1964), further investigation of Parnate *alone* was not pursued. It became of more immediate interest to determine the possible effect of methionine *per se* on urinary indole excretion.

To accomplish this, we undertook studies with rats on complete-synthetic amino-acid diets, a test-situation whereby conditions could be controlled better than in human subjects and large amounts of methionine could be fed over a prolonged period of time (Sprince *et al.*, 1964, 1965a, and 1965b). The purpose of this research was to determine the effect of excess dietary methionine (or its metabolites, e.g. homocysteine and cysteine) on the *in vivo* metabolism of tryptophan from which urinary indoles are known to arise. Two key metabolites known to originate from tryptophan in the rat by different metabolic pathways were chosen for study. These were N^1-methylnicotinamide and indoleacetic acid (see Fig. 1). Creatinine was also considered because methionine is involved in its formation by way of transmethylation.

Methods. Sprague-Dawley male rats (approximately 40 days old, weighing 150 g) on arrival were placed on a control casein diet of the following composition (g/100 g of diet): casein, 30·0; corn starch, 46·0; yellow dextrin, 2·0; non-nutritive fiber (cellulose), 4·0; NRRL salt mix No. 446, 3·0; cottonseed oil, 14·0; and vitamin supplement in corn starch, 1·0.[1] After attaining a weight

[1] One gram of corn starch-vitamin supplement supplied the following vitamins in mg/100 g of diet: *p*-aminobenzoic acid, 11·02; ascorbic acid (coated 97·5% ascorbic acid), 101·75; biotin, 0·04; Ca pantothenate, 6·61; choline dihydrogen citrate, 371·52; folic acid, 0·20; *i*-inositol, 11·02; menadione, 4·96; nicotinic acid, 9·92; pyridoxine·HCl, 2·20; riboflavin, 2·20; thiamin·HCl, 2·20; vitamin A (dry stabilized, 500,000 U.S.P. units/g), 3·97; vitamin B_{12} (0·1% in mannitol), 2·98; vitamin D_2 (dry, 500,000 U.S.P. units/g), 0·44; vitamin E acetate (25%, 250 I.U. vit. E/g), 48·50; and corn starch q.s., 420·47.

of approximately 200 g, generally in 8 to 10 days, these rats were then placed on the following test diets (8 rats/diet): (1) diet (CASEIN) = 30% casein control diet of above; (2) diet (CS−N) = a complete-synthetic amino-acid diet deficient in nicotinic acid or nicotinamide, but containing 0·806% DL-methionine and 0·358% DL-tryptophan and described in detail in the next paragraph; (3) diet (CS−N+4%M) = same as (CS−N), but plus 4% methionine (total methionine content = 4·806%); (4) diet (CS−N+HC ⇌ 4% M) = same as (CS−N), but plus homocysteine equivalent to 4% methionine on a mole basis; (5) diet (CS−N+CY ⇌ 4%M) = same as (CS−N), but plus cysteine equivalent to 4% methionine on a mole basis; (6) diet (CS−N−M) = same as (CS−N), but minus methionine; and (7) diet (CS−N−M−T) = same as (CS−N), but minus both methionine and tryptophan. The above diets were prepared by General Biochemicals.

The exact composition of diet (CS−N) was as follows (g/100 g of diet): L-arginine·HCl, 1·209; L-histidine·HCl·H_2O, 0·484; L-isoleucine, 0·448; L-leucine, 0·717; L-lysine, 1·227; DL-methionine, 0·806; DL-phenylalanine, 0·806; DL-threonine, 0·896; DL-tryptophan, 0·358; DL-valine, 1·254; DL-alanine, 0·358; L-asparagine, 0·896; L-glutamic acid, 4·569; glycine, 1·792; DL-serine, 0·448; L-tyrosine, 0·896; cottonseed oil, 7·175; salt mix (Wesson), 3·587; sodium bicarbonate, 1·525; sucrose, 59·677; non-nutritive fiber (cellulose), 8·780; and cod liver oil, 1·794. Vitamins added were (mg/100 g of diet): thiamin·HCl, 0·538; riboflavin, 0·538; pyridoxine·HCl, 0·538; calcium pantothenate, 2·687; choline chloride, 179·2; biotin, 0·0449; folic acid, 0·179; *i*-inositol, 89·580; menadione, 0·448; vitamin B_{12} (0·1% in mannitol), 4·479; and α-tocopherol, 17·917. This diet was prepared by General Biochemicals (J. R. Thomson formulation minus nicotinic acid).

During the test period, rats were maintained as follows. Rats were housed and fed in Hoeltge rat metabolism cages (one rat per cage). Daily records were kept of rat weight, food consumption and urine volume for a period of 3 weeks. At the beginning of the test period (zero time) and at weekly intervals thereafter for 3 weeks, 24-hr urine samples were collected under toluene, pooled for each group, and stored in a deep freeze (−15°C) until used for assay. Urinary determinations were made for creatinine (CR), N^1-methyl-nicotinamide (MNA), and indoleacetic acid (IAA). CR was assayed by the standard alkaline-picrate method (Folin, 1914). MNA was measured by Sarett's method (Sarett, 1943) with a minor modification. This consisted of treatment with 0·5 N HCl (0·1 of total volume) at 40°C for 5 min in a glass-stoppered tube, just prior to addition of benzidine reagent. IAA was determined both as free, unhydrolyzed IAA (FIAA) and total, acid-hydrolyzed IAA (TIAA). A paper chromatographic method for IAA was developed to avoid possible interference from a closely related chromatographic spot normally found in rat urine and tentatively identified as indoleacetylglycine.

Briefly the IAA method was as follows. Urine (2–5 ml) unhydrolyzed, or hydrolyzed by acidification to 1 N with HCl and heating at 80°C for 15 min, was adjusted to pH 5–5·5, diluted to convenient volume (10–20 ml), saturated with $(NH_4)_2SO_4$, extracted with ethyl ether, the ether extract evaporated to dryness, and dissolved in 95% ethanol to convenient volume (2–5 ml). An aliquot of the ethanol extract (≎ approx. 0·5–1·5 mg urinary CR) was then subjected to two dimensional paper chromatography (*first* solvent, isopropanol/ammonium hydroxide/water, 80/10/20; *second* solvent, isopropanol/pyridine/25% aqueous dimethylamine-glacial acetic acid mixture adjusted to pH 6·2/water, 75/10/5/10) and sprayed with Ehrlich benzaldehyde-nitrite reagent (Sprince, 1960). Two blue spots resulted: one was the tentatively identified indoleacetylglycine spot (R_f = 0·55, 0·35, respectively); the other was the IAA spot (R_f = 0·51, 0·65, respectively). The blue IAA spot was extracted into 2 ml alcoholic-HCl solution (1 part 3 N HCl+1 part 95% ethanol) and the optical density read at 580 mμ. For rapid one-way chromatographic separations, good results have also been obtained with the second solvent system *per se*.

Results. The effects of excess dietary methionine and its metabolites, homocysteine and cysteine, are self-evident from Figs. 5, 6, 7 and 8. Results are given for the mean urinany excretion of CR, MNA, and IAA, both free (FIAA) and total (TIAA), at the beginning of the experiment (zero time) and at weekly intervals thereafter for the 3-week test period.

(a) *Weight response*. To compare the effect of the various test diets on the urinary metabolites, it was necessary to correct for variability in rat weight response to the different diets. This was done by calculating the amount of metabolite excreted per 24 hr per kilogram rat. Mean rat weight changes in grams/day and mean food consumption in grams/day for the entire 21-day test period were respectively as follows: CASEIN, (+5·0) (14·3); (CS−N), (+2·5) (13·1); (CS−N+4% M), (+0·2) (8·9); (CS−N+HC ≎ 4% M), (−1·0) (7·4); (CS−N+CY ≎ 4% M), (+2·3) (13·1); (CS−N−M), (−3·0) (5·4); and (CS−N−M−T), (−2·7) (6·7). Excess dietary methionine retarded growth in the rat, an observation previously reported by others (Brown and Allison, 1948; Stekol and Szaran, 1962). Growth retardation was even greater with excess dietary homocysteine, but practically nil with cysteine compared to diet (CS−N) as control. As expected, in the absence of methionine, growth was inhibited to the point where weight loss occurred.

(b) *Urinary* CR. In the case of urinary CR (Fig. 5), it is obvious that with all test diets, only minor changes occurred during the 3-week test period despite the marked variability in weight response. At zero time, the mean urinary CR excretion for all groups from A to G in mg/24 hr/kg rat was calculated to be 30·8±0·62 S.E. (standard error).

(c) *Urinary* MNA. With urinary MNA, a marked drop in excretion (from a mean zero-time value for all test groups of 16·6±0·58 S.E. mg/24 hr/kg rat) was observed with diets containing an excess of methionine, homocysteine, or

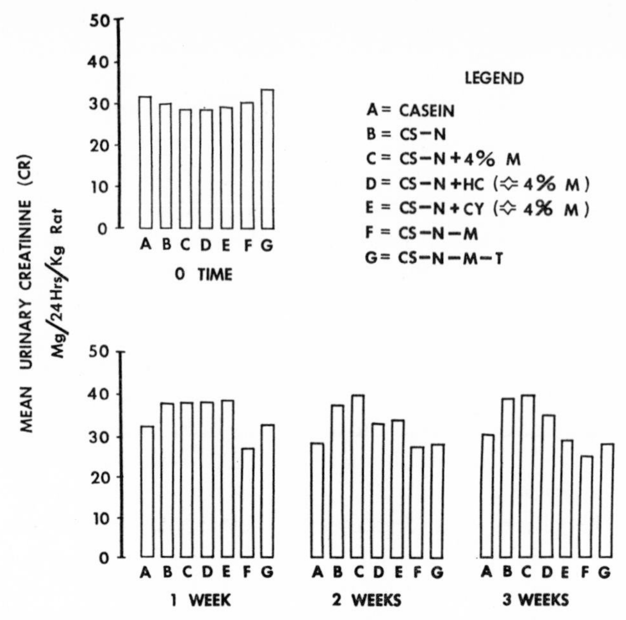

FIG. 5. Mean urinary creatinine (CR) excretion in rats on different diets.

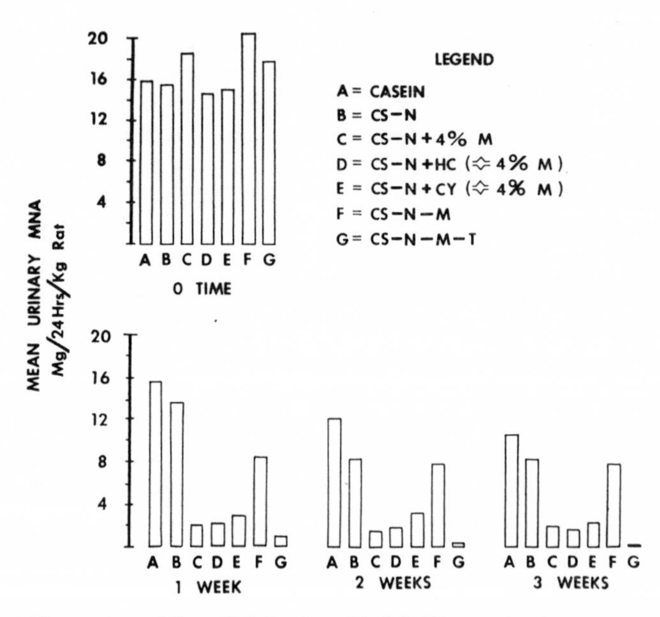

FIG. 6. Mean urinary N^1-methylnicotinamide (MNA) excretion in rats on different diets.

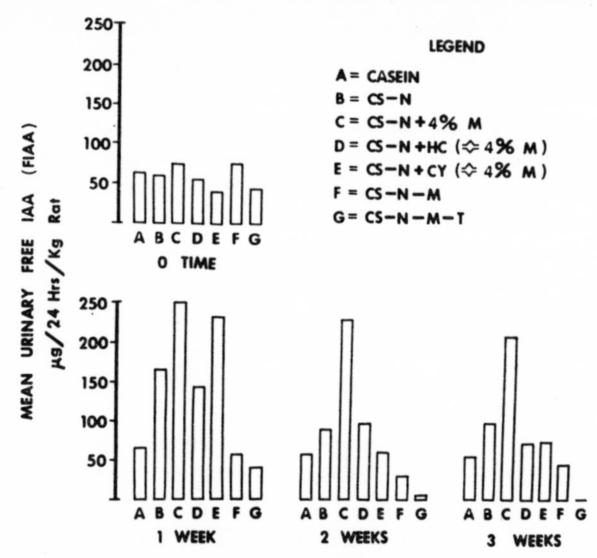

FIG. 7. Mean urinary free indoleacetic acid (FIAA) excretion in rats on different diets.

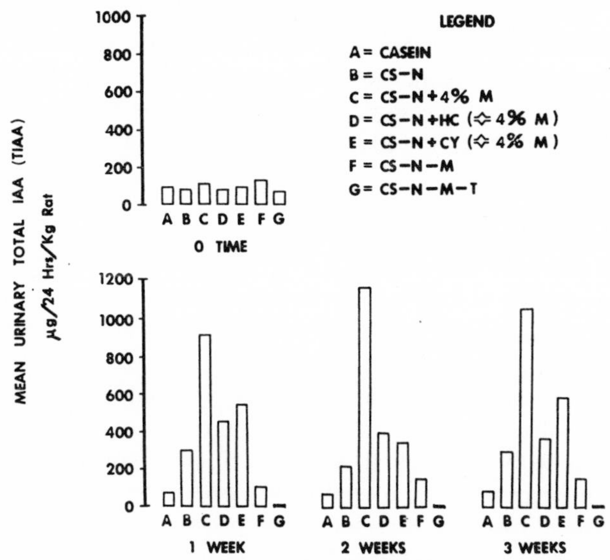

FIG. 8. Mean urinary total indoleacetic acid (TIAA) excretion in rats on different diets.

cysteine in comparison with control diets (CS – N) and casein (Fig. 6). Curiously enough, the diet deficient in methionine showed very little drop, suggesting that tissue protein was furnishing endogenous methionine for the formation of MNA. On the other hand, the observed decreases, especially with excess methionine and homocysteine, approached the value obtained with the diet deficient in both tryptophan and methionine, a condition wherein MNA formation must necessarily be minimal. Decreased urinary MNA excretion associated with excess dietary methionine has been previously reported in the human (Horwitt *et al.*, 1956), but the significance of this finding has not been fully appreciated. The degree of diminution of urinary MNA observed in our studies suggests the possibility of an inhibitory effect exerted by methionine or its metabolites at some point along the metabolic pathway from tryptophan to MNA. This, however, remains a problem for future study.

(d) *Urinary* IAA. Concomitantly with the decrease in urinary MNA, an increase in both free and total IAA was noted (Figs. 7 and 8 respectively). At zero-time, the mean FIAA value for all test groups was calculated to be $60{\cdot}1 \pm 4{\cdot}55$ S.E. μg/24 hr/kg rat; the mean TIAA value for all test groups, $89{\cdot}5 \pm 7{\cdot}59$ S.E. μg/24 hr/kg rat. During the 3-week test period, it is obvious that a marked increase in both urinary FIAA and TIAA occurred with the diet containing excess methionine compared to the control diets (CS – N) and casein. The increases with diets containing excess homocysteine and excess cysteine, however, were less clear-cut. Thus, it appears that in our studies an excess of dietary methionine not only decreased urinary MNA but also increased urinary IAA, suggesting a shift in tryptophan metabolism from the nicotinic acid pathway to the IAA pathways. This is a point also requiring further study.

DISCUSSION

An excess of dietary methionine could affect tryptophan metabolism *in vivo* in a number of ways. Not the least to be considered is a possible alteration of intestinal microflora which could result in changes of levels of MNA and IAA excreted in urine. However, preliminary experiments in this laboratory with excess methionine injected intraperitoneally in rats lead us to a consideration of tissue metabolism as an important factor in the methionine effect.

From a speculative standpoint, excess methionine could affect the tissue metabolism of tryptophan in a number of ways. These are as follows:

A. *Inhibition of oxidative enzymes of tryptophan metabolism.* A number of oxidative enzymes (more recently called "oxygenases" by Hayaishi, 1964) are known to be involved in the intermediary metabolism of tryptophan. The most prominent of these are (a) tryptophan pyrrolase, (b) kynurenine hydroxylase, (c) 3-hydroxyanthranilic acid oxidase, (d) tryptophan-5-hydroxylase, and (e) monoamine oxidase. Despite the fact that some of these enzymes may require sulfhydryl (–SH) groups for activity, it is not unreasonable to suppose that large amounts of homocysteine and cysteine arising from the metabolism of excess methionine could result in a concentration of –SH groups high enough to inhibit the activity of such enzymes. For a report suggesting the possibility of such inhibitions, see Lagnado and Sourkes (1956). The decreased excretion of urinary MNA observed in our rat studies could be explained on this basis. Work is in progress in our laboratories to examine this point further.

B. *Liberation of free tryptophan from bound tryptophan in the blood or tissues.* Studies by McMenamy and associates (1958, 1963) have shown that L-tryptophan is bound to serum albumin predominantly at one site in a highly stereospecific manner. The possibility thus exists that an excess of methionine could prevent the binding of *free* tryptophan at, or could release *bound* tryptophan from, highly specific binding sites in the blood or tissues. Increased amounts of *free* tryptophan would then be available for metabolic transformation over its various pathways (Fig. 1). Such an effect could account for our observation of increased urinary excretion of free and total indoleacetic acid in our rat studies with excess methionine. The likelihood of this possibility would be all the more increased if the inhibition of the oxidative enzymes discussed in the preceding paragraph (section A) were operative. To examine this point further, we are now undertaking tryptophan assays on the above rat urines.

C. *Formation of N-methylated indolic amines* (*i.e. N,N-dimethyl derivatives of tryptamine and serotonin*). The possible formation of these psychoactive amines has already been discussed. It is of interest that these compounds have been claimed to have MAO inhibitory activity (Govier *et al.*, 1953). The increased excretion of urinary tryptamine and IAA-conjugate in our clinical studies and of IAA in our rat studies suggests that methionine loading may raise intermediary tryptamine levels in the body to the point where the N,N-dimethyl derivatives could be formed. However, our *in vivo* studies in man and in the rat gave no evidence for such compounds in the urine. Nevertheless, the feeling still persists that such N,N-dimethyl derivatives may be formed (Berlet *et al.*, 1964; Park *et al.*, 1965); and, in this regard, the extraction of much larger urine volumes than were used in our studies may be worthy of consideration. Moreover, it remains to be determined whether or not the administration of an MAO inhibitor (e.g. Parnate) to animals fed excess methionine over a prolonged period of time could give rise to such compounds. Such studies are currently in progress in our laboratory.

D. *Formation of O-methylated* (*methoxy*) *metabolites.* A number of metabolites originating from tryptophan have been reported to form methoxy (–OCH_3) derivatives which can be detected in urine upon occasion. These are: (a) 5-methyoxytryptamine in the urine of rheumatic subjects (Haddox and Saslow, 1963), (b) 8-methoxyxanthurenic acid in the normal urine of man (Price and Dodge, 1956) and in rat urine only under certain conditions

(Roy *et al.*, 1961), and (c) 3-methoxyanthranilic acid in normal human urine (Kido *et al.*, 1963). Questions now arise as to whether or not these methoxy metabolites may be increased in the urine after methionine load and whether or not they could act as metabolic feedback inhibitors in the nicotinic acid pathway. Such feedback inhibitions also could explain the reduced urinary MNA excretion observed in our rat studies. This latter point is of special interest in view of the observation that 3-methoxyanthranilic acid can inhibit nicotinic acid formation from tryptophan in *Neurospora* (Mitchell *et al.*, 1948).

Another important consideration with regard to O-methylation arises from the work of Axelrod (1959) and that of Friedhoff (Friedhoff and Van Winkle, 1962; Friedhoff, this symposium). This is the possibility that the methoxylation of phenols may serve as an inactivation or detoxication mechanism for certain phenolic compounds involved in psychoactivity (e.g. dopamine, norepinephrine and epinephrine). As a metabolic process of this nature, phenolic methoxylation would normally form small amounts of *monomethoxy* derivatives of these compounds (e.g. 3-methoxytyramine, normetanephrine, and metanephrine respectively). In certain forms of mental illness, however, phenolic methoxylation might be elevated to such a high level of activity that "abnormal" *dimethoxy* derivatives would be formed. Such a possibility finds support from the reports of Friedhoff and Van Winkle (above) that 3,4-dimethoxyphenylethylamine (and possibly 3,4-dimethoxyphenylacetic acid) is found in schizophrenic urine but not in normal urine. Within the framework of this concept, it might be worth while to look for increased urinary levels of the three methoxy metabolites of tryptophan cited above in conditions of mental disturbance. Data have yet to be obtained in this regard.

Finally, it is of additional interest to note that 5-methoxytryptamine is contained in the molecule of the pineal gland hormone, melatonin (Lerner *et al.*, 1960); that pineal gland extracts have been implicated in schizophrenia (Altschule, 1957; Eldred *et al.*, 1960); and that the N,N-dimethyl derivative of 5-methoxytryptamine has been claimed to effect behavioral alterations in the rat (Gessner and Page, 1962).

E. *Formation of α-methylated metabolites.* Recently, the possibility has been considered that catechol amines methylated in the α-position ($-CH(CH_3)-NH_2$) can be formed in the body and may be related to mental depression (Friend, 1964). This investigator claims to have obtained preliminary data purporting to show that α-methylnorepinephrine has been found in the urine of a depressed patient on no drugs. If this claim can be confirmed it would be of interest to test the effect of methionine load on this type of metabolic methylation.

F. *Effect on pyridoxal phosphate activity.* The metabolism of methionine to form homocysteine, cystathionine, and cysteine involves enzymes requiring pyridoxal phosphate in the case of the latter two metabolites. A high methionine intake is known to increase pyridoxine depletion, an observation which, it has been suggested, may be related to increased synthesis of pyridoxal phosphate-containing enzymes and/or the loss of pyridoxal phosphate itself (Nutrition Reviews, 1964). Loss of pyridoxal phosphate could occur by way of formation of an indole-pyridoxal complex (Scott, 1961). A claim for the appearance of such an indole-pyridoxal complex in the urine of schizophrenic patients has already been made (Huszak and Durko, 1964). It is tempting to consider this claim of Huszak and Durko with reference to our own findings wherein an increased excretion of urinary indoles was observed after methionine load. Thus, the possibility exists that a methionine load or increase by metabolic disturbances could raise the level of body indoles to a point where complex formation with pyridoxal phosphate (mobilized for increased enzyme activity) could occur. The loss of the indole-pyridoxal phosphate complex in the urine could result in pyridoxal phosphate deficiency symptoms known to involve psychic and nervous disturbances (Sourkes, 1962). Further consideration of this possibility awaits future study.

SUMMARY

1. Metabolic interrelationships of tryptophan and methionine in relation to mental illness are reviewed. Data are presented of clinical studies in the human and basic studies in the rat.

2. Clinical studies with schizophrenic and psychoneurotic patients revealed that a combination of a monoamineoxidase (MAO) inhibitor (Parnate) and L-methionine gave rise to higher levels of urinary indoles than did either component alone. A correlation with behavioral change was observed.

3. Basic studies in rats were undertaken to determine the effect of methionine *per se* on the excretion of urinary indoles. Studies with synthetic test diets containing tryptophan but deficient in nicotinic acid revealed that an excess of dietary methionine (4%) lowered the urinary level of N^1-methylnicotinamide and raised the urinary level of indoleacetic acid. Urinary creatinine levels showed only minor changes. The methionine metabolites homocysteine and cysteine fed in excess also lowered urinary N^1-methylnicotinamide; their effect on indoleacetic acid excretion, however, was less certain.

4. As a working hypothesis, it is suggested that, *in vivo*, excess methionine may favor the channeling of tryptophan metabolism into indoleacetic acid production by inhibiting the nicotinic acid pathway or stimulating those pathways leading to the formation of indoleacetic acid. From a speculative standpoint, excess methionine and/or its metabolites could involve disturbances in tryptophan metabolism by way of inhibition of oxidation (oxygenase) reactions, liberation of free tryptophan from the bound state, formation of N-methylated metabolites, formation of O-methylated metabolites, formation of alpha-methylated metabolites (?), and stimulation (and/or depletion) of pyridoxal phosphate activity. These possibilities are briefly discussed.

REFERENCES

ALEXANDER, F., CURTIS, III, G. C., SPRINCE, H. and CROSLEY, A. P. (1963) L-Methionine and L-tryptophan feedings in non-psychotic and schizophrenic patients with and without tranylcypromine, *Journal of Nervous and Mental Disease*, **137,** 135–42.

ALTSCHULE, M. D. (1957) Some effects of aqueous extracts of acetone-dried beef-pineal substance in chronic schizophrenia, *New England Journal of Medicine*, **257,** 919–22.

AXELROD, J. (1959) Metabolism of epinephrine and other sympathomimetic amines, *Physiological Reviews*, **39,** 751–76.

AXELROD, J. (1961) Enzymatic formation of psychotomimetic metabolites from normally occurring compounds, *Science*, **134,** 343.

BENTLEY, H. R., MCDERMOTT, E. E. and WHITEHEAD, J. K. (1950) Action of nitrogen trichloride on proteins–synthesis of the toxic factor from methionine, *Nature*, **165,** 735.

BERLET, H. H., BULL, C., HIMWICH, H. E., KOHL, H., MATSUMOTO, K., PSCHEIDT, G. R., SPAIDE, J., TOURLENTES, T. T. and VALVERDE, J. M. (1964) Endogenous metabolic factor in schizophrenic behavior, *Science*, **144,** 311–13.

BROWN, J. H. and ALLISON, J. B. (1948) Effects of excess dietary DL-methionine and/or L-arginine on rats, *Proceedings of the Society for Experimental Biology and Medicine*, **69,** 196–8.

BRUNE, G. G. and HIMWICH, H. E. (1962a) Indole metabolites in schizophrenic patients, *A.M.A. Archives of General Psychiatry*, **6,** 324–8.

BRUNE, G. G. and HIMWICH, H. E. (1962b) Effects of methionine loading on the behavior of schizophrenic patients, *Journal of Nervous and Mental Disease*, **134,** 447–50.

CARSON, N. A. J., CUSWORTH, D. C., DENT, C. E., FIELD, C. M. B., NEILL, D. W. and WESTALL, R. G. (1963) Homocystinuria: a new inborn error of metabolism associated with mental deficiency, *Archives of Diseases of Childhood*, **38,** 425–36.

ELDRED, S. H., BELL, N. W. and SHERMAN, L. J. (1960) A pilot study comparing the effects of pineal extract and a placebo in patients with chronic schizophrenia, *New England Journal of Medicine*, **263,** 1330–5.

FABING, H. D. and HAWKINS, J. R. (1956) Intravenous injection of bufotenine in humans, *Science*, **123,** 886–7.

FISCHER, E., FERNÁNDEZ LAGRAVERE, T. A., VÁZQUEZ, A. J. and DISTEFANO, A. O. (1961) A bufotenin-like substance in the urine of schizophrenics, *Journal of Nervous and Mental Disease*, **133,** 441–4.

FOLIN, O. F. (1914) On the determination of creatinine and creatine in urine, *Journal of Biological Chemistry*, **17,** 469–73.

FRIEDHOFF, A. J. and VAN WINKLE, E. (1962) Isolation and characterization of a compound from schizophrenic urine, *Nature*, **194,** 897–8.

FRIEDHOFF, A. J. and VAN WINKLE, E. (1966) New developments in the investigation of the relationship of 3,4-dimethoxyphenylethylamine to schizophrenia, this Symposium, pp, 19–21.

FRIEND, D. G. (1964) Role of synthetic drugs in therapy of mental illness. *In Molecular Modification in Drug Design* (F. W. Schueler, Chairman), *Advances in Chemistry Series*, **45,** pp. 148–61, Washington, D. C.; American Chemical Society.

FRIMPTER, G. W., HAYMOVITZ, A. and HORWITH, A. (1963) Cystathioninuria, *New England Journal of Medicine*, **268,** 333–9.

GAITONDE, M. K. and RICHTER, D. (1957) The metabolism of S^{35}-methionine in the brain. *In Metabolism of the Nervous System* (D. Richter, Ed.), pp. 449–55, New York; Pergamon Press.

GERRITSEN, T., VAUGHN, J. G. and WAISMAN, H. A. (1962) The identification of homocystine in the urine, *Biochemical and Biophysical Research Communications*, **9,** 493–6.

GESSNER, P. K. and PAGE, I. H. (1962) Behavioral effects of 5-methoxy-N:N-dimethyltryptamine, other tryptamines, and LSD, *American Journal of Pysiology*, **203,** 167–72.

GOVIER, W. M., HOWES, B. G. and GIBBONS, A. J. (1953) The oxidative deamination of serotonin and other 3-(β-aminoethyl) indoles by monoamine oxidase and the effect of these compounds on the determination of tyramine, *Science*, **118,** 596–7.

HADDOX, JR., C. H. and SASLOW, M. S. (1963) Urinary 5-methoxytryptamine in patients with rheumatic fever, *Journal of Clinical Investigation*, **42,** 435–41.

HARRIS, H., PENROSE, L. S. and THOMAS, D. H. H. (1959) Cystathioninuria, *Annals of Human Genetics*, **23,** 442–53.

HAYAISHI, O. (1964) Oxygenases, *Proceedings of the Plenary Sessions, 6th International Congress of Biochemistry, July 26–August 1, 1964, New York*. Federation of American Societies for Experimental Biology.

HEYMAN, J. J. and MERLIS, S. (1963) Transmethylation of nicotinamide in schizophrenics and normals. II. The effect of psychotropic drugs on the transmethylation of nicotinamide in the schizophrenic, *Recent Advances in Biological Psychiatry*, **5,** 211–20.

HIMWICH, W. A. and COSTA, E. (1960) Behavioral changes associated with changes in concentrations of brain serotonin, *Federation Proceedings of American Societies for Experimental Biology*, **19,** 838–45.

HORWITT, M. K., HARVEY, C. C., ROTHWELL, W. S., CUTTER, J. L. and HOFFRON, D. (1956) Tryptophan-niacin relationships in man, *Journal of Nutrition*, **60,** Supplement 1, 43 pages.

HUSZAK, I. and DURKO, I. (1964) Formation of indole-pyridoxal complex in the urine of schizophrenics, *Acta Biochimica Polonica*, **11,** 389–93.

IBER, F. L., ROSEN, H., LEVENSON, S. M. and CHALMERS, T. C. (1957) The plasma amino acids in patients with liver failure, *Journal of Laboratory and Clinical Medicine*, **50,** 417–25.

KETY, S. S. (1961) Possible relation of central amines to behavior in schizophrenic patients, *Federation Proceedings American Societies for Experimental Biology, Symposium and Reports*, **20,** 894–6.

KIDO, R., TSUJI, T. and MATSUMURA, Y. (1963) The identification of 3-methoxy-anthranilic acid, additional tryptophan metabolite, in human urine, *Biochemical and Biophysical Research Communications*, **13,** 428–30.

KRAWCZYNSKI, J. (1961) The influence of serotonin, D-lysergic acid diethylamide and 2-brom-LSD on the incorporation of S^{35}-methionine into brain proteins and on the level of ATP in the brain, *Journal of Neurochemistry*, **7,** 1–4.

LABROSSE, E. H., KOPIN, I. J., FELIX, Jr., W. R. and WESTLAKE, R. J. (1964) Urinary tryptamine and indole-3-acetic acid excretion by schizophrenic patients: Use of the tryptamine/indole acetic acid ratio as an index of monoamine oxidase inhibition, *Journal of Psychiatric Research*, **2,** 185–97.

LAGNADO, J. R. and SOURKES, T. L. (1956) Inhibition of amine oxidase by metal ions and by sulfhydryl compounds, *Canadian Journal of Biochemistry and Physiology*, **34,** 1185–94.

LAUER, J. W., INSKIP, W. M., BERSOHN, J. and ZELLER, E. A. (1958) Observations on schizophrenic patients after Iproniazid and tryptophan, *A.M.A. Archives of Neurology and Psychiatry*, **80,** 122–30.

LERNER, A. B., CASE, J. D. and TAKAHASHI, Y. (1960) Isolation of melatonin and 5-methoxyindole-3-acetic acid from bovine pineal glands, *Journal of Biological Chemistry*, **235,** 1992–7.

MCMENAMY, R. H. and ONCLEY, J. L. (1958) The specific binding of L-tryptophan to serum albumin, *Journal of Biological Chemistry*, **233,** 1436–47.

MCMENAMY, R. H. and SEDER, R. H. (1963) Thermodynamic values related to the association of L-tryptophan analogues to human serum albumin, *Journal of Biological Chemistry*, **238,** 3241–8.

MITCHELL, H. K., NYC, J. F. and OWEN, R. D. (1948) Utilization by the rat of 3-hydroxyanthranilic acid as a substitute for nicotinamide, *Journal of Biological Chemistry*, **175,** 433–8.

OATES, J. A. and SJOERDSMA, A. (1960) Neurological effects of tryptophan in patients receiving a monoamine oxidase inhibitor, *Neurology*, **10,** 1076–8.

OLSON, R. E., GURSEY, D., and VESTER, J. W. (1960) Evidence for a defect in tryptophan metabolism in chronic alcoholism, *New England Journal of Medicine*, **263,** 1169–74.

PARK, L. C., BALDESSARINI, R. J. and KETY, S. S. (1965) Methionine effects on chronic schizophrenics, *Archives of General Psychiatry*, **12,** 346–51.

POLLIN, W., CARDON, Jr., P. V. and KETY, S. S. (1961) Effects of amino acid feedings in schizophrenic patients treated with Iproniazid, *Science*, **133**, 104–5.

PRICE, J. M. and DODGE, L. W. (1956) Occurrence of the 8-methyl ether of xanthurenic acid in normal human urine, *Journal of Biological Chemistry*, **223**, 699–704.

Review article (1964) Dietary methionine and activity of enzymes related to cysteine metabolism, *Nutrition Reviews*, **22**, 188–90.

RODNIGHT, R. (1961) Body fluid indoles in mental illness, *International Review of Neurobiology*, **3**, 251–92.

ROY, J. K., PRICE, J. M. and BROWN, R. R. (1961) Studies concerning the formation of the 8-methyl ether of xanthurenic acid, *Journal of Biological Chemistry*, **236**, 145–8.

SARETT, H. P. (1943) A direct method for the determination of N-methyl derivatives of nicotinic acid in urine, *Journal of Biological Chemistry*, **150**, 159–64.

SCOTT, T. A. (1961) An enzymic method for the estimation of L-tryptophan, *Biochemical Journal*, **80**, 462–4.

SHAPOT, V. S. (1957) Brain metabolism in relation to the functional state of the central nervous system. *In Metabolism of the Nervous System* (D. Richter, Ed.), pp. 257–62, New York; Pergamon Press.

SMITH, B. and PROCKOP, D. J. (1962) Central-nervous-system effects of ingestion of L-tryptophan by normal subjects, *New England Journal of Medicine*, **267**, 1338–41.

SOURKES, T. L. (1962) *Biochemistry of Mental Disease*, pp. 228–30, New York; Harper and Row (Hoeber Medical Division).

SPRINCE, H., HOUSER, E., JAMESON, D. and DOHAN, F. C. (1960) Differential extraction of indoles from the urine of schizophrenic and normal subjects, *A.M.A. Archives of General Psychiatry*, **2**, 268–70.

SPRINCE, H. (1960) A modified Ehrlich benzaldehyde reagent for detection of indoles on paper chromatograms, *Journal of Chromatography*, **3**, 97–8.

SPRINCE, H. (1961) Indole metabolism in mental illness, *Clinical Chemistry*, **7**, 203–30.

SPRINCE, H. (1962) Biochemical aspects of indole metabolism in normal and schizophrenic subjects, *Annals of the New York Academy of Science*, **96**, 399–418.

SPRINCE, H., PARKER, C. M., JAMESON, D. and ALEXANDER, F. (1963) Urinary indoles in schizophrenic and psychoneurotic patients after administration of tranylcypromine (Parnate) and methionine or tryptophan, *Journal of Nervous and Mental Disease*, **137**, 246–51.

SPRINCE, H., PARKER, C. M. and JAMESON, D. (1964) Effect of methionine on the urinary excretion of N^1-methylnicotinamide and indoleactic acid, *Abstracts*, **5**, 402, Sixth International Congress of Biochemistry, New York, July 26 to August 1, 1964.

SPRINCE, H., PARKER, C. M., JAMESON, D., and JOSEPHS, JR., J. A. (1965a) Effect of methionine and its metabolites on tryptophan metabolism, *Federation Proceedings of American Societies for Experimental Biology*, **24**, 169, Forty-Ninth Annual Meeting, Atlantic City, N.J., April 9–14, 1965.

SPRINCE, H., PARKER, C. M., JAMESON, D. and JOSEPHS, JR., J. A. (1965b) Effect of methionine on nicotinic acid and indoleacetic acid pathways of tryptophan metabolism *in vivo*, *Proceedings of the Society for Experimental Biology and Medicine*, **119**, 942–6.

STEKOL, J. A. and SZARAN, J. (1962) Pathological effects of excess methionine in the diet of growing rats, *Journal of Nutrition*, **77**, 81–90.

SZARA, S. (1961) Hallucinogenic effects and metabolism of tryptamine derivatives in man, *Federation Proceedings of American Societies for Experimental Biology*, **20**, 885–8.

TOWER, D. B. (1961) The neurochemistry of convulsive states and allied disorders. *In Chemical Pathology of the Nervous System* (J. Folch-Pi, Ed.), pp. 307–46, New York; Pergamon Press.

WALSCHE, J. M. (1959) Biochemical studies in hepatic coma. *In Lectures on the Scientific Basis of Medicine*, Vol. **8**, pp. 407–28, New York; Oxford University Press.

WOOLLEY, D. W. (1962) *The Biochemical Basis of Psychoses*, New York; John Wiley and Sons, Inc.

STUDIES ON PERIODIC CATATONIA

F. A. JENNER

Physician in Charge, Medical Research Council,
Unit for Research on the Chemical Pathology of Mental Disorders,
Hollymoor Hospital, Northfield, Birmingham 31

UNFORTUNATELY, and despite persistent attempts and the expenditure of enormous sums of money, little has been achieved in demonstrating physical mechanisms of much relevance in the aetiology of the neuroses and functional psychoses. There are exceptions, though even the genetic studies of Kallman (1946), Slater (1965), Rüdin (1923), etc., can now be criticized. That some psychotic states are produced by drugs is generally accepted for example, the depression due to Rauwolfia alkaloids and the schizophreniform states due to amphetamine addiction. Finally one must mention the revered, but equally neglected, work of Gjessing (1932–60). Gjessing showed nitrogen balance changes occurred in phase with the mental state in the clockwork-like recurring states of periodic catatonia. Some of these patients he cured by treating them with massive doses of thyroxine given to deplete their nitrogen stores. This work has been in part but not completely confirmed by Hardwick and Stokes (1941) and Mall (1952).

Though it is quite clear that the cytochemical architecture of the brain must be relevant to cerebral function, and that the latter is the basis for mentation, the clinician is much more profitably engaged studying the family background and immediate psychological problems than amine metabolism. The psychiatrist may, nevertheless, do more by blindly manipulating the latter with drugs than he can achieve in his attempts to alter the psychological outlook and the social environment. Unfortunately everything is relevant.

The methodological difficulties of research in this field are enormous. The literature is a burlesque compounded of naïveties of the clinical or biochemical problem or both; it has been well reviewed by Bleuler (1954) and Kety (1959). Hence the attraction of cases which show recurrent and predictable changes in behaviour and symptomatology.

Interest in the periodic psychotic has been so great that one authority with a considerable justification has said, "No field has been more overworked." Be that as it may, the problems remain and such symptoms can still be shown to recur despite our efforts.

Attempts to find cases quite analogous to Gjessing's has demonstrated how difficult this is. This may be due to improved social conditions and hospital environments which ameliorate the symptoms. Some feel it is due to drug therapy. It is, however, in some part certainly due to the fact that such cases are easily missed. They are only found by longitudinal studies; the symptomatology is not specific.

That some psychotic conditions do recur with remarkable clock-like regularity is well substantiated by Kraepelin (1913), Bleuer (1911), Menninger-Lerchenthal (1959), Crammer (1959a), and many others. The best review of the clinical aspects of the subject is that by Menninger-Lerchenthal. Richter (1960) however, has produced some of the most interesting speculations. The latter writers agree, and our studies confirm the fact that the 48-hr psychotic rhythm can be the most persistent and regular one observed. Alternate days of mania and depression can persist for decades of a patient's life. Other cycles of 72, 96, and 120 hr have also been repeatedly reported. The longer the cycle, however, the less precise the timing.

The special significance of 48 hr is difficult to understand. The usual suggestion that it is a doubled diurnal rhythm is not very enlightening. Jenner (1965) published an electronic analogue of how such a rhythm might arise from a 24-hr clock, itself monitored by external events.

That the actual rhythm is dependent upon environmental factors has been clearly demonstrated by Goodwin, Jenner, Lobban and Sheridan (1964). We studied a patient with a well-established 48-hr psychosis and a control living together in an isolated chamber and in a 22-hr time régime. That is in eleven real days, the subjects lived through 12 days of meals, sleep, and lighting. During this period the 48-hr psychosis became a 44-hr psychosis.

Though renal excretory patterns with 48-hr components occur in such psychotic patients (see Jenner, 1963) living in 22-hr time and exhibiting a 44-hr rhythm of behaviour, the 48-hr components are not consistently changed to 44-hr patterns. This is particularly true of potassium, and therefore suggests that its changes are not of central importance in the psychotic mechanism.

Despite the obscurity of the physical factors, and despite the clear demonstration of the importance of the environmental factors, the persistence for decades of severe disturbances of behaviour and mood every other day does seem enough to suggest the relevance of physical rather than simply psychodynamic factors in such syndromes. It might, however, be suggested that this is a learnt response, but even so any reason for learning such a pattern of behaviour is quite unknown. Further, the syndrome has been reported following cerebral catastrophies (Scheiber, 1901).

One very striking example, however, of the complex relationship between sociological and biochemical factors is illustrated by a case reported by Crammer (1959a). This is a man now in his late fifties; he has a 6- to 8-day cycle of behaviour which has lasted for 14 years, except on five occasions following moves from one hospital to another. If this patient is moved the cycle becomes obliterated for between 5 and 6 months. It then reappears in the new environment and with exactly the same pattern as was exhibited before. In a study of this and other patients, to be published later, we have been able to clearly demonstrate the enormous importance of suddenly being placed in a strange environment. The precisely recurring periodic psychotic enables one to demonstrate such factors at a level of statistical significance which is usually very hard to achieve in psychiatry. The recurrence of the same pattern of behaviour suggests the underlying clock is still present.

A number of workers have shown that many patients with such syndromes have remissions which persist for intervals which are equivalent to a precise number of missed beats in the cycle (see Menninger-Lerchenthal). We have not been able to adequately confirm this as our own studies have always been of very short cycles.

These two factors, (1) that admission to hospital and presumably other non-specific stresses can temporarily alter the syndrome, and (2) that there can be missed beats in the rhythm probably add to the number of cases missed if not specially looked for. A third factor was brought out by Gjessing which could be summarized by suggesting that the clock-like genes can have variable penetrance. In a number of his patients the symptoms did not recur regularly until the diet and environmental régime were rigidly controlled. The degree of control was such that few would feel it justifiable to repeat this work in our present era of comparative therapeutic optimism. In psychiatry one syndrome merges imperceptibly into another, and it would seem in this respect the periodic psychoses are no exceptions.

Fortunately for the research worker cures do occur in which the environmental factors are of little consequence and the timing remains precise come what may. They in particular force one to consider the whole question of their relationship to other biological clocks.

The study of biological clocks has become a major field in research, though it has, like almost everything, a long history. To summarize such studies in a few words is not possible, and further, its relevance to psychiatry is even more difficult to assess. The field is, however, a fascinating one. It can be stated that approximately 24-hr endogenous clocks are ubiquitous in living things. The effects of such clocks can be clearly shown in the pattern of animal behaviour under constant environmental conditions (see Janet Harker, 1964; Bunning, 1963, etc.). Rats, squirrels, cockroaches, etc., persistently show periods of sleep and activity of rhythm approximately 24-hr duration for months on end without any environmental clues of the actual time. More recent experiments on man in caves, the Arctic, or specially designed bunkers (see, for example, Aschoff and Wever, 1962) also confirm that this is true for us as well as other animals.

Despite the above, few would fail to understand what Richter means, though they might not agree with him in detail when he states that man depends less on his clock to control his behaviour than do animals, as long as the man is well. The diurnal change in mood in depression is a classical example of how he might be influenced by his clock when ill. Richter considers the clock to be hypothalamic, and to be pushed into the background by the enlargement of the cortex, through the later stages of mammalian and particularly primate evolution.

Throughout the animal kingdom precision seems to be predominantly given to the otherwise only approximately 24-hr clock by light and darkness. Though Aschoff (1962) has shown that intensity of light might control the period of the free-running rhythm of man in an isolated environment, there is little other evidence available from human studies which demonstrates this effect in man. Nevertheless, that rhythms in the renal excretion of water and electrolytes in man are influenced by light is well established. Sharp (1960) blindfolded one group and showed that this caused differences in sodium and water excretion not seen in otherwise similarly treated controls. Lobban and Tredger (1964) have shown that the totally blind have a comparative absence of normal rhythms when compared with the partially or normally sighted. This is most strikingly true if the subject has been blind from birth. Further, many of the indigenous population in Alaska, where light and darkness follows almost 6-month cycles, have limited renal excretory rhythms (see Lobban, 1960 and 1965).

Studies of how light affects metabolism and behaviour have also been stimulated by the finding that light falling on the retina changes the concentration of melatonin, a derivative of 5-hydroxytryptamine which occurs in the pineal. There is good evidence available that this is achieved via neural pathways from the retina to the superior cervical ganglia and from there to the pineal. Much needs to be done to decide on the significance of this finding for humans. There is, however, considerable evidence that in rodents this pathway and mechanism leads to changes in activity and oestral cycles. No doubt work is continuing throughout the world on these fascinating areas of humoral control of behaviour. One can assume that these pathways are at least affected by large numbers of tranquillizing drugs, and we must be humbled by all the theories which could perhaps be added to our present fund of suggestions of how the drugs we use work (see Cohen, 1964).

The most important studies of abnormal rhythms of behaviour in animals seem again to be those of Richter (1957). He found that damage to the thyroid or the pituitary, hypothalamic tumours, and forced swimming to exhaustion could each produce abnormal behaviour rhythms in rats. After such treatment the rat developed, for example, a 19 to 21-day cycle of hyper and hypo activity. This persists for the rest of the animal's life unless it is treated with large doses of thyroxine. The relevance of this finding to the clinical problems of the periodic psychoses has never been fully explored. We are at present repeating this work and hope to be able to demonstrate how far it is, or is not, to be compared with the clinical problem.

One suggestion which immediately arises from Richter's work is that the patient with a periodic psychosis has experienced something analogous to the rat's swimming to exhaustion.

No evidence for simple physical exhaustion as a precipitant of such psychoses exists. On the other hand, the cases studied do not appear to arise in perfectly adjusted personalities who one day start to have periodic psychoses. It is not easy to quantify impressions, but it would be true to say that impotence of the patient or partner, inability to carry sexual relations to a mature marital conclusion, being jilted, being unable to express one's own needs and aggression are all factors which have been striking in the premorbid personalities of patients whom I have studied. This is somewhat in conflict with the case reports of Gjessing.

The actual symptoms displayed by patients with periodic psychoses are very varied, though in some degree most can be seen as variations of the manic depressive type of psychosis. Gjessing's study of periodic catatonia as a type of dementia praecox (he did not like the word "schizophrenia") was at least in part an historical accident of which he was aware. He again and again insisted that his studies gave him little ground to suggest they were applicable to the whole field of the functional psychoses. Nevertheless he tended to see them as studies on the border region between dementia praecox and the manic depressive psychoses. The real difficulty in repeating them in part arises from the difficulty of controlling diet in very disturbed patients, and all the problems of maintaining such a régime for months on end before one is able to decide when to give thyroxine.

This we have succeeded in doing in only one case, but for over a year, and now we have exhibited thyroxine as indicated by Gjessing. This patient has had phases of mania alternating with depressive cum catatonic stupor lasting for 4 years. The immediate impression is very encouraging, though it would be wrong to be too optimistic until a year or more has elapsed without any recurrence.

Nitrogen-balance studies in the more rapidly changing patients have produced negative results, but in one patient with a long-standing alternate day psychosis it has been possible on three occasions to stop the cycle for between 10 and 14 days. Unfortunately this patient then developed auricular fibrillation and treatment had to stop only to allow the cycle to re-emerge. Work in this field is very slow and a great number of control studies are required to assess whether the results achieved are more adequately explained in terms of the stress caused by enormous doses of thyroxine (up to 10 mg a day), or whether they are due to more specific pharmacological effects of thyroxine. We have little evidence to suggest that they are due to nitrogen depletion, but this possibility suggested by Gjessing is still quite conceivable.

Other aspects of our studies have included attempts to explain the water-balance changes described by Crammer (1959b) and in part on his most striking patient. Though the results of our work (Goodwin and Jenner) are not completely definitive, it can be categorically stated that to a large extent such changes are brought about by a periodically changing output of a vasopressin-like substance. Whether this substance is the normally occurring antidiuretic hormone or not must be the subject of further work. Nevertheless the water-balance changes it brings about seem to precede the change in mental state as has already been clearly indicated by Crammer. The changes in water balance have been shown in our work to be mainly associated with expansion and contradiction of the extracellular space. Unlike the diuresis and anti-diuresis to be expected from changing levels of antidiuretic hormone, our studies have shown that this is accompanied in the periodic psychotic by an associated naturesis and antinaturesis.

In what way, if at all, the redistribution of body water causes the changes in mental state is not easy to answer; it can, however, be stated that such large changes are rare if they occur at all in most stressful situations

Other changes which occur predictably and with the same regularity as the symptoms in some patients include changes in the height of the ECG *t* wave, the mean abundance of the α rhythm of the EEG and its harmonic mean, the level of serum cholesterol, the renal excretion and serum levels of cate-cholamines, the urinary free amino acids excreted per day, and, without fail, the rate of secretion of saliva by the parotid glands. The complicated details of the phase relationships of these factors to the symptoms cannot be presented in a limited space. The significance of such factors in the hierarchy of events producing the symptoms is also unknown.

The study of the periodic psychoses is still in a state where one must continue to find the pieces of the jigsaw. It is not at all possible to coherently assemble them to produce any composite picture. Nevertheless one can still hope that such a picture, when assembled, may throw interesting light on factors which can influence mental state. Even if that hope fails, then certain psychosomatic factors will have been found which are of importance in related fields.

REFERENCES

ASCHOFF, J. and WEVER, R. (1962) Spontanperiodik des Menschen bei Ausschluss aller Zeitgeber, *Die Naturwissenschaften*, **15**, 337–42.

BLEULER, E. (1911) *Dementia praecox oder Gruppe der Schizophrenien*, F. Deuticke.

BLEULER, M. (1954) *Edokrinologische Psychistrie*, Georg Thieme, Stuttgart.

BUNNING, E. (1963) *Die physiologische Uhr*, Springer, Berlin.

COHEN, R. A. (1964) Some clinical, biochemical, and physiological actions of the pineal gland—Clinical Staff Conference, *Ann. Int. Med.* **61,** 1164.

CRAMMER, J. L. (1959a) Periodic psychoses, *Brit. Med. J.* **1,** 545–9.

CRAMMER, J. L. (1959b) Water and sodium in two psychotics, *Lancet*, **1,** 1122–6.

GJESSING, R. (1932) Beiträge zur Kenntnis der Pathophysiologie der Katatonen Stupors I and II, *Arch. Psychiat. Nervenkr.* **96,** 319–91, 393–473.
GJESSING, R. (1935, 1939) Beiträge zur Kenntnis der Pathophysiologie der Katatonen Erregung III and IV, *Arch. Psychiat. Nervenkr.* **104,** 355–441; **109,** 525–95.
GJESSING, R. (1953, 1960), Beiträge zur somatologie der periodischer Katatonie, V–X, *Arch. Psychiat. Nervenkr.* **191,** 191–219, 220–46, 247–96, 297–322; **200,** 350–65, 366–89.
GOODWIN, J. C., JENNER, F. A., MARY LOBBAN and SHERIDAN, M. (1964) Renal rhythms in a patient with a 48 hour cycle of psychosis during a period of life on an abnormal time routine, *J. Physiol.* **176,** 18P.
HARDWICK, S. W. and STOKES, A. B. (1941) Metabolic investigations in periodic catatonia, *Proc. roy. Soc. Med.* **34,** 733–56.
HARKER, JANET (1964) *Physiology of Diurnal Rhythms*, Cambridge University Press.
JENNER, F. A. (1963) Biochemical aspects of disorders of mood. In *Neurometabolic Disorders in Childhood*, Ed. K. Holt, Livingstone, Edinburgh.
JENNER, F. A. (1965) A psychotic analogue. In *Biomechanics and Related Bio-engineering Topics*, Ed. R. M. Kenedi, Pergamon Press, Oxford.
KALLMAN, F. J. (1946) The genetic theory of schizophrenia, *Amer. J. Psychiat.* **103,** 309.
KETY, S. S. (1959) Biochemical theories of schizophrenia, *Science*, **129,** 1528–32 and 1590–6.
KRAEPELIN, E. (1913) *Kinische Psychiatrie*, 8 Aufl., J. A. Barth, Leipzig.
LOBBAN, MARY (1960) The entrainment of circadian rhythms in man, *Cold Harbor Spring Symposia on Quantitative Biology*, **25,** 325–32; and (1965) *Circadian Clocks*, Ed. Ascoff, to be published.
LOBBAN, MARY C., and TREDRE, B. (1964) Renal Diurnal Rhythms in Blind Subjects, *J. Physiol.* **170,** 29P.
MALL, G. (1952) Beiträg zur Gjessing ischen Thyroxinbehandlung der periodischen Katatonien, *Arch. Psychiat. Nervenkr.* **187,** 381–403.
MENNINGER-LERCHENTHAL, E. (1959) *Periodizität in der Psychopathologie*, Wilhelm Maudrich, Bonn.
RICHTER, C. P. (1957) in *Recent Progress in Hormone Research*, **13,** 105–59.
RICHTER, C. P. (1960) Biological clocks in medicine and psychiatry: shock phase hypothesis. *Proc. nat. Acad. Sci. Washington*, **46,** 1506.
RÜDIN, E. (1923), *Studien über Verebrung und Entstehung Geistig Störungen*, Julius Springer, Berlin.
SCHEIBER (1901) *see* Menninger-Lerchenthal above.
SHARP, G. W. G. (1960) The effect of light on the morning increase in urine flow, *J. Endocrin.* **21,** 219–23.
SLATER, E. (1965) the latest review in *Clinical Aspects of Genetic Mental Disorders* in *Biochemical Aspects of Neurological Disorders*, Second Series, Blackwell, Oxford.

GENERAL DISCUSSION[1]

DISCUSSION AFTER DR. BERLET'S PAPER

FRIEDHOFF: Dr. Berlet, are there any relationships between creatinines in any of the amino acids and the urinary volumes?

BERLET: In some cases we find a relationship between urine volume and the excretion rates of creatinine. This was the case in one of the schizophrenic patients but only during one of the two observation periods. No such relationship was found during the second observation period of this patient. There was no correlation at all in the second schizophrenic patient.

FRIEDHOFF: Was there a positive correlation?

BERLET: Yes, a positive correlation.

RODNIGHT: We noticed when we were measuring urinary tryptamine that it was correlated with urinary volume.

PERRY: I wanted to ask: How do you obtain your timed urine collections? How do you, with psychotic or mentally defective patients, assure yourself that you are really getting 24-hr urine collections and that you are not getting say 21 hr on one day and 28 hr on the next day. Were you catheterizing your patients?

BERLET: No, we did not, but we did have strict control over our patients as far as their going to the bathroom was concerned. All the patient's doors were locked on the ward and only under the supervision of an aide were the patients permitted to use the toilets. For 24-hr specimens we start collecting with the second morning specimen for 24 hr—the first morning specimen of the patient being added to the previous day's specimen. This can introduce a variable of probably considerable extent. However, there is one other fact in our favor. Some of these increases of creatinine were sustained for several days. If you had, for instance, one day a 28-hr specimen and the next day a 20-hr, you would get an increase and a decrease the next day. But it would hardly account for a sustained increase over 4 or 5 days.

RICHTER: I believe you said that the rise in tryptamine excretion is determined by the breakdown of protein rather than by the kidney metabolism, but I wonder if these two alternatives are really incompatible? Accepting your view that the breakdown of protein is the primary factor, this would produce a general rise in amino-acid levels and therefore in the amines produced from them. The amine oxidase in the kidney and other tissues would be bombarded with amines, and due to competitive inhibition of the amine oxidase by other amines it would be quite reasonable to expect an increase.

BERLET: We considered the rises of tryptamine an indication that the kidneys get more tryptophan to break down through the blood-stream. There are some experiments, some of them quoted this morning (Erspamer, V. and Bertaccini, G., *Arch. Int. Pharmacol. Pharmacodyn.* **137,** 6, 1962; Erspamer, V. and Nobili, N. B., *Arch. Int. Pharmacol. Pharmacodyn.* **137,** 24, 1962) which show that, when the kidneys get hold of tryptophan as a precursor, the step between the blood-stream and the final excretion in the urine involves primarily a decarboxylation of amino acids. It would be appropriate to determine plasma tryptamine concentrations in order to evaluate the exact role of the kidneys with respect to urinary tryptamine. In a new series of patients we are now investigating the relationship between daily variations of urinary tryptamine and total indole-3-acetic acid as one further step in this direction.

HORWITT: One question and then a comment. What is the average volume of your urine?

BERLET: This depends on the individual patient. In one patient we had 1500–2000 ml/24 hr as an average; in the other we had only 1000 ml or less.

HORWITT: How did they vary from day to day, the volume? What was the degree of variation?

[1] The discussion refers to the papers of Drs. Berlet, Brune, Sprince and Jenner.

BERLET: We have published an observation in *Nature* (Berlet, H., Pscheidt, G. R., Spaide, J. K. and Himwich, H. E., *Nature*, **203,** 1198, 1964) which shows that with the onset of behavioral worsening, we find in some cases a dramatic increase of urine volume too. I think that in general this is known to occur in mental patients in relation to behavioral changes.

HORWITT: The reason I ask is because when we first started setting up metabolic wards with schizophrenic patients, we found that we were getting variations with creatinine excretion. We started off on the assumption that this was technical rather than blaming it on schizophrenia. One of the ways we straightened this out was by arranging for the patient to take two extra glasses of water during the 24 hr that we were collecting urine. In other words, we went for large volumes in order to wash out the bladder and to be sure the patients could not hold on to the urine. The schizophrenic may not cooperate too well when we wanted him to empty his bladder in the morning. But by having a large volume we got away from this. This was first done about 20-odd years ago during our first thiamine study. We did achieve good creatinine urine levels in this way. We worked on the assumption that if we did not have creatinine excretions something was wrong with our technique. In this connection, how do you explain the fact that so many of us have no trouble getting good creatinine baselines on our patients when we run twenty at a time and you do not? In other words, if we were running amino-acid analysis, and did not have a level that was considered proper for a given patient which corresponded to his mass weight, we just did not analyze that sample. I am trying to figure out what are the differences—have I missed some points that are important?

BERLET: To make a drastic point, you may have eliminated your better patients, from the metabolic point of view, from your study in this way.

HORWITT: But we did not eliminate them—we just went back and took their urine the next day to achieve consistent results. This is what could happen to somebody once in thirty times.

BERLET: We feel strongly that is not an isolated phenomenon. Creatinine is part of the overall metabolic variability in these patients and if you disregard the creatinine then somehow you sort patient material into two different groups—maybe some show it, maybe some do not. As to your question that other investigators did not report this variation, there are several reports in the literature questioning the constancy of urinary excretion rates of creatinine for a 24-hr period or from day to day (Consolazio, C. F., Johnson, R. E. and Pecora, L. J., *Physiological Measurements of Metabolic Functions in Man*, p. 262, Blakiston Div., McGraw-Hill Book Co., New York, 1963; Vestergaard, P. and Leverett, R., *J. Lab. Clin. Med.* **51,** 211, 1958).

HORWITT: Your diet was meat-free, I take it.

BERLET: No.

HORWITT: Did the amounts vary?

BERLET: No, the total protein intake was kept constant at approximately 70 g/day, milk and cheese being the other main sources of protein besides meat.

HORWITT: How did you control then the creatinine in your meat?

BERLET: We figured out that the amount of meat to be consumed ought to be fairly large to account for an increase, for instance of 0·7 g of creatinine in 24 hr, especially since muscle contains little or no creatinine at all.

JENNER: I just wanted to say that we have done quite a lot of studies on creatinine and our answer comes somewhere in between what you are implying and Dr. Himwich's results. Nevertheless, we have found some changes in conditions which would seem very difficult to explain if they were not endogenous in some form. Our patients are kept on completely fluid diets all the time. They are kept in bed during studies and in some of the studies I, in fact, lived with a very disturbed patient myself to make sure the collections were correct. The vast majority of people have constant creatinine output but certain periodic catatonics in the phase of stupor put out more creatinine—I think there is muscle breakdown due to inactivity. I think that the test made during catatonic excitement also occasionally shows an increased output perhaps because the diet is inadequate to satisfy the metabolic requirement. But that is one group. I also have one or two others who have sporadic unexplained large outputs of creatinine under conditions in which they were living on fluid diets in bed and which in fact in one which I will show you later in a slide I was actually living with him to make sure the collections were adequate (see paper of Jenner in this volume).

SPAIDE: Dr. Horwitt, what was the length of time during which you made continuous 24-hr urine collections from the same patients for creatinine analyses?

HORWITT: Ten years.

SPAIDE: Were creatinine analyses made on daily collections or on aliquots from pooled collections?

HORWITT: Now I must admit that there are occasions when the patient is ill or when we might not get good creatinine reproducibility. We did not get these 50–100% variations like those just reported. We would get a variation between 10 and 25% on a given patient. I am not questioning the fact that you got them, I am trying to explain why you got them.

SPAIDE: If you used pooled urine collections for creatinine determinations or if you averaged your daily results, you probably failed to see the variations since the high and low values even out in the average. I would also like to add that at the present time we are making daily collections from patients who are receiving the general hospital diet. The meat intake is not controlled. We are finding similar variations in urinary creatinine excretion which makes it seem unlikely that our previous fluctuations might have been due to the intake of meat by our patients. Schottstaedt *et al.* (*J. Psychosomatic Res.* **1,** 292, 1956) have studied creatinine excretion in normal patients and also found that the amount of meat in the diet did not seem to affect the variation in the urinary creatinine excretion.

HORWITT: There are hundreds of people in the country working on chromatographic techniques, many of them with schizophrenics. They are still using the creatinine to determine whether or not the technician did a good job to collect the urine. When we find one which is wrong, which is not very often, we go back and get another one the next day. I also want to stress this fact at this point of making sure your schizophrenic gets enough fluid when you are making such a collection. This we find did straighten out a lot of the errors that we had years ago.

SPAIDE: In this regard, I would like to say that in some of the patients with the largest urine volume we see the greatest variations in creatinine excretion.

HORWITT: Not going in and out of nitrogen balance?

SPAIDE: We are not determining nitrogen balance in these patients.

HORWITT: This would be different from data I have seen from Worcester, from Elgin, and dozens of places down through the years and I just do not know what the difference is. You must have something that is very important.

HIMWICH: As Dr. Horwitt emphasizes, our result with creatinine were not to be anticipated from orthodox concepts but perhaps the conditions under which these concepts were derived were highly specialized and not of general applicability. Shortly after the turn of the century (1905), Folin showed that in mentally ill patients using a meat-free diet, creatinine excretion was constant. As presented in the historical introduction of the paper of Schottstaedt *et al.*, this finding has not received unequivocal support. Recently it has been shown, for example, that the ingestion of a diet devoid of creatine and creatinine but adequate in protein lowers creatinine excretion by as much as 30% (Bleiler, R. E. and Schedl, H. P., *J. Lab. Clin. Med.* **59,** 945, 1962). It is not improbable that investigators in the field of schizophrenia have thrown out urine with increased creatinine levels without determining whether or not these creatinine levels correlated with the intensity of the psychotic symptoms. Yet to throw out such observations because they do not agree with standards obtained under special conditions certainly creates an error when applied to another kind of dietary condition and indeed this shuts out further explorations in this field.

SZARA: I was wondering what your criteria were for exacerbation of motor activity and if it was possible to separate the exacerbation of motor activity from the increase of psychotic symptoms.

BERLET: Our measurements were primarily clinical. First the patient is seen by the physician every day. In addition we had weekly interviews by several physicians. This evaluation gives of course only a one-day impression, but our psychiatric aides on the various wards were recording for each patient certain points which appeared important in this condition, such as eating habits, time awake, time asleep, pacing, whether the patients were restless or quiet or sitting. This score was recorded in three periods during the day. For instance,

8 hours from 6 a.m. to 2 p.m., 2 p.m. to 10 p.m. and from 10 p.m. to 6 a.m. I think the second question of yours was how can we distinguish between motor activity and psychotic symptoms. In this type of patient we cannot. Increases of psychotic symptoms in these patients were always somehow connected with increases of motor activity and anxiety, so we cannot distinguish between the specific effects of the schizophrenic experiences like hallucinations or the specific effects of the motor activity associated with it.

SPRINCE: Then motor activity is actually part of your measurement of psychotic activity.

BERLET: In fact, as I pointed out. Time did not permit us to go into this aspect very much. Our feeling is that motor activity and anxiety are primary causes of these changes in so far that they aid in producing a negative energy balance together with a possibly centrally caused reduction of food intake. Thus we have two factors, the increased motor activity and the decreased energy supply, both acting together to finally cause this pattern.

SPRINCE: How about the days when the patients participated actively in a ball game or taking a dance lesson without being more psychotic and more marked.

BERLET: For our experimental purposes, these patients were confined to the ward permanently, so they did not have scheduled physical exercise.

HIMWICH: Dr. Berlet has just said that our behavioral measurements were not quantitative and he is correct, partly because in this clinical field it is difficult to obtain quantitative methods. But we made no attempt to correlate small differences in urinary products with behavior. We took into consideration only tremendous outbursts of activity occurring during periods of aggravations in psychotic symptoms. Thus we were interested rather in large differences, practically qualitative in character.

DISCUSSION AFTER DR. BRUNE'S PAPER

KETY: Dr. Brune has mentioned some of the psychiatric effects of the administration of amino acids. Our results are somewhat different. Although it is true that with a number of amino acids which were tried by Cardon and Pollin and myself, only tryptophan and methionine were associated with any observable changes in the patient's behavior; the effects associated with tryptophan were quite different from those with methionine. Tryptophan produced changes like those which had previously been reported in non-schizophrenic individuals by Sjoerdsma and his associate (Oates, J. A. and Sjoerdsma, A., *Neurology*, **10,** 1076, 1960) and in chronic schizophrenics by Lauer and co-workers (Lauer, J. W., Inskip, W. M., Bernsohn, J. and Zeller, E. A., *AMA Arch. Neurol. Psychiat.* **80,** 122, 1958) which could hardly be called an exacerbation of psychosis. There seemed to be a greater relaxation of the patient, a freer association, in fact the syndrome was very similar to what one might expect if the patient were under the influence of a mild dose of alcohol. With methionine, on the other hand, there was a clear occurrence of an intensification of psychotic symptoms. However, we have not inferred from that that there was an actual exacerbation of the schizophrenic process and this in fact is a very crucial issue. We have not found a means psychiatrically, at least, to pursue the question further. We have not been able to differentiate a toxic psychosis super-added to the schizophrenia of these individuals from an intensification of the schizophrenic process itself, whatever that may be, nor do we see immediately any obvious way of doing that. Nor can we rule out completely an intensification of the idiosyncratic schizophrenic symptoms of the patients on the basis of a mild psychological disturbance which methionine might have produced in these patients but which was potentiated by the fact that they were schizophrenics. In fact, the situation is so complicated and psychiatric discriminations at the present time are still so broad and unsharp that we have felt it best to wait and try to approach this question on the basis of more specific biochemical studies. I think the most that one could say was that these effects of methionine were compatible with a methylation hypothesis but they were equally compatible with a large number of alternative hypotheses which have not been ruled out. Dr. Brune, did you have an occasion to examine the effect of methionine on some of these methylated derivatives in the urine like bufotenin or dimethyltryptamine?

BRUNE: I entirely agree with Dr. Kety when he says that the behavioral changes observed in schizophrenic patients after administration of the combination of either trytophan or methionine and a monoamine oxidase inhibitor should not be interpreted in terms of an actual intensification of schizophrenia. We do not know what schizophrenia is except for the fact that it is a poorly defined diagnostic category. Any attempt of a concept of schizophrenia is confronted with this crucial fact. In my paper I tried to point out that psychotic behavior similar to the patterns of psychotic behavior observed in schizophrenic patients may occur in various pathogenic conditions we do not subsume under the diagnosis of schizophrenia. Therefore it appears impossible to draw conclusions from observed behavioral patterns on the underlying pathological process. This also includes that it is sometimes difficult, if not impossible, to differentiate between so-called toxic psychoses and so-called endogenous psychoses. In regard to the behavioral effects of the combination of tryptophan and a monoamine oxidase inhibitor, I got the impression from the paper of Pollin, Cardon and Kety as well as from that of Lauer and his co-workers, that beside the behavioral effects described by Sjoerdsma in mentally healthy people, that there was also a flare-up of psychotic patterns in some schizophrenic patients during that treatment. Lauer *et al.* stated in their paper that even though it was not statistically demonstrated, one general trend became apparent, namely the shift toward acute psychosis.

We have not examined the urine of schizophrenic patients on methylated tryptamines during the treatment with methionine and isocarboxazid, but we made some studies while the patients received betaine in combination with isocarboxazid. We found a substance with the paper chromatographic characteristics of bufotenin in three out of five schizophrenic patients during the combined treatment as well as during treatment with placebo. In two schizophrenic patients as well as in three mental defective patients we could not detect this compound.

HOLMSTEDT: This story about bufotenin in urine never has appealed to me. If we look at this historically, why are people at all suspecting bufotenin of being a hallucinogenic agent? First of all, it stems from the custom in Siberia where some tribes were known several hundred years ago to eat the fly agaric. Now the fly agaric does not contain bufotenin, but during the 1930s Professor Wieland in Germany examined a related species which does contain small amounts of bufotenin. Apparently people have associated these two facts with each other, which is wrong in the first place.

KETY: There is a more cogent observation which is that snuff which is used by West Indian tribes was found by Horning to contain bufotenin (Fish, Horning and Johnson, *J. Am. Chem. Soc.* **77**, 5892, 1955).

HOLMSTEDT: That is right, and I will give you the full details about that tomorrow. But bufotenin still is not a hallucinogenic agent, whereas dimethyltryptamine, which is contained in the same drug, is.

BRUNE: In my paper I referred to the observations reported by Fabing and his group (*Am. J. Psychiat.* **113**, 409, 1956).

HOLMSTEDT: Well, they gave increasing doses of bufotenin intravenously to volunteers and observed violent reactions with the highest dose. The patients became very sick and I would not draw any conclusions that this was a psychotic-like episode.

BRUNE: Fabing and his co-workers reported that those people who were treated with higher doses of bufotenin experienced color hallucinations, slight disorientation as well as such symptoms as a tingling spreading from head to extremities, constriction of the chest, purpling of the skin, nausea and other symptoms. After stopping the intravenous injection there developed a gradual relaxation, lassitude, withdrawal followed by euphoria. Thus it appears that there were some psychotomimetic effects. This, however, brings up another question, namely what are the effects of an amine when it is endogenously formed in the body and what are its effects when it is injected intravenously? There is no doubt that various amines may play a role in brain function. But they may also have marked effects on the vasal system and especially when they are injected intravenously. Serotonin may serve as an example. Therefore it appears possible that an endogenously determined alteration of the brain levels of certain amines may in the first place be associated with a disturbed function of some brain regions, whereas after intravenous application of certain amines the reactions of the vasal system including vasoconstrictions and/or vasodilations with all their consequences on the function of the various organs of the body may be predominant and thus may overshadow to a more or less degree the clinical correlates of the actual effects of the amine on brain function. I would think that this should be observed in interpreting the clinical effects of some psychoactive compounds and especially when these compounds are injected intravenously.

HOLMSTEDT: But bufotenin does not penetrate into the brain, at least unappreciably, compared to some other indoles.

BRUNE: As far as I know, bufotenin does penetrate into the brain. In addition, I would think, it is not only a matter of how much of a substance penetrates into the brain, but also how powerful this compound is to alter brain function. Very small quantities of LSD, for instance, may induce marked behavioral changes.

KETY: I believe, apropos the bufotenin psychomimetic action, I must agree with Dr. Holmstedt that the evidence that this compound is psychotomimetic is still quite unclear. The Fabing studies were done with doses which produced a tremendous degree of somatic disturbance. He reported that the patient's face became blue and showed other signs of what may have been rather severe asphyxia. These are some unreported observations where Isbell, in a controlled situation, was not able to satisfy himself that bufotenin was a psychotomimetic agent.

RODNIGHT: You mentioned our work on bufotenin in urine. If I remember rightly, we found by adding bufotenin to 24-hr samples of urine that we could detect it above about 10 μg a day. What sort of levels were obtained at Dr. Himwich's laboratory?

BRUNE: We used paper chromatographic procedures when we studied the question of the urinary excretion of methylated tryptamines in schizophrenic and mental defective patients (Brune, G. G. and Himwich, H. E., *Recent Advances in Biological Psychiatry*, Vol. **5**, p. 144, J. Wortis, Ed., Plenum Press, New York, 1963). Therefore we cannot give exact quantitative results. We observed, however, that bufotenin could be readily detected by our method when its concentration was 20 μg/1000 ml or higher. Based upon visual examination and in comparison with the authentic compound, we would estimate that the amount of the bufotenin-like substance observed in the urine of some schizophrenic patients was of a magnitude of about 20–30 μg/day. In general the bufotenin-like spot was larger in size and more intensive in color during the combined medication than during the placebo period.

PERRY: I was not quite clear from your talk how often you find bufotenin. Could you tell us how many of your patients, of your schizophrenic subjects for instance, excreted it, and am I right in understanding that those subjects who did not excrete it normally also did not excrete bufotenin when they were given methionine or betaine?

BRUNE: That is right. We investigated five schizophrenic patients and observed that only those three patients excreted the bufotenin-like compound during the betaine-isocarboxazid régime and they had not previously excreted it when they were on placebo (Brune, G. and Himwich, H. E., *J. Nerv. Ment. Dis.* **134,** 447, 1962).

HORWITT: The introduction of the study on methionine feeding raises a problem of whether or not you get exacerbation of symptoms when one makes the patient physiologically uncomfortable. This reminds me of some work we did many years ago and some more recently. Nutritional deficiences were produced in schizophrenic patients, and in almost every case when this happened, sometimes inadvertently, the remark of everybody associated with the ward, including the psychiatrists, psychologists and attendants, was that the patient was going through an activation stage. His schizophrenia became more acute. This means that he could react unfavorably to something which is physiologically undesirable like any other individual. You may remember that Keys in his work on starvation reported pseudo-psychotic episodes in his so-called normals which may have been true psychotic episodes. And then, of course, are the starvation experiences, not experiments, starvation in the concentration camps where you had similar reports of psychotic behavior. In any case, if one takes a schizophrenic patient and treats him in a manner where he is even less comfortable than he was before, it should not be surprising that you may get an exacerbation of symptoms. Is not the administration of 20 g of methionine, recognized by any person who knows anything about nutrition, physiology or amino-acid balance, a procedure which will give you a terrific disturbance of the nitrogen balance?

BRUNE: Obviously not. When you give methionine, a relatively large amount of methionine, actually nothing will happen. The situation, however, is different when you combine methionine with a monoamine oxidase inhibitor. In that case there are marked behavioral changes.

HORWITT: I will agree that there may be a different picture if you add monoamine oxidase inhibitor on top of a large excess of methionine.

BRUNE: With methionine alone, even with doses as high as 20 g/day, we did not see much of behavioral changes in our patients.

HORWITT: This may be a good approach and it deserves much more study. I would like to call attention to some evidence which most people here are not acquainted with. Back in 1954 we had occasion for different reasons to give eight patients about 350 mg of methionine every day for 8 weeks and then follow that with more than a gram of choline for 13 weeks. These were schizophrenic patients. We followed the various biochemcal parameters among which was methylnicotinamide in the urine. One thing noted is that at this level we did not have any evidence of a difference in psychotic behavior.

KETY: Dr. Horwitt may not have remembered some of the controls which we tried in the methionine study because we were aware of these problems which he raises. It is true that the patients on methionine do not feel good. They have gastrointestinal symptoms although these can be rendered less severe if the methionine is given in capsule form and not mixed with chocolate and other things which make it taste even worse. Nevertheless, the patient still has rather obvious gastrointestinal symptoms and mild nausea and looks rather ill. In order to control the effect of these symptoms we gave these same patients 15 g of ammonium chloride a day which produced the same sort of symptoms. They did not show an exacerbation of psychotic sysmptoms. On that basis, we felt that we were not able any longer to entertain the notion that it was simply a response to the feeling of malaise which was associated with methione and which had even more association with the ammonium chloride. I am afraid I cannot support entirely the requirement of a monoamine oxidase inhibitor for methionine effects although we found this to be the case in our first report. We have since tried a course of methionine at the same level without monoamine oxidase inhibitor in one of our positive reactors and his response was qualitatively similar to what he had before but perhaps less intense.

BRUNE: As was pointed out in one of my slides, we observed slight behavioral changes in two out of seven schizophrenic patients while the patients received methionine alone. We were, however, not really sure whether or not this was a significant finding. At any rate, the behavioral effects we observed during the combined treatment with methionine and isocarboxazid were much more pronounced than with methionine alone.

HORWITT: Dr. Kety, I think I was misunderstood. When I talked of patient discomfort, I was not thinking only about how he feels subjectively so much as I was thinking of the fact that with 20 g of methionine, one completely upsets the amino-acid balance of an individual. This is more than just physiological discomfort. This causes very strong negative nitrogen balance. We know that all you have to do is add maybe two times the requirement of an amino acid to throw an animal or a patient into negative balance. These things are important and they should not be interpreted as being just a methionine effect. We are affecting twenty other amino acids.

KETY: I agree that methionine may be doing all sorts of things biochemically and for that reason we have not been able to say that the methionine is producing its effects by transmethylation. But to the point you made before about a simple intensification of schizophrenia on the basis of making the patient sick. . . .

HORWITT: I meant making him sick physiologically because something is wrong with his other enzymatic systems.

SMYTHIES: Surely we can meet Dr. Horwitt's objection by saying that all the other amino acids you fed in large quantities would have this effect of upsetting the amino-acid metabolism.

KETY: But not upsetting it the way methionine might. Methionine produces many biochemical changes other than transmethylation in a way which the other amino acids we used might be replicable.

SMYTHIES: Any one amino acid given in excess would upset the general balance.

KETY: I would assume that he was making a more sophisticated argument that methioine may be operating by dozens of different pathways than transmethylation.

SMYTHIES: Surely you can answer that point by asking what is in common between betaine and methionine except that they are methyl donors? It is not reasonable to suppose that methionine is giving the effect by one mechanism and betaine by some other method.

KETY: Certainly the report by Drs. Brune and Himwich on betaine makes an effect on transmethylation a stronger possibility (Brune, G. G. and Himwich, H. E., *Recent Advances in Biological Psychiatry*, Vol. **5**, p. 144, J. Wortis, Ed., Plenum Press, New York, 1963).

SMYTHIES: The other point you raise, Dr. Kety, the very important clinical point about whether you can distinguish a schizophrenic who is getting worse and a schizophrenic who has a superimposed toxic psychosis, I would like to hear from the clinical psychiatrists present whether this is a clinically viable distinction that can be made with confidence. I feel that one could, but if you wanted to test it you could give a genuine deliriant like atropine to your schizophrenics which really does produce toxic psychosis. This is the crucial point. Would the schizophrenic with atropine psychosis be detectable?

KETY: Perhaps there are some psychiatrists who might want to address themselves to that point. We were not able to convince ourselves that it would be possible to differentiate a toxic psychosis superimposed on schizophrenia or an intensification of schizophrenia as a result of non-specific psychological variables. In a small series of normals, methionine in association with monoamine oxidase inhibitors does produce mental effects. These effects, as best we could describe them, were like taking one or two Martinis—there was light-headedness and a trace of euphoria, not at all like what was seen in the schizophrenics. That does not mean, however, that the same kind of manifestation in schizophrenia might not produce a much more flagrant kind of exacerbation. However, in answer to that we should point out that both tryptophan and methionine in normals produce similar light-headedness but the tryptophan in these schizophrenics did not exacerbate psychosis.

SZARA: I would like to add something which is quite relevant to this particular experiment that Dr. Kety has described and to those which have been reported by Sjoerdsma after giving tryptophan or methionine load. These patients reported having a feeling of light-headedness like having two martinis. When we started our work with dimethyltryptamine about 10 years ago in order to find out whether the dimethyltryptamine is hallucinogenic or not, the first patients who received small doses said at the beginning of the drug effects, "I feel like having a couple of beers". They did compare psychotomimetic effects to the effect of alcohol but later on, as the drug effects became more intense, they said, "Oh, oh, this is not alcohol at all—it is something quite different". I was wondering whether the subjects to whom you gave methionine-tryptophan load and who felt light-headed like after two martinis, had just a small hallucinogenic effect which they mistook for an alcoholic effect, or would it have been possible for them to say that is different (Sai-Halasz, Brunecker and Szara, *Psychiat. et Neurologia*, **135,** 285, 1958).

KETY: Well, those who have given tryptophan and monoamine oxidase inhibitors to non-schizophrenic individuals have to stop the administration of tryptophan, as we did, because of the onset of rather severe neurological disturbances and I do not know that one has been able to test Dr. Szara's point by increasing the dosage.

HIMWICH: I would like to continue further the discussion of Dr. Szara in regard to this similarity and difference between giving any methionine alone or methionine and an MAOI. In the first place, I do not think you can compare the severity of the effects with methionine alone and methionine and MAOI. Now the symptoms you get are both very much like yours, Dr. Szara, and very much like Dr. Kety's—I thought Dr. Brune was going to say that. In almost half of our patients the most apparent effect was like a toxic psychosis and in a little more than half exacerbations occurred like the spontaneous exacerbations of the schizophrenic symptoms (Brune and Himwich, *J. Nerv. Ment. Dis.* **134,** 447, 1962). These two different groups of symptoms appeared again last year on our second study with methionine and tranylcypromine. This time it was a smaller percentage that had a toxic-like psychosis but we still had some where the toxic psychosis was predominant and others with a flare-up that reminded us of schizophrenic symptoms. Frequently, and particularly in our second study, the symptoms that seemed toxic frequently preceded those which reproduced in exaggerated form the usual symptoms characteristic for the patient (Berlet *et al.*, *Arch Gen. Psychiat.* **13,** 521, 1965).

BRUNE: May I say one more word on the problem of the occurrence of toxic psychoses in schizophrenic patients during methionine and isocarboxazid treatment. In our papers we have not inferred from our observations that a toxic psychosis had occurred in our schizophrenic patients during the treatment with methionine or betaine together with a monoamine oxidase inhibitor. On the other hand we were not able to rule out that any toxic effects had occurred. We described our observations in terms of two behavioral components which became evident during the study.

One behavioral component appeared to be a recurrence or intensification of individual psychotic patterns observed during spontaneous activations of the psychosis, while the other components were exemplified by euphoria, sedation and mental confusion, symptoms which were not seen during spontaneous exacerbations of the psychosis. The latter behavioral changes, however, are frequently observed during intoxications, i.e. after drinking alcohol.

We did not try to make a further differentiation as to a toxic psychosis or an endogenous psychosis or a toxic psychosis superimposed on endogenous psychosis. We just wanted to point out that there are similarities but also dissimilarities in behavior during spontaneous activations of the psychoses and during activations of the psychoses occurring during treatment with methionine or betaine together with a monoamine oxidase inhibitor. We feel that these differences represent a factor which limits the significance of the behavioral observations in terms of an underlying biochemical mechanism of the psychoses in schizophrenic patients. Considering all aspects of the study we arrived at the conclusion that the observed behavioral effects during administration of methionine and betaine in combination with a monoamine oxidase inhibitor are compatible with the view that a defect of transmethylation processes including a greater formation of methylated psychoactive amines may play a role in psychotic behavior of schizophrenic patients, but that from these studies alone no conclusive statement can be made at the present time.

KETY: Dr. Baldessarini had an opportubity to see some patients with a methionine-induced exacerbation of psychosis, although these were not marked as some of the earlier ones, and since he is planning to be a psychiatrist and is already a pretty good one, it may be interesting to hear his observations upon the question of toxic versus schizophrenic psychosis.

BALDESSARINI: In general the "reactors to methionine" that we saw appeared to be more psychotic. I did not have the impression that they were sick, delirious or toxic (Park, Baldessarini and Kety, *Arch. Gen. Psychiat.* **12,** 346, 1965).

SPRINCE: Now was this with methionine alone?

BALDESSARINI: The effect was noted only when methionine was given with a MAO inhibitor, but even then, not very frequently. Methionine or MAO inhibitor alone did not produce psychotic exacerbations in the doses we used.

SPRINCE: Have you noticed any behavioral alteration with methionine alone? Has anyone?

KETY: In one case. In one of the most positive reactors in our first report we were recently testing the requirement for monoamine oxidase inhibitor and got with methionine alone a very intense psychotic exacerbation which was perhaps less intense than the first but met all of the requirements. But, of course, in this patient one raises the question of whether he was already conditioned to this kind of process and having perceived the methionine effects, whether he might not have gone through the rest of the reaction in that way rather than on a biochemical basis.

SPRINCE: How many were tried with methionine alone?

KETY: Two of our reactors were tried with methionine alone, some 2 years after the first report and one of these gave this response—the other did not.

SZARA: We had an opportunity to give dimethyltryptamine to schizophrenic patients and in about half of the cases even the card-carrying psychiatrist in our team was not able to distinguish the drug effects from the psychotic symptoms of these particular patients. In other cases the patients reported that the drug effects were different from their usual symptoms.

SNYDER: It might be very hard to ascertain, but would you say that the schizophrenics were less responsive to DMT than normals as they are less responsive to LSD than normals?

SZARA: We did not have a systematic study comparing LSD with dimethyltryptamine, but given the same dose of dimethyltryptamine to schizophrenics and normals, the schizophrenics responded less than the normals, if a comparison can be made at all.

MANDELL: The work of Dr. Berlet *et al.* appears important not only as a specific example of the occurrence of a metabolic shift associated with an exacerbation of psychiatric symptomatology but as a refreshing change of research tactics from the search for a stable metabolic indicator to a more dynamic view of possible metabolic mechanisms in psychosis. A "one gene—one enzyme" model, such as applies in phenylketonuria, may not fit an approach to diseases with as much fluctuation in status and responsivity to the environmental factors as the schizophrenias. A research program making use of longitudinal-repeated measurement studies using each patient as his own control, promises to elucidate dynamic metabolic factors and has the added power of the greater control for individual differences than cross-sectional studies. This approach minimizes the possibility of losing changes of potential importance in the noise of population variance.

A logical word of caution, and one with which I know the Galesburg group has been struggling, concerns the problem of non-specific changes; ones which are the result of acute upsets, independent of a mechanism involved with the pathogenesis of psychiatric disease directly. One which has been mentioned already concerns a decrease in nutritional intake and a shift to a state of negative nitrogen balance. Another, to which we have some pertinent data, concerns metabolic concomitants of the glucocorticoid elevations associated with severe disturbances. Sachar *et al.* (*Psychosom. Med.* **25,** 510, 1963) have shown that patients with acute schizophrenic reactions manifest massive elevations in urinary excretion of 17-hydroxycorticoids. In experiments we have going on using ring-labelled C^{14}-tryptophan infusion before and after ACTH, we have shown 200% rises in kynurenine excretion and 150% increases in indole-3-acetic acid excretion over control values in experimental human subjects. N-acetyltryptophan, 5-hydroxyindoleacetic acid and indolyloeryloglycine as general indications of corticoid mobilization of tryptophan from protein and a general "wash-out" effect, do *not* change (*Stress and Adaptation*, Forest Hospital Foundation Publications, Des Plaines, Ill., 43, 1965). Knox *et al.* (*Brit. J. Exp. Pathol.* **32,** 237, 1961) and others have demonstrated glucocorticoid induction of both hepatic tryptophan pyrrolase and tryptophan (tyrosine) transaminase in rat liver which may account for this differential effect. In any case, it appears that adrenal activation alone may account for some of the increase in excretion in indole-3-acetic acid reported in these studies. The general problem of cause versus concomitance is brought sharply into focus in attempting to ascertain the significance of the very interesting findings that Dr. Berlet and co-workers have brought to our attention today.

BRUNE: Dr. Mandell's work represents an excellent methodological set-up. Testing the various biochemical parameters in close association with clinical psychiatry, I hope, will give us further information on the question of underlying biochemical mechanisms of psychotic behavior.

BERLET: I think Dr. Mandell has mentioned a very important point concerning the biochemical effects of methionine. One of them is, for instance, the release of nitrogen from the body by large doses of methionine (Brown, J. H. and Allison, J. B., *Proc. Soc. Exp. Biol. Med.* **69,** 196, 1948). It is also known that this nitrogen-releasing effect of methionine may affect certain amino acids in a selective manner, for instance alanine, glutamic acid, histidine and several others (Klain, G. J., Vaughan, D. A. and Vaughan, L. N., *J. Nutrition*, **80,** 337, 1963). In addition methionine induces certain enzyme systems in the liver, for instance arginase and tryptophan pyrrolase. It is of considerable interest that methionine was recently found by Munro *et al.* to raise plasma levels of hydrocortisone. This effect was obtained with methionine only but not with other amino acids tested (Munro, H. N., Steele, M. and Hutchinson, W. C., *Nature*, **199,** 1182, 1963).

DISCUSSION AFTER DR. SPRINCE'S PAPER

BALDESSARINI: Dr. Sprince pointed out that a methionine load decreased methyl nicotinamide in urine of rats. In working with nicotinamide, and realizing that nicotinamide is methylated by the methyl group of methionine as Cantoni showed some time ago, we suspected that giving nicotinamide might lower tissue methyl donor, S-adenosyl methionine, and in fact we found that it did not. I am not sure of the significance of this finding.

SPRINCE: Apropos of this point, Dr. Horwitt may recall that he too found a decreased excretion of N^1-methylnicotinamide upon feeding methionine to human subjects. This paper was published some time ago (*J. Nutrition*, Suppl. 1, p. 43, 1956).

HORWITT: I would like to say a word of praise to Dr. Sprince and I would like to encourage more studies of this kind. It seems that the use of the whole animal as opposed to *in vitro* studies of nerve stimulation should be promoted more vigorously in this field. It is plain that what people call nutritional techniques are really studies of the whole animal to determine what is controlling what as a consequence of metabolites absorbed through the intestinal tract.

For what it is worth, Dr. Kety, I should mention something which most people here have not possibly seen because it was published in nutritional journals. I do not know how it applies to the finding here, but in any case it should be mentioned that methionine will lower the antioxidant requirements of the whole animal (Horwitt, M. K., *From Symposium on Foods: Lipids and their Oxidation*, ed. by H. W. Schultz, E. A. Day and R. O. Sinnhuber, Avi Publishing Co., Westport, Conn. p. 390, 1962). What this means I am not sure—when it was first developed a year or two ago we were mystified by it; we still are. The antioxidant requirement is the function of the amount of vitamin E, ascorbic acid and selenium in the tissues (Horwitt, M. K., *Fed. Proc.* **24**, 68, 1965). The requirement for these antioxidants varies in proportion to the polyunsaturation fatty acids which enter the tissues. The brain, especially in young animals, may be peculiarly susceptible to an imbalance of the peroxidizable fatty acids and the biological antioxidant, vitamin E. Furthermore, just changing the fatty acids in the brain by dietary means can cause larger differences in certain enzymatic activities studied *in vitro* (Century, B., Witting, L. A., Harvey, C. C. and Horwitt, M. K. *Am. J. Clin. Nutrition*, **13**, 362, 1963).

BRUNE: Have you observed any behavioral changes in your rats when they were on higher doses of methionine?

SPRINCE: We did try a very primitive type of learning test involving rats swimming in a T-maze (Wilpizeski, C. R. and Hamilton, C. L., *Psychopharmacologia*, **6**, 475, 1964). This test was designed to evaluate learning ability in a very stressful situation, i.e. to find on which side of the T-maze an escape ladder was situated. Our data, however, with methionine-fed rats showed no differences from normal rats.

BERLET: Did any one of your diets contain methionine and nicotinic acid or was the nicotinic eliminated from all the diets you used?

SPRINCE: Nicotinic acid was completely eliminated from all the synthetic amino-acid diets. The synthetic diets containing an excess of methionine, homocysteine or cysteine also contained the original amount of methionine in the diet. We wanted to be sure that the excess effect of homocysteine and cysteine could be compared with excess methionine, all animals starting from the same base line with respect to methionine content in the diet (Sprince, Parker, Jameson and Josephs, *Fed. Proc.* **24**, 169, 1965).

BERLET: If I understand you correctly, only the 30% control diet contained the nicotinic acid.

SPRINCE: Correct. Only the 30% casein control diet contained nicotinic acid. This diet is a good normal high-protein diet for rats. It may be worth noting that our observation of the reduced urinary level of N^1-methylnicotinamide in the methione-fed rats could be due, theoretically, not only to an enzymic inhibition along the pathway from tryptophan to N^1-methylnicotinamide, but also to a more rapid transformation of N^1-methylnicotinamide to pyridone derivatives which were not measured in our studies. However, it should be remembered that in the rat the chief urinary metabolite of nicotinic acid is N^1-methylnicotinamide so that the latter alternative is not likely. This latter point recalls the claim of Heyman and Merlis (*Recent Advances in Biological Psychiatry*, Vol. **5**, Plenum Press, J. Wortis, Ed., p. 211, 1963) that N^1-methylnicotinamide level is lower and the N^1-methyl-2-pyridone-5-carboxamide level is higher in the urine of schizophrenic patients than in normal controls.

BERLET: Is nicotinamide excreted as such along with methylnicotinamide?

SPRINCE: In the rat, nicotinamide is excreted in small amounts along with the chief metabolite which is N^1-methylnicotinamide. In our studies, we did not assay for nicotinamide, only for N^1-methylnicotinamide.

Excess *tryptophan* fed to rats on the nicotinic acid-deficient diet will increase the urinary output of *both* N^1-methylnicotinamide and indoleacetic acid. However, excess *methionine* fed to rats under similar conditions results in a *decrease* of N^1-methylnicotinamide and an *increase* in iodoleacetic acid in the urine. This leads us to the hypothesis that excess dietary methione may be inhibiting the metabolic pathway from tryptophan to N[1]-methylnicotinamide and/or stimulating the formation of indoleacetic acid. Other possible explanations might be considered, namely the effect of methionine on renal tubule physiology or intestinal bacteria. In attempt to rule out the role of intestinal bacteria, we did try intraperitoneal injections of large doses of methionine (adjusted to pH 7·2) for 1 week and obtained urinary excretion patterns of the aforementioned metabolites similar to those found with excess dietary methionine. We have hesitated to try sulfa drugs or antibiotics. Methionine is known to antagonize the action of sulfa drugs on intestinal bacteria, and questions could be raised about the effect of antibiotics on metabolic pathways. Despite these possible limitations, we should try the effect of gut sterilization and plan to do so. Ideally, of course, one should use germ-free animals.

KETY: I think for what it is worth I might point out that in Dr. Alexander's paper to which you just referred, Dr. Sprince, in which he concluded that methionine and Parnate produced similar behavioral changes in psychoneurotic as in schizophrenic patients, we of course are very much interested in that because one of the crucial points is whether the methionine effect is characteristic of schizophrenics. But we did not feel, after reading the extensive case histories which he was careful to report, that they supported that conclusion. Although there were some behavioral changes in the psychoneurotic patients, they were not at all qualitatively or quantitatively like what occurred in the schizophrenic patients. Would you comment on that?

SPRINCE: As often happens in psychiatric evaluations of this type, there was not always unanimity of opinion among the clinical observers as to the nature of the behavioral alterations which developed. It was generally agreed that neither of the two psychoneurotics tested showed evidence of hallucinations. On the other hand, both of these psychoneurotics showed at least several of the mental and nervous responses listed by Alexander *et al.* (*J. Nerv. Ment. Dis.* **137,** 135, 1963) as evidence of behavioral alteration.

DISCUSSION AFTER DR. JENNER'S PAPER

HORWITT: Is it proper to open my remarks with an apology? This is an apology to Dr. Himwich's group with reference to my criticism of their creatinine excretion studies. My assumption was that they were working with schizophrenics as a group. I was not completely aware that they were discussing specific patients who were exceptions to the normal pattern and that they were studying a phenomenon that could more closely be related to a cycle like that found in manic-depressives.

BERLET: We picked these two patients because they showed a greater variability, so this is the fact I mentioned in the discussion. The two patients showed it—we have some more now under study but it seems that this variability of behavior applies to all schizophrenics we have studied thus far.

SNYDER: Dr. Jenner, you brought up for discussion the pineal gland and melatonin, an area in which we are doing research and about which I might make a few comments. As you well know, most biological clock-like functions that have been studied are endogenous and can go on for weeks at a time or much longer in constant darkness and under very constant conditions. We are studying a particular biological clock in the pineal gland of rats which regulates the serotonin content of the pineal gland. Apparently in terms of reversing the clock—by changing the lighting pattern—the pineal clock responds much more rapidly to changes in external lighting than to other biological clocks in general. In fact, in regard to the synthesis of melatonin, another rhythmic function of the pineal gland, it appears that this is a one-dial rhythm which may be totally endogenous, completely controlled by lighting changes. These facts suggest that the pineal gland may be the master clock of the body.

JENNER: Yes, that is right. The urinary potassium is the last one to lose 24-hr rhythm and that is why I showed it in the results of our study. At experimental midnight the urinary potassium is what you would expect by real time at midday, when in fact it was midday.

EFRON: Am I correct in assuming that the patients were cataleptic?

JENNER: Well, some of them but not all of them.

EFRON: The reason I am asking is that I would like to try to counteract the catalepsy with some drugs.

JENNER: Most tranquilizers or most phenothiazines do reduce the amplitudes of periodic cycles, there is not much doubt of that. At the same time the periodicity can remain unchanged.

EFRON: I produced catalepsy in animals by three different types of drugs: bulbocapnine, huge doses of morphine and butyrophenones. The catalepsy caused by the butyrophenone can be counteracted by reserpine or quinolazines, both affecting the levels of amines. Morphine catalepsy can be counteracted by WIN 20,228. But I could not counteract catalepsy caused by bulbocapnine.

JENNER: I was rather surprised—I thought these studies would demonstrate a reliable independent endogenous clock, especially as one cannot change such a regular thing by many exogenous factors. Now if we made the day 18 hr instead of 22 perhaps adaptation to the environment may not have occurred.

We have not found any pharmacological method that alters the rhythm. You can alter the amplitude or destroy it but we cannot shorten the rhythm, or change the rhythm. Some say that imipramine will do this but I have not seen this.

KETY: I believe it is also Dr. Curt Richter's experience with his rats that he finds it extremely difficult to alter the endogenous rhythm by means of any chemical or pharmacologic agent.

SPRINCE: As an aside, I note that Dr. Jenner in his abstract mentions tryptamine and the possible beneficial use of thyroxine. It may be of interest to note that papers have appeared showing a relationship between thyroxine and urinary tryptamine. For example, a twofold increase in urinary tryptamine has been reported in thyrotoxicosis (Levine, R. J., *et al.*, *J. Clin. Endocrin. Metabolism*, **22**, 1242, 1962). This information may be relevant to Dr. Jenner's findings.

SCHILDKRAUT: Two questions. First, is there any change in this rhythm during periods of physical illness? I think this is something which Gjessing has observed. The question is in regard to drug effects. You noted that phenothiazines will damp out the cycles. Have you tried imipramine or lithium in these patients?

JENNER: They have all had lithium and they have all had imipramine. Lithium reduces the mania but was not very helpful.

BERLET: Consolazio *et al.* in physiological measurements report that they find evidence of an effect of physical exercise on creatinine excretion. On the other hand, there is some work published in 1956 by Schottstaedt *et al.* (Schottstaedt, W. W., Grace, W. J. and Wolff, H. G., *J. Psychosom. Res.* **1**, 292, 1956) investigating the effect of different emotional situations on the excretion of electrolytes and creatinine. They reported an enhanced excretion of creatinine and electrolytes during emotional stress. However, the point was made that in a situation where the stress was removed physical activity was somewhat reduced too. It happens that both emotional factors and physical activity act together.

SZARA: In our institute, Dr. Weil-Malherbe has been doing some work with the catechol excretion pattern of the seven original astronauts measuring eight catechol metabolites in the urines collected during stressful situations like simulated flying and actual space shots. Several of the metabolites measured, especially VMA, were good indicators of sympatho-adrenal activation if severe stress occurred.

BERLET: We have been discussing this point and we tried to reconcile our observations with previous observations. The point is probably that we are dealing with selected individuals when we are working with mental patients during periods of drastic psychic and metabolic upheavals.

COMPARATIVE NEUROPHYSIOLOGICAL STUDIES OF PSYCHOTOMIMETIC N-DIMETHYLAMINES AND N-DIETHYLAMINES AND THEIR NON-PSYCHOTOMIMETIC CONGENERS DEVOID OF THE N-DIMETHYL OR N-DIETHYL CONFIGURATIONS

HAROLD E. HIMWICH

Thudichum Psychiatric Research Laboratory,
Galesburg State Research Hospital, Galesburg, Illinois 61401

IN THIS paper we shall review some of our results obtained with psychomimetic and non-psychomimetic congeners of three classes of indoleamines: 4-substituted indoleamines, 5-substituted indoleamines, and lysergic acid diethylamide (LSD-25). These observations were made by Brodey *et al.* (1963), Schweigerdt and Himwich (1964) and Schweigerdt *et al.* (1966) respectively. We shall also mention some pilot experiments made by Dr. Yuji Takeo with mescaline and 3,4-dimethyoxyphenylethylamine. The psychomimetic congeners of the indoleamines are in general characterized by possessing a N-dimethylamine or a N-diethylamine structure while the non-psychomimetic congeners are devoid of either of these two chemical configurations. The results of the congeners of the 4-substituted indoleamines, the 5-substituted indoleamines, LSD-25 and the preliminary experiments with the two methoxy catecholamines are presented in that order.

METHOD

Adult albino rabbits weighing from 2·5 to 3·0 kg were used throughout these studies. Animals were tracheotomized under ether and local pontocaine anesthesia, curarized and artificially respired. Brain wave recordings were made on an eight-channel Grass Model III D electroencephalograph (EEG). Monocoaxial electrodes were implanted according to the maps of Sawyer *et al.* (1954) in the anterior cortex (motor) (anterior 3, lateral 4, vertical plus 9); amygdala (anterior 2, lateral 5·5, vertical plus 5); caudate nucleus (anterior

3, lateral 4, vertical plus 4·5); posterior cortex (limbic) (posterior 4, lateral 4, vertical plus 8·5); hippocampus (posterior 4, lateral 4, vertical plus 5·5); thalamus (VPL) (posterior 4, lateral 4, vertical minus 1); and reticular substance (posterior 10, lateral 2, vertical minus 9). For purposes of convenience, these will be referred to as EEG, even though they were direct tissue recordings from cortical and subcortical sites. Histological examinations were undertaken and the placements of electrodes were verified. In addition to the observations on intact animals in the course of these experiments three sections of the brain were performed (Fig. 1) and our observations include one or more sections on each animal. One transection (1) was at the precollicular prepontine level rostral to the midbrain, another (3) was at the post-collicular

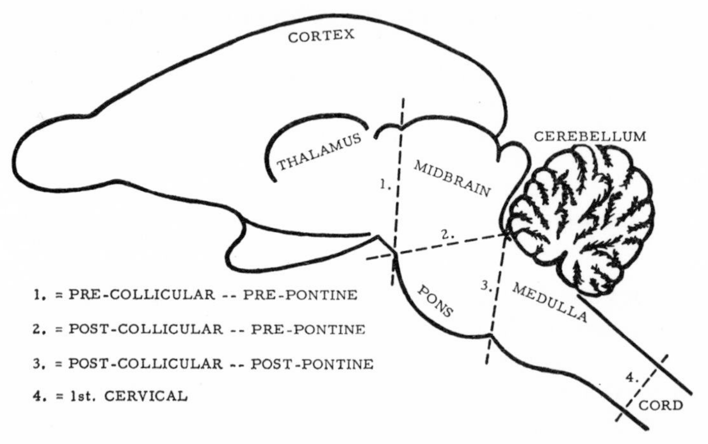

FIG. 1. Schematic representation of the rabbit brain showing planes of transection; in the present experiments transections 1, 3 and 4 were employed.

post-pontine level caudal to the midbrain, and still another (4) was made at C_1. Following each experiment, the animals were sacrificed and the brains removed to ascertain if the transections was complete and in the prescribed plane. All drugs were dissolved in distilled water and injected into the femoral vein via a polyethylene cannula. With 5-hydroxytryptophan (5-HTP), however, in addition to the intravenous route, intracarotid injections were also made. In all experiments blood pressure readings on the animals were monitored by a polyethylene cannula inserted into the femoral artery and connected to a mercury manometer. Animals with tracings that did not show normal maintenance of blood pressure following transection were excluded from the study.

RESULTS

4-*substituted indoleamines*. Fifty-nine albino rabbits received 4-substituted indoleamine compounds (Fig. 2). The latter were five in number:

(1) *o*-phosphoryl-4-hydroxy-N-dimethyltryptamine (psilocybin), (2) 4-hydroxy-N-dimethyl tryptamine (psilocin), (3) 4-methyl-alpha-methyl tryptamine (MP-809), (4) 4-hydroxy-alpha-methyl tryptamine (MP-14), and (5) 1-methyl psilocybin. Each of these five indoleamines evoked an EEG alert reaction in rabbits with intact brains. Figure 3 illustrates the difference between the EEG pattern before and after the injection of non-psychotomimetic MP-809.

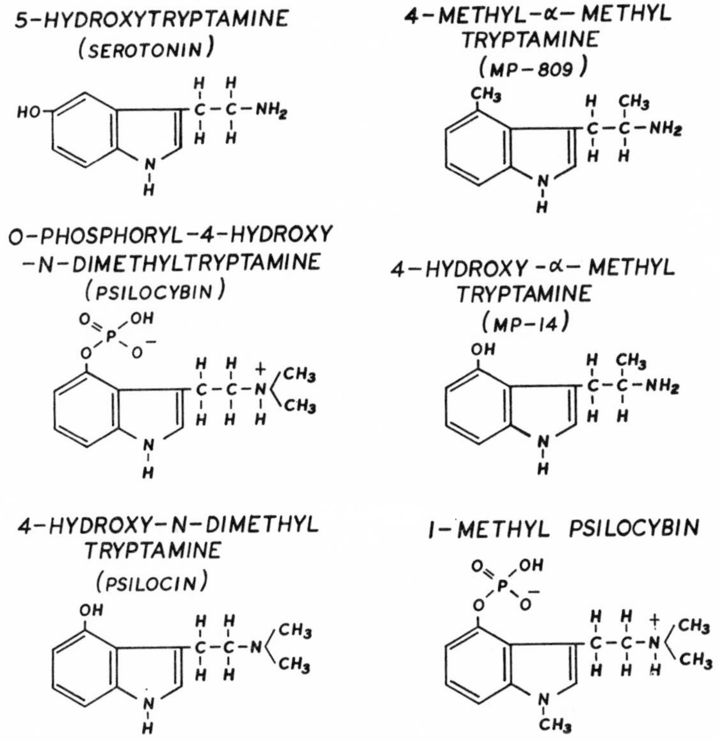

FIG. 2. Chemical structures of serotonin and 4-substituted indoleamines investigated in the present study.

As a next step we transected the rabbit brain at the pre-collicular pre-pontine level (Transection 1, Fig. 1) and EEG alerting could be no longer obtained (Fig. 4). In contrast, a post-collicular post-pontine transection did not prevent the EEG arousal after the injection of MP-809. There was a significant difference between MP-809, however, and its congener, psilocin. Despite psilocin, post-collicular, post-pontine preparation (Transection 3, Fig. 1) did not exhibit alerting (Fig. 5) which, however, was produced after transection at the cervical level. Thus the midbrain preparation was adequate to sustain EEG arousal to the non-psychomimetic congener but with the encephale isolé the psychomimetic one was successful.

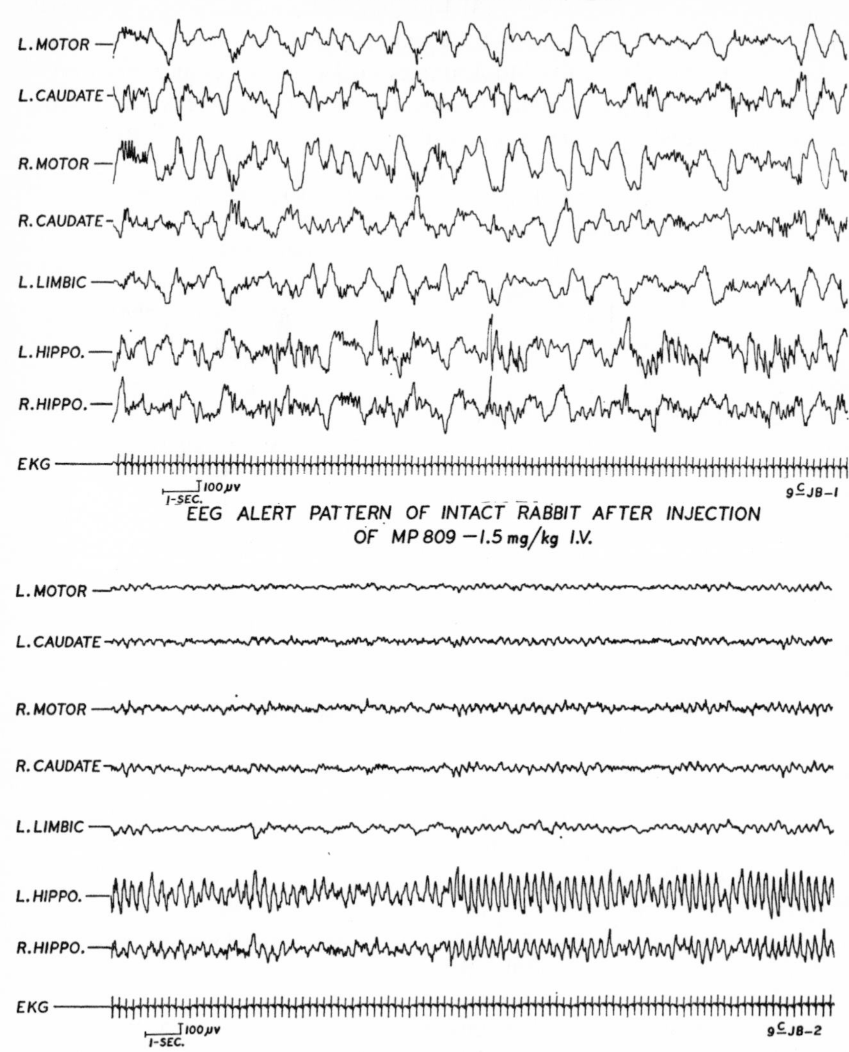

FIG. 3. Top series of tracings: Cerebral electrical activity of a curarized unanesthetized rabbit showing typical synchronized patterns of high-voltage waves and 14/sec spindles. Lower series of tracings: Cerebral electrical activity of rabbit with intact brain after administration of 1·5 mg/kg of MP–809. Notice the desynchronization characterized by low amplitude and absence of sleep spindles and slow waves. As can be seen, the alerting patterns of the hippocampus are different from those of all other brain structures. The leads are (reading downward) (1) left motor cortex, (2) left caudate nucleus, (3) right motor cortex, (4) right caudate nucleus, (5) left limbic cortex, (6) left hippocampus, (7) right hippocampus, (8) EKG.

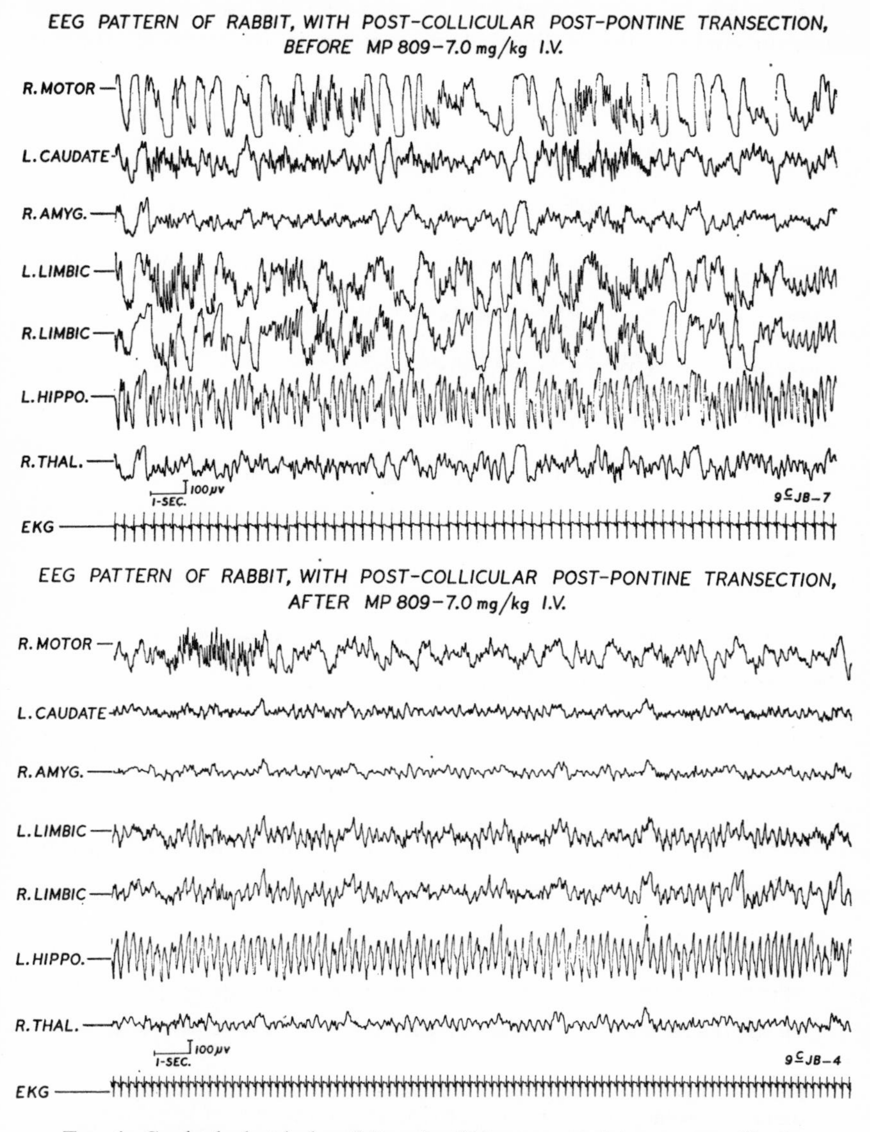

FIG. 4. Cerebral electrical activity of rabbit, transected in a post-collicular post-pontine plane, after MP-809 7·0 mg/kg. The pattern observed in the lower series of tracings resembles EEG arousal presented in the lower series of tracings of Fig. 3 and differ from them only in the somewhat higher amplitudes of the cortical brain waves.

5-substituted indoleamines. We next went on to an examination of bufotenin and serotonin in seventy-three animals, and of these two congeners only bufotenin contains the N-dimethylamine group in its chemical structure

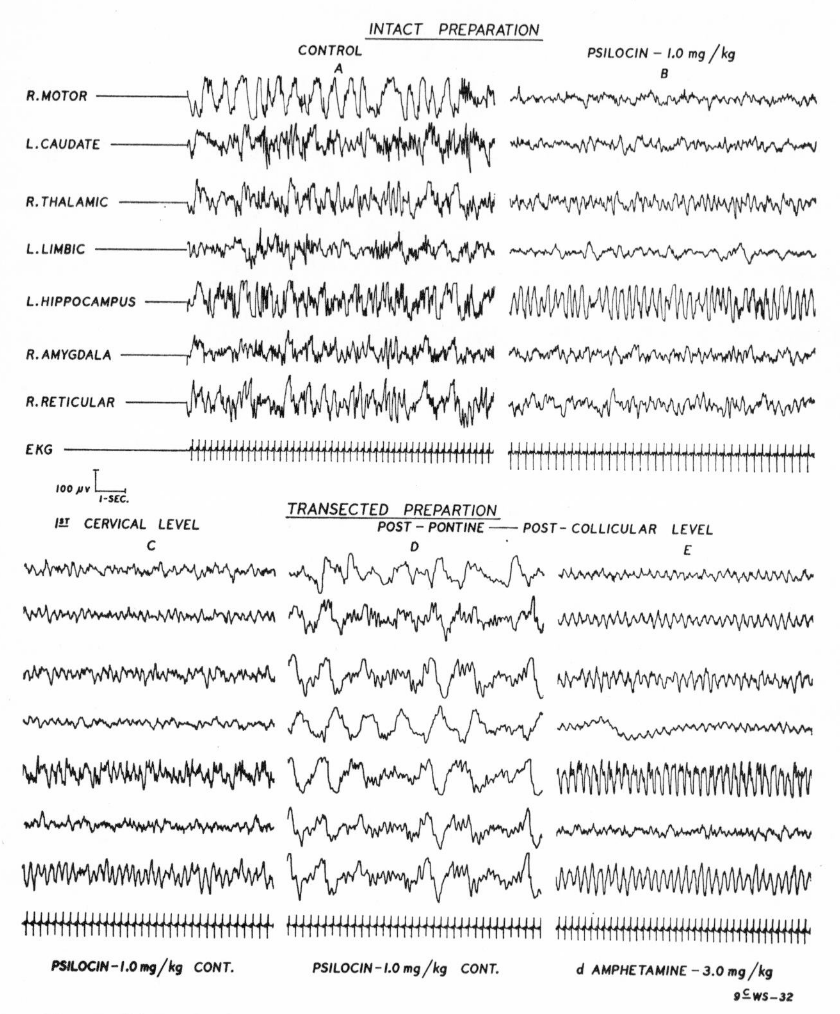

FIG. 5. (A) Predrug resting rhythm, (B) psilocin alerting with intact brain, (C) continued maintenance of psilocin alerting after transection of spinal cord at first cervical vertebra, (D) loss of EEG arousal after second transection caudate to midbrain, and (E) arousal restored by *d*-amphetamine.

(Fig. 6). Because the brain is relatively impermeable to serotonin, we injected 5-HTP instead. Previous work with 5-HTP revealed that four intracarotid injections of 5-HTP, each of 11 mg given about 5 min apart, evoked a persistent alerting pattern which endured at least $\frac{1}{2}$ to 1 hr after the fourth injection (Costa *et al.*, 1960). These observations also revealed a significant increase in the serotonin content of the brainstem. We therefore again employed the same technique in our present experiments with intravenous bufotenin and intracarotid or intravenous injections of 5-HTP in order to increase brain serotonin. Again we obtained EEG alerting after a total dose of 44 mg intracarotidly or approximately four times as much intravenously, an alert which was also obtained in rabbits transected at the post-collicular post-pontine site (Transection 3, Fig. 1) (Fig. 7). In contrast bufotenin could not induce alerting at the midbrain level but after the first cervical section the EEG arousal reaction was consistently observed (Fig. 8). Thus though bufotenin and serotonin after injection of 5-HTP evoked the alerting reaction in the midbrain preparation, bufotenin was effective at a lower level in the brainstem.

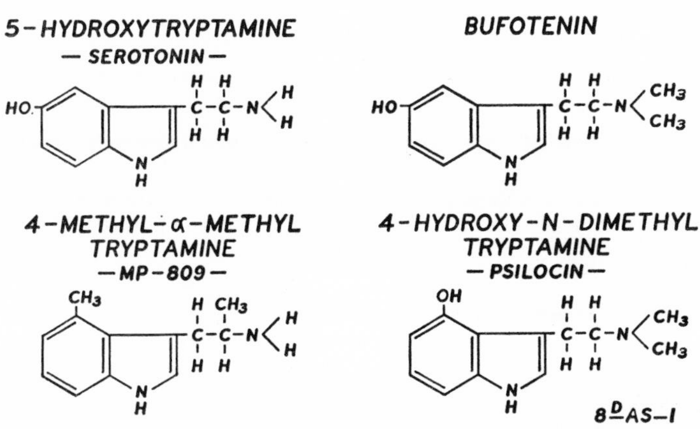

FIG. 6. Chemical structures of serotonin, bufotenin, MP-809 and psilocin.

LSD-25 and 9 congeners. It would seem that we have even a better opportunity to test our concept because of the greater number of possibilities presented by LSD and its congeners (Fig. 9). In these observations we studied a total of ninety-six albino rabbits. For those congeners that gave alerting, minimal dosage was determined and in most instances larger doses were administered to assure alerting. Five of these ten compounds produced alerting: LSD-25, LAE, LSM, MLD and DAM. LSD-25 was able to maintain alerting even after cord transection at the level of C_1 (Fig. 10). In view of the inability of this drug to evoke EEG alerting in animals transected at the post-collicular post-pontine level it would seem that LSD-25 possesses a potent locus of action in the lower brainstem region. Thus this psychomimetic N-diethyl indoleamine appears to have the same ability to evoke alerting at the lower brainstem level as do N-dimethyl indoleamines. In contrast, LSM, MLD and DAM did not exhibit EEG alerting in the encephale isolé preparations. The latter findings are in agreement with those reported

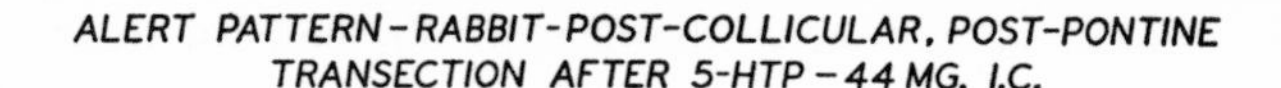

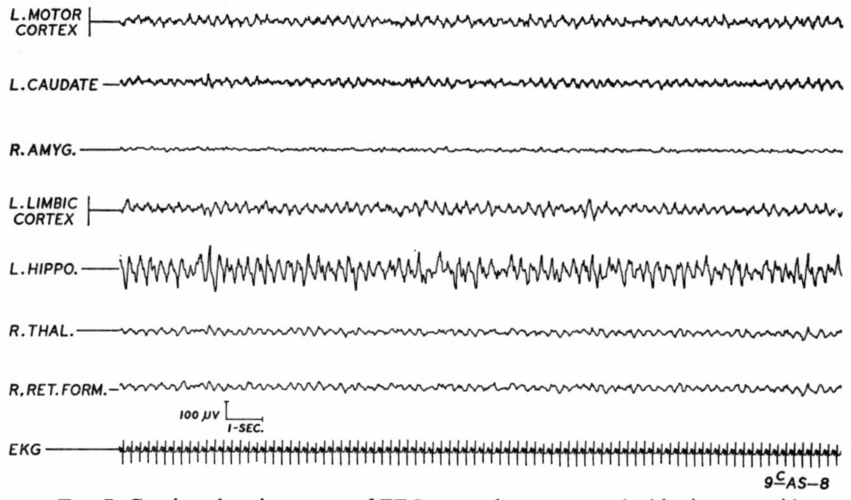

Fig. 7. Continued maintenance of EEG arousal patterns evoked by intracarotid injection of 44 mg 5-HTP in a rabbit after transection in a post-collicular post-pontine plane.

ALERT PATTERN - RABBIT WITH FIRST CERVICAL TRANSECTION
AFTER BUFOTENIN - 2100 γ/KG. I.V.

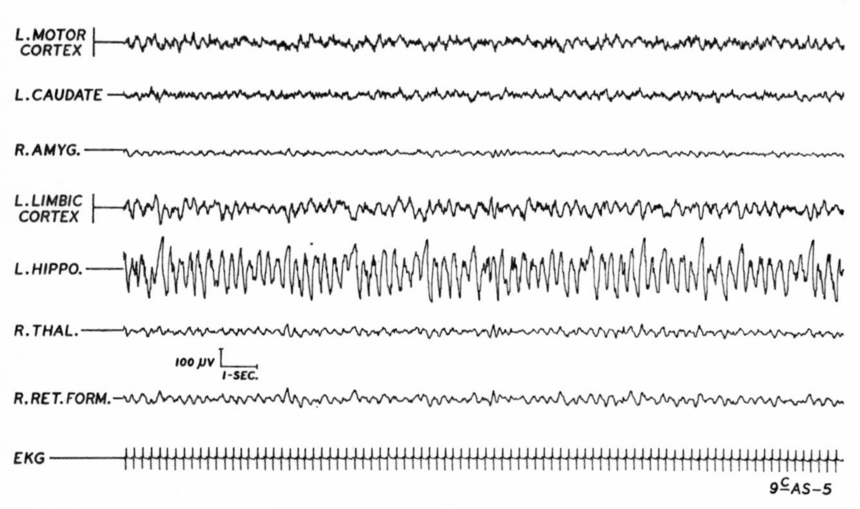

Fig. 8. Continued maintenance of alert pattern after bufotenin (2100 μg/kg i.v.) transection of the spinal cord of a rabbit at the first cervical segment.

CHEMICAL STRUCTURES OF COMPOUNDS

COMPOUNDS ABBR.	STRUCTURAL FORMULA	COMPOUNDS ABBR.	STRUCTURAL FORMULA
D-LYSERGIC ACID DIETHYLAMIDE * LSD	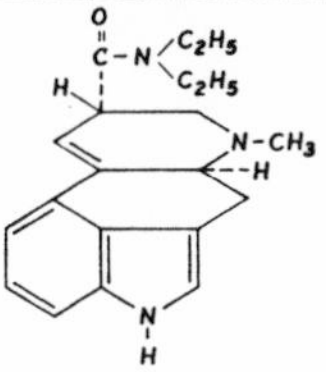 O=C-N(C_2H_5)(C_2H_5); H; N-CH$_3$; H; N-H	D-ISO-LYSERGIC ACID DIETHYLAMIDE D-ISO-LSD	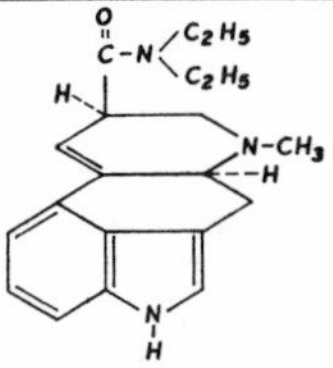 O=C-N(C_2H_5)(C_2H_5); H; N-CH$_3$; H; N-H
D-LYSERGIC ACID MONOETHYLAMIDE * LAE	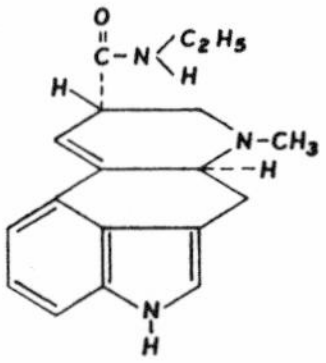 O=C-N(C_2H_5)(H); H; N-CH$_3$; H; N-H	L-LYSERGIC ACID DIETHYLAMIDE L-LSD	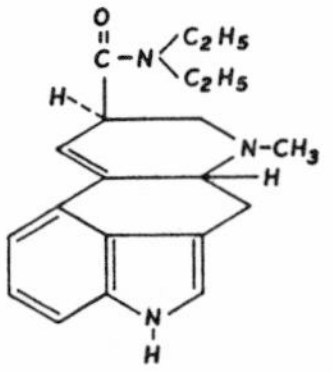 O=C-N(C_2H_5)(C_2H_5); H; N-CH$_3$; H; N-H
D-LYSERGIC ACID * LA	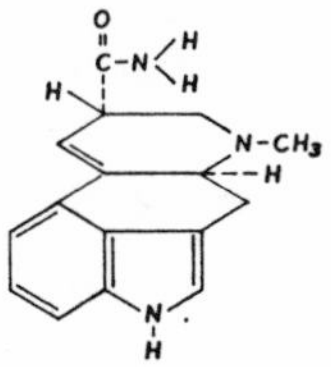 O=C-N(H)(H); H; N-CH$_3$; H; N-H	D-LYSERGIC ACID DIMETHYLAMIDE * DAM	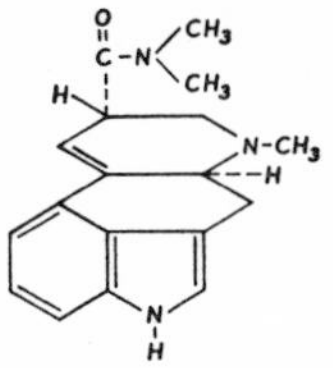 O=C-N(CH_3)(CH_3); H; N-CH$_3$; H; N-H
D-LYSERGIC ACID MORPHOLIDE * LSM	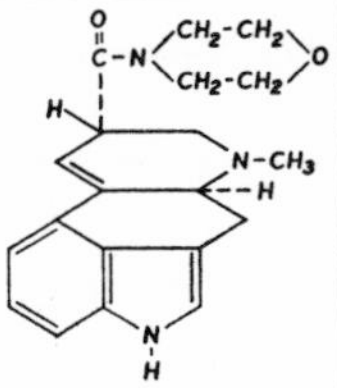 O=C-N(CH_2-CH_2)(CH_2-CH_2)O; H; N-CH$_3$; H; N-H	2-BROM-D-LYSERGIC ACID DIETHYLAMIDE BOL	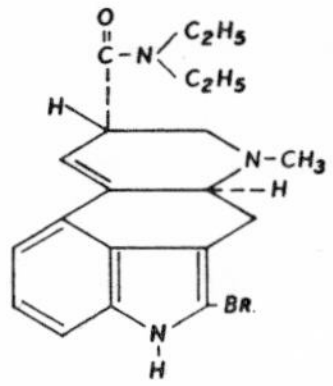 O=C-N(C_2H_5)(C_2H_5); H; N-CH$_3$; H; BR; N-H
D-I-METHYL-LYSERGIC ACID DIETHYLAMIDE * MLD	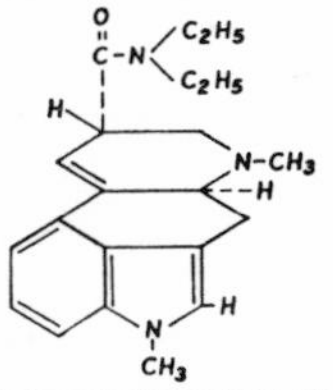 O=C-N(C_2H_5)(C_2H_5); H; N-CH$_3$; H; H; N-CH$_3$	I-METHYL-D-LYSERGIC ACID BUTANOLAMIDE UML	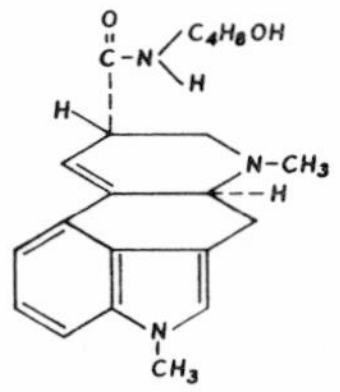 O=C-N(C_4H_8OH)(H); H; N-CH$_3$; H; N-CH$_3$

* HAVE HALLUCINOGENIC ACTIVITY. 8^{D}AS-2

FIG. 9. Chemical structures of LSD-25 and congeners.

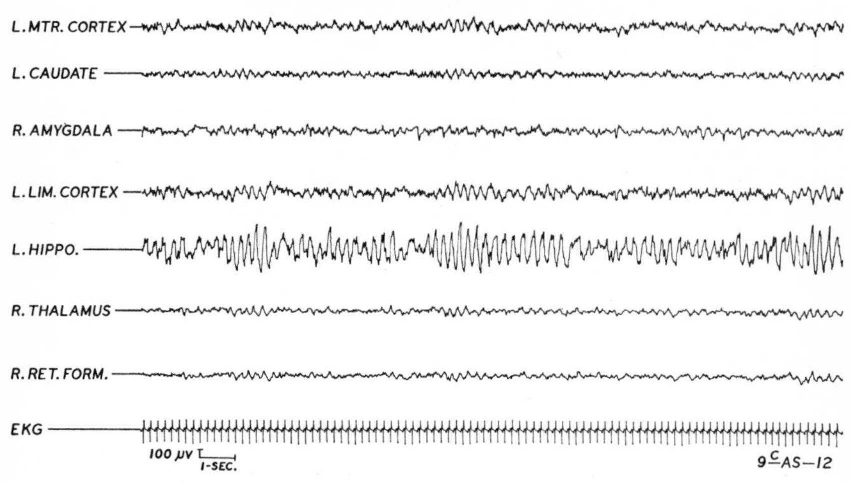

FIG. 10. Continued maintenance of LSD-25 alerting after transection of the spinal cord at the first cervical segment.

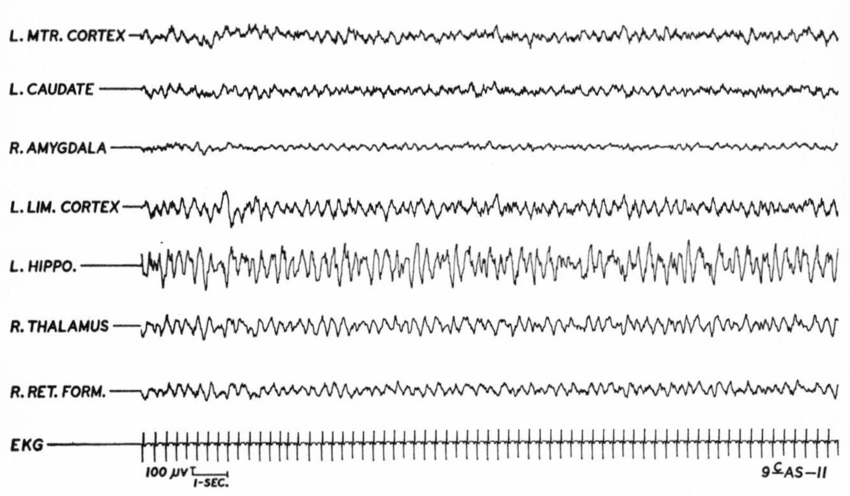

FIG. 11. Continued maintenance of EEG arousal pattern evoked by LAE after transection in a post-collicular post-pontine plane.

by Philip Bradley (1958) that in the cat LSD-25 alerting could be neither initiated nor maintained after cervical transection. Bradley suggests that the action of LSD-25 may be to sensitize receptors at the level of the reticular formation so that they become sensitive to afferent impulses arriving via collaterals and especially those coursing centripetally up the spinal cord. This is similar to our observations with LSM, MLD and DAM which also failed to evoke alerting in the C_1 transected animal. On the other hand, unlike the cat, in the rabbit LSD was still effective in the encephale isolé animal. Thus it seems likely that tonic reticular inputs from super-spinal levels were adequate to elicit EEG arousal with LSD-25 in cervical transected rabbits. That this may be a species difference in rabbits, which could sustain EEG activation after C_1 transection, is indicated by the fact that psilocin and bufotenin may likewise maintain alerting in the cervical transected rabbits. It is noteworthy that the five congeners active in evoking alerting are all regarded as being clinically hallucinogenic (Solms, 1956; Abramson *et al.*, 1955; Isbell *et al.*, 1956). It is interesting that LAE (Fig. 11) with a single ethyl group effected EEG alerting in animals transected caudal to the midbrain level and therefore exhibits a higher site of action at the midbrain level. It seems likely, therefore, that either a diethyl or monoethyl constituent is necessary to evoke alerting though acting at different levels.

One hallucinogen, LA, without an ethyl group in the N position failed to elicit EEG activation. The substitution of a diethyl group in DAM or the closure of the two ethyl groups into a morpholine ring in LSD-25 did not change the ability of these substances to induce EEG alerting. With the addition of a methyl group in the indole ring (MLD) or the substitution of one ethyl radical with a hydrogen (H) as in LAE, a period of latency is seen before the drug-induced arousal. This delay suggests either that these drugs do not pass the blood-brain barrier readily or that some active intermediate is formed in the intervening period. With the exception of BOL the non-hallucinogenic compounds D-iso-LSD, L-LSD and UML failed to elicit alerting. We found it necessary, however, to administer BOL in total dosages which approach toxic levels to obtain even brief periods of activation in some animals. In general, our results show that those psychomimetic congeners of LSD-25 containing the N-diethylamine group act similarly to the indoles containing the N-dimethylamine configurations in exhibiting a locus of action in the lower brainstem level. Furthermore, it is suggested that the indole group and either the N-diethylamine or N-dimethylamine structures are strategically important in producing changes in the site of EEG activation as well as in psychomimetic behavior and both parts of the psychomimetic molecule are necessary to produce alerting.

We have now begun to extend our observations to the catecholamines and have initiated our studies with observations on mescaline and dimethoxyphenylethylamine, of which Dr. Arnold Friedhoff very kindly supplied samples. Previous work has revealed that mescaline can evoke marked and long-enduring EEG alerting reactions in the intact organism (Himwich, 1959). These observations we have confirmed.

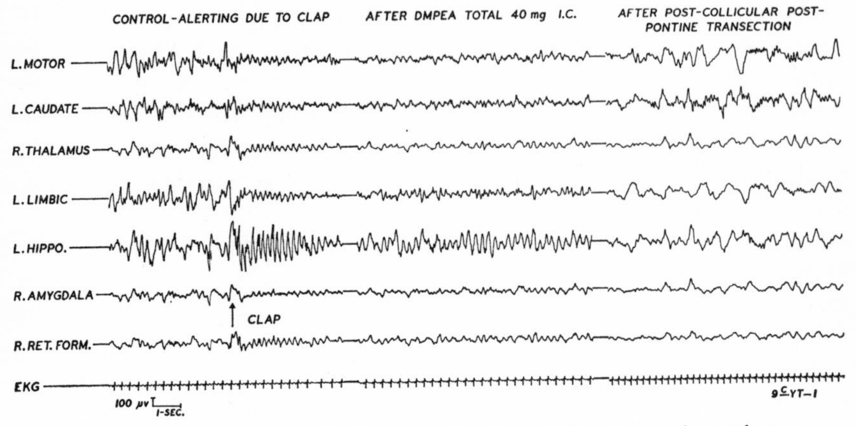

FIG. 12. The alert pattern is shown under three different experimental conditions. In the left-hand series of tracings the alert pattern is evoked as a result of the sound of clapping of the hands. The middle series of tracings reveal the alert pattern evoked by three injections of 10 mg/kg i.v. of mescaline to an animal with intact central nervous system. The series of tracings on the right reveal that this pattern is maintained after transection at C_1.

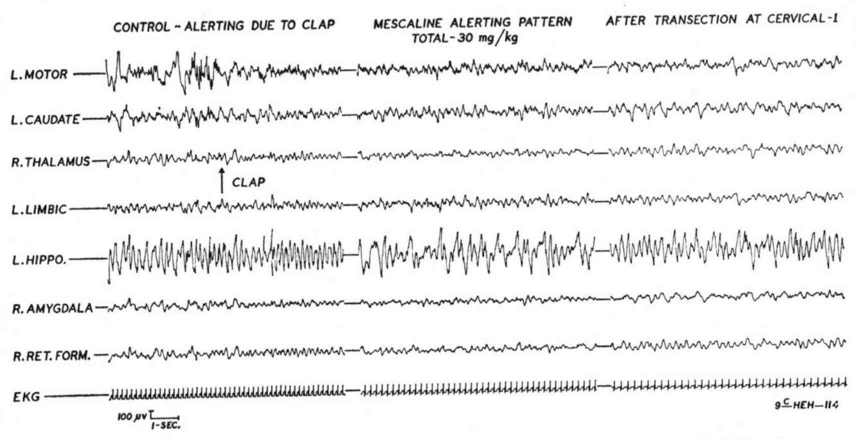

FIG. 13. The left-hand series of tracings reveals the alert pattern evoked by the sound of clapping of the hands. In the middle series of tracings the alerting is produced by four intracarotid injections of 10 mg each of dimethoxyphenylethylamine. The series of tracings on the right reveal that alerting can neither be evoked nor maintained in rabbits transected in the post-collicular post-pontine plane.

In our pilot experiments now going on, mescaline failed to evoke EEG alerting in rabbits sectioned caudal to the midbrain but transections in the C_1 plane left this ability unimpaired. Furthermore, if the animals were transected first, injections of mescaline still excited EEG alerting (Fig. 12). In regard to dimethoxyphenylethylamine, it is of special significance that the pattern for evoking EEG alerting is similar to that of mescaline, ineffective at the midbrain level but successful in the lower brainstem (Fig. 13). We are going to continue observations with these two compounds and in addition study other O-methoxy catecholamines. These preliminary observations, however, reveal that O-methoxy psychotomimetic catecholamines, like N-diethylamine or N-dimethylamine indole compounds, share the characteristic of evoking EEG alerting in the encephale isolé animal but not in those sectioned just caudal to the midbrain.

ACKNOWLEDGMENT

We are happy to thank Drs. R. Bircher and L. Achor of the Sandoz Pharmaceuticals for generous samples of the 4- and 5-substituted indoleamines.

REFERENCES

ABRAMSON, H. A., JARVIK, M. E., KAUFMAN, M. R., KORNETSKY, C., LEVINE, A. and WAGHER, M. (1955) LSD–25. I. Physiological and perceptual response, *J. Psychol.* **39,** 3–60.

BRADLEY, P. B. (1958) The central action of certain drugs in relation to the reticular formation of the brain, H. H. Jasper, L. D. Proctor, R. S. Knightson, W. C. Noshay and R. T. Costello, eds., *Reticular Formation of the Brain*, pp. 123–49, Little, Brown & Company, Boston.

BRODEY, J. F., STEINER, W. G. and HIMWICH, H. E. (1963) An electrographic study of psilocin and 4-methyl-alpha-methyl tryptamine (MP–809), *J. Pharmacol. Exper. Therap.* **140,** 8–18.

COSTA, E., PSCHEIDT, G. R., VAN METER, W. G. and HIMWICH, H. E. (1960) Brain concentrations of biogenic amines and EEG patterns of rabbits, *J. Pharmacol. Exper. Therap.* **130,** 81–88.

HIMWICH, H. E. (1959) Discussion. P. B. Bradley, P. Deniker and C. Radouco-Thomas, eds. *Neuro-Psychopharmacology*, pp. 129–33, Elsevier, New York–Amsterdam.

ISBELL, H., BELLEVILLE, R. E., FRASER, H. F., WIKLER, A. and LOGEN, C. R. (1956) Studies on lysergic acid diethylamide (LSD–25). I. Effects in former morphine addicts and development of tolerance during chronic intoxication, *AMA Arch. Neurol. Psychiat.* **76,** 468–78.

SAWYER, C. H., EVERETT, J. W. and GREEN, J. D. (1954) The rabbit diencephalon in stereotaxic coordinates, *J. Comp. Neurol.* **101,** 801–24.

SCHWEIGERDT, A. K. and HIMWICH, H. E. (1964) An electrographic study of bufotenin and 5-hydroxytryptophan, *J. Pharmacol. Exper. Therap.* **144,** 253–9.

SCHWEIGERDT, A. K., STEWART, A. and HIMWICH, H. E. (1966) An electrographic study of LSD-25 and nine congeners, *J. Pharmacol. Exper. Therap.* **151,** 353-9.

SOLMS, H. (1956) Relationships between chemical structures and psychoses with the use of psychotoxic substances, *J. Clin. Exp. Psychopathol. & Quart. Rev. Psychiat. Neurol.* **17,** 429–33.

GAS CHROMATOGRAPHIC ANALYSIS OF SOME PSYCHOACTIVE INDOLE BASES

BO HOLMSTEDT

Department of Toxicology, Swedish Medical Research Council,
Karolinska Institutet, Stockholm 60, Sweden

WITH the many methods available for the isolation and identification of indoles, recently summarized by Hanson (1965), one might rightly ask what position gas liquid chromatography (GLC) occupies in this context.

I will not attempt here to point out the general applicability of GLC to the separation and determination of biologically occurring compounds. Excellent general surveys are already available (Burchfield and Storrs, 1962; Szymanski, 1964). Instead I will summarize some of the research carried out in our department in recent years concerned with the identification of psychoactive tryptamines in South American drugs. By presenting the sequence of events leading to the final identification of some of these indole bases I think the audience will get a good idea of the usefulness of gas liquid chromatography as compared to other methods. The result of this research with regard to details of botany, ethnography and pharmacology has already been published (Wassén and Holmstedt, 1963; Holmstedt, 1965). We are concerned here mostly with the analytical procedures.

About 10 years ago E. C. Horning and co-workers isolated from the seed of *Piptadenia peregrina*, a leguminous plant, indole alkaloids which were identified by means of paper chromatography, colour reactions, fluorescence and infrared spectra (Stromberg, 1954; Fish *et al.*, 1955; Fish and Horning, 1956). They found the seed to contain dimethyltryptamine (DMT) and bufotenine (5-OH-DMT) and also the N-oxides of those two compounds (Fig. 1).

A snuff made of the seeds of *Piptadenia peregrina* has been used by South American Indian tribes to produce hallucinations and the interest of Horning and co-workers arouse from these properties of the drug. As you know, synthetic DMT is now used experimentally by psychiatrists to produce short-lasting states of illusions and hallucinations (Szara *et al.*, 1957, 1961; Böszörményi and Grunecker, 1957).

Ethnological and botanical explorations in recent years indicate, however, that *Piptadenia peregrina* is not the main constituent in all snuffs used by the South American Indians. Powders of other botanical origin have, for instance, been collected by Schultes (1954) who found them to be prepared from two species of Myristicaceae (*Virola calophylla* Warburg and *V. calophylloidea* Markgraf). A specimen of the powder used for inhalation by the Waica tribe was placed at the author's disposal by courtesy of Mr. Georg J. Seitz of Rio de Janeiro, and it was judged interesting to compare this to the Paricà powder previously analysed.

The Waica Indians belong to a group of ethnologically related tribes called the Yanonàmi who inhabit the region between the Rio Negro and Rio Branco in north-west Brazil and who have been thoroughly investigated by Zerries (1964) and Becher (1960). Their intoxicating snuff is called *epená* and its main constituent is species of *Virola*. It is a fine brownish-grey powder which may very well have been sifted. Primarily, and during all stages of the analysis, it gives a positive Ehrlich reaction indicating the presence of indoles.

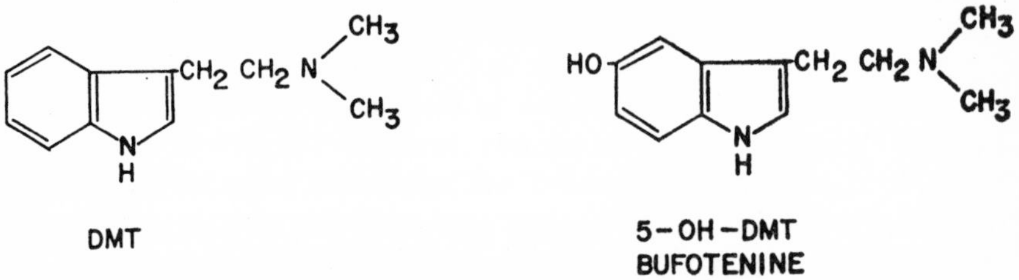

DMT

5-OH-DMT
BUFOTENINE

FIG. 1. Formulas for N,N-dimethyltryptamine (DMT) and 5-hydroxy-N,N-dimethyltryptamine = bufotenine (5-OH-DMT).

During the course of work with this native drug both bioassay and conventional biochemical techniques were used. Eventually, it was found that gas chromatography provided the best means of identification of the components in the alcaloid fraction. With regard to the techniques they have all been completely described and can be found in Holmstedt *et al.* (1964), Horning *et al.* (1964) and Holmstedt (1965). No detailed analytical description will therefore be given here.

For isolation of the organic basis the drug was treated according to the procedure described by Fish *et al.* (1955). The isolation procedure was followed in detail and the steps followed with tests using Ehrlich's reagent. The main constituents were further isolated by preparative paper chromatography run descendingly in 20% KCl. Two spots giving positive reaction with Ehrlich's reagent were identified in this way, a slow-running one giving a dark blue colour and a fast-running one giving a red-blue colour. For the sake of convenience we called these fractions A and B respectively.

The fractions A and B were compared paper chromatographically to a large number of synthetic tryptamine derivatives in several solvent systems. Because of the occurrence of bufotenine in similar plant material attention was first focused on this compound. The oxidation product of bufotenine as described by Fish *et al.* (1955) was also put on paper. An experiment of this kind is shown in Fig. 2. It will be seen that neither bufotenine nor bufotenine-N-oxide are identical with the other compounds investigated.

When all the tryptamines available to us during this stage of the investigation were compared to fractions A and B, two of them had Rf values com-

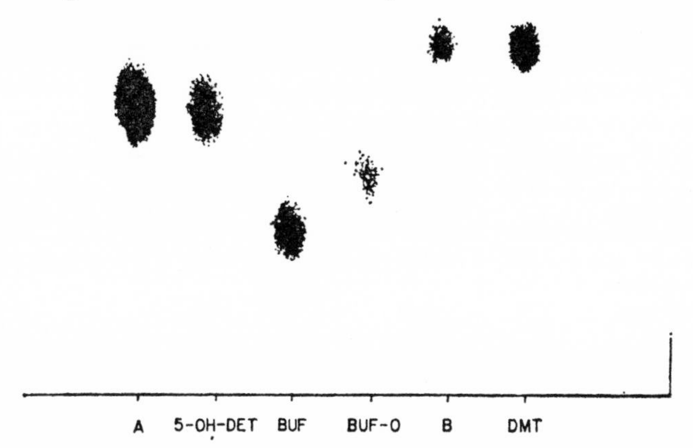

FIG. 2. Paper chromatogram. Solvent *n*-butanol–acetic acid–aqua (120:30:50). Time 16 hr

Rf values:

Fraction A	0·72
5-OH-N,N-diethyltryptamine (5-OH-DET)	0·72
Fraction B	0·78
N,N-dimethyltryptamine (DMT)	0·78
Bufotenine (BUF)	0·60
Bufotenine oxide (BUF-O)	0·65

From HOLMSTEDT, *Arch. Internat. Pharmacodyn.* (1965).

HO— (indole) —$CH_2CH_2N(C_2H_5)_2$; N H

5—OH—DET

CH_3O— (indole) —$CH_2CH_2N(CH_3)_2$; N H

5—MeO—DMT

FIG. 3. Chemical formulas of 5-hydroxy-N,N-diethyltryptamine and 5-methoxy-N,N-dimethyltryptamine.

parable to those of the fractions. They were respectively 5-hydroxy-N,N-diethyltryptamine (5-OH-DET) and N,N-dimethyltryptamine (DMT) (Fig. 3). The Rf values in three solvent systems are presented in Table 1. No other compounds available at the time showed any similarity with fractions A and B in this respect.

The paper chromatograms thus gave no evidence for the presence of bufotenine in fractions A and B, but strongly indicated the identity of the fractions with 5-OH-DET and DMT respectively.

The occurrence of DMT in the drug came as no surprise, since it had been isolated from similar material before but the presence of a N,N-diethyl-substituted amine (5-OH-DET) presented problems. Not many alcaloids containing ethyl groups exist and to the author's knowledge none containing

TABLE 1

Substance	Rf value Solvent n-butanol, acetic acid glacial, water, 120:30:50	Rf value Solvent n-propanol ammonia 5:1	Rf value Solvent t-butanol, water, formic acid 207:87:6
Fraction A	0·71	0·90	0·73
5-OH–N,N-diethyl-tryptamine base	0·71	0·89	0·72
Fraction B	0·80	0·91	0·69
N,N-dimethyl-tryptamine (hydrogen oxalate) DMT	0·80	0·91	0·69

From HOLMSTEDT, *Arch. Internat. Pharmacodyn.* (1965).

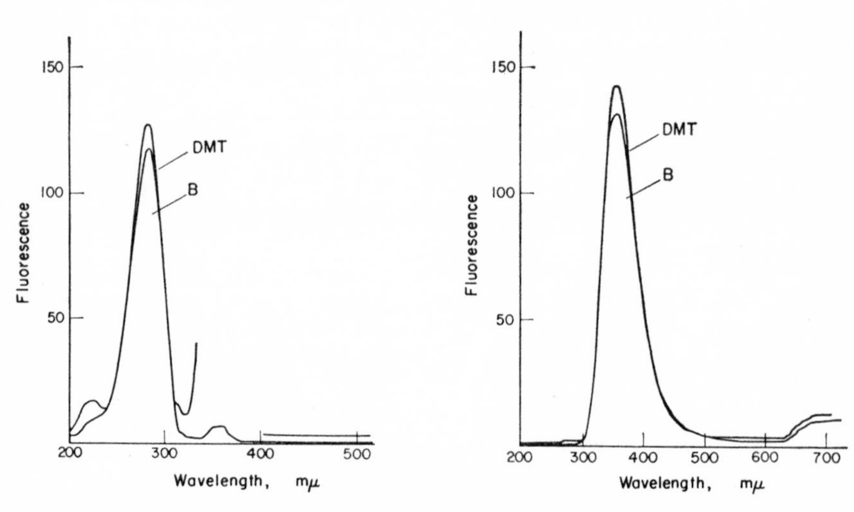

FIG. 4. Comparison of N,N-dimethyltryptamine (DMT) and fraction B (B). Medium aqua. Left activation spectrum. Right fluorescence spectrum at activation maximum 278 mμ. Fluorescence peak at 350 mμ.
From HOLMSTEDT, *Arch. Internat. Pharmacodyn.* (1965).

a diethyl group. For all practical reasons ethyl groups may be considered biosynthetical rarities (Jackson *et al.*, 1962). Because of this in the following work we concentrated our efforts upon solving the identity of fraction A.

Thin-layer chromatography disclosed one difference from the paper chromatography in that synthetic 5-OH-DET gave a yellow colour instead of a blue one. It was, however, not possible to achieve anything but a group separation of the tryptamines in the *epená* extract. The spot given by the extract had an Rf value between those of DMT and 5-OH-DET and a blue colour. No trace of the yellow tinge of 5-OH-DET could be refound in the group-separated extract which made us somewhat suspicious.

Next we tried spectrophotofluorometry. Activation and fluorescence spectra of fractions A and B, 5-OH-DET and DMT were run and recorded (Figs. 4 and 5). These spectra were run in water solutions with both fractions and the test substances and the magnification of the Aminco–Bowman instrument

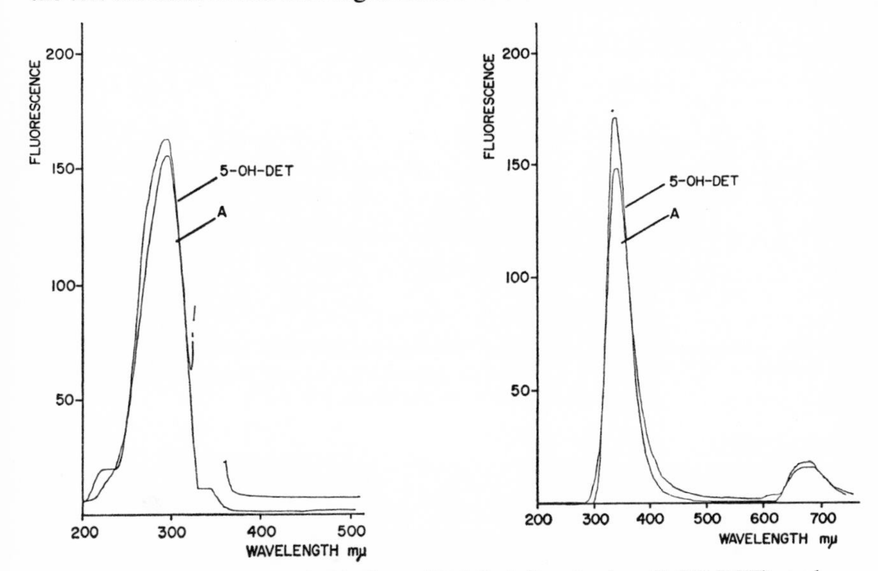

FIG. 5. Comparison of 5-hydroxy-N,N-diethyltryptamine (5-OH-DET) and fraction A (A). Medium aqua. Left activation spectrum. Right fluorescence spectrum at activation maximum of 295 mμ. Fluorescence peak at 340 mμ.

was adjusted to give approximately the same heights of the spectra. As seen from the curves the spectra are superimposable and for all practical reasons identical. It is well known that fluorescence spectra of 5-substituted indoles when run in 3 N HCl show a shift of the peak to higher wavelengths (Udenfriend, 1962). This occurred also with our fraction A as will be seen from Fig. 6 where in acid solution a peak is obtained in the region of 540 mμ. This at least gave us the valuable information that the compound represented by fraction A was substituted in the 5-position, since the shift described is not known to occur with indoles substituted in the 4, 6 or 7.

For bioassay of serotonine-like activity a modification of the method of Vane (1957, 1959) was used. Serotonine (5-HT) was served as a standard and bufotenine was included in the experiments. Fraction A was compared both to a standard solution of 5-OH-DET and a solution run on paper in 20% KCl under conditions identical to those of fraction A. The concentration of the supposed 5-OH-DET in fraction A was calculated spectrophoto-

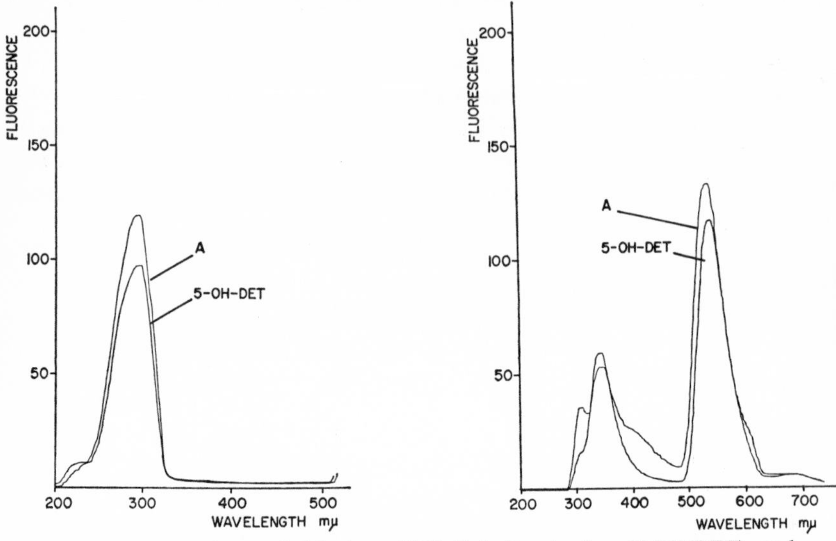

FIG. 6. Comparison of 5-hydroxy-N,N-diethyltryptamine (5-OH-DET) and fraction A (A). Medium 3 N HCl. Left activation spectrum. Right fluorescence spectrum at activation maximum 295 mμ.

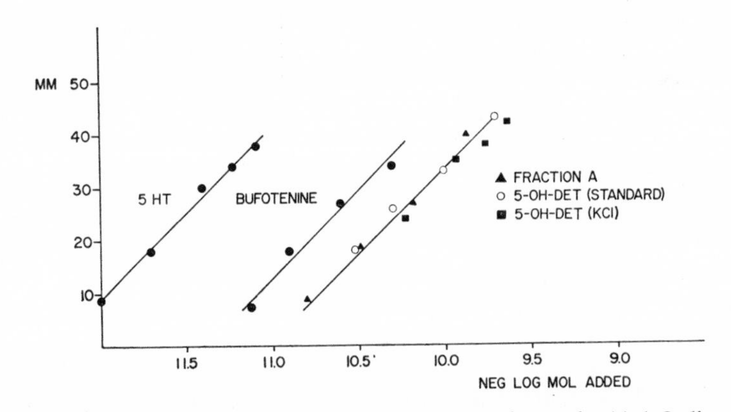

FIG. 7. Bioassay of tryptamine derivatives. Abscissa neg. log. mol. added. Ordinate contraction height in mm. Modified rat fundus strip preparation according to Vane. 5 HT = 5-hydroxytryptamine. Explanation see text. Volume of test bath 5 ml. Volume of active substance added 0·25 ml.

fluorimetrically based upon comparison with standard solutions of known concentration. As seen from the curve, Fig. 7, the dose response curves of fraction A and 5-OH-DET are identical, whether the latter one is run on paper or not. In no case did the curve for bufotenine coincide with other curves. Judged from the data accumulated so far 5-OH-DET could therefore very well be identical with component A in the extract in spite of its "unlikely" chemical structure.

At this stage I went to Houston to work with Evan Horning and one of the problems we decided to tackle was the identity of fraction A for which we thought, as it turned out rightly, GLC would be the ideal method. A study was therefore first made of GLC methods for distinguishing several different kinds of indole amines related to tryptamine. This necessitated the determination of conditions suitable for the GLC separation and identification of indole amines substituted in various ways. Very little information was available at the start of the work about the GLC behaviour of indole bases related to tryptamine. Much work was therefore devoted to the preparation of suitable columns, packings and coating. The details will be found in Holmstedt *et al.* (1964), and the general procedures have recently also been summarized by Fales and Pisano (1964). The latter authors described in 1963 the separation

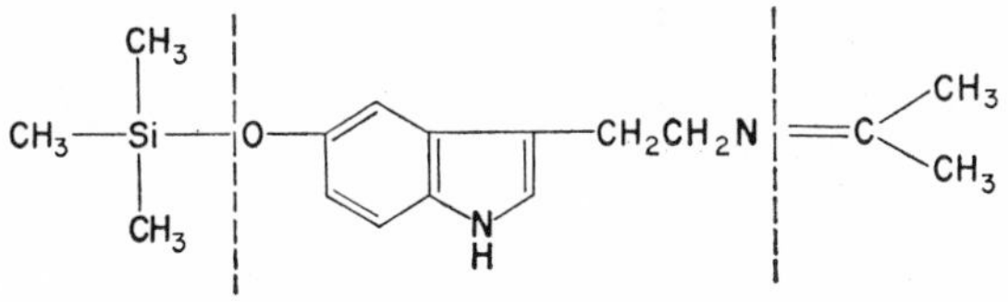

CH_3—Si(CH_3)(CH_3)—O—[indole]—CH_2CH_2N=C(CH_3)(CH_3)

FIG. 8. Serotonine treated with hexamethyldisilazane in acetone. Left part formation of trimethylsilylether. Right part formation of eneamine (Schiff's base).

of several indole bases, and Brochmann-Hanssen and Svendsen (1962) demonstrated that trimethylsilyl (TMSi) ethers were suitable derivatives for the GLC separation of phenolic alkaloids.

The trimethylsilylations carried out with hexamethyldisilazane in solution serves to block OH groups in the compound, although increasing molecular weight lowers the boiling point of the compounds. It has been extensively used in gas chromatographic analysis of steroids (Luukainen *et al.*, 1961). We took advantage of this method also with the amines (Fig. 8, left part). Another reaction which was taken advantage of was the formation of eneamines (Schiff bases) (Fig. 8, right part). These condensation products of amines with acetone were not isolated; they are formed readily and are best used in gas chromatographic work without isolation. The completeness of the reaction can be followed in each instance by disappearance of the free amine.

If acetone is used during the extraction procedure it must be with the knowledge that it reacts with primary amines with the elimination of water to form Schiff's bases. This behaviour can often be utilized to determine whether an amine is primary or secondary since the latter do not commonly react in this manner. The Schiff's bases elute slightly later than the parent amines on non-polar phases and exhibit less tailing due to conversion of the NH_2 to an N-isopropylidene group (Fig. 8, right part). The formation of trimethylsilylethers and Schiff's bases represents only two of the reactions

TABLE 2
RELATIVE RETENTION TIMES FOR INDOLE BASES RELATED TO TRYPTAMINE

Compound	F-60-Z,[a] 182°C	NGS,[b] 216°C
Antracene	1·00[c]	1·00[d]
N,N-Dimethyltryptamine	1·05	1·68
N,N-Diethyltryptamine	1·71	2·14
4-Trimethylsilyloxy-N,N-dimethyltryptamine	2·89	—
5-Trimethylsilyloxy-N,N-dimethyltryptamine	3·19	3·21
6-Trimethylsilyloxy-N,N-dimethyltryptamine	3·70	3·74
7-Trimethylsilyloxy-N,N-dimethyltryptamine	2·23	1·72
5-Trimethylsilyloxy-N,N-diethyltryptamine	5·10	3·96
Tryptamine	1·00	—
Acetone condensation product of tryptamine	1·86	3·26
5-Methoxytryptamine	2·74	—
Acetone condensation product of 5-methoxytryptamine	4·50	9·50
5-Methoxy-N,N-dimethyltryptamine	2·69	5·10
Serotonine	3·10	—
Acetone condensation product of serotonine	8·74	—
Trimethylsilyl ether of acetone condensation product of serotonine	5·29	—
		NGS[e], 227°C
4-Hydroxy-N,N-dimethyltryptamine	3·46	7·22
5-Hydroxy-N,N-dimethyltryptamine	5·77	15·0
6-Hydroxy-N,N-dimethyltryptamine	5·92	15·9
7-Hydroxy-N,N-dimethyltryptamine	4·41	11·9
5-Hydroxy-N,N-diethyltryptamine	8·11	—

[a] Conditions: 6 ft × 4 mm glass U-tube; 7% F-60 and 1% EGSS-Z; 182°C; 18 psi.
[b] Conditions: 6 ft × 4 mm glass U-tube; 10% NGS; 216°C; 19 psi.
[c] Anthracene time, 7·0 min.
[d] Anthracene time, 6·6 min.
[e] Anthracene time, 4·9 min; 21 psi.

From HOLMSTEDT *et al.*, *Analyt. Biochem.* (1964), and HORNING *et al.*, *Analyt. Chem.* (1964).

to which the indoles can be subjected. Later on, other derivatives have also been used successfully (Horning *et al.*, 1964).

The relative retention times for indole bases related to tryptamine and their derivatives will be found in Table 2. Naturally occurring compounds related to tryptamine may contain a variety of side chain structures. N-substitution usually leads to altered retention times when methyl (or ethyl) groups are introduced. Because of the data from the paper chromatography one could suspect the presence of ethyl groups. One chief consideration was therefore the effective separation of compounds with $—CH_2CH_2N(CH_3)_2$ and $—CH_2CH_2N(C_2H_5)_2$ side chains. Figure 9 conclusively demonstrates the longer retention time of compounds with a $—CH_2CH_2N(C_2H_5)_2$ side chain.

The biological hydroxylation of indoles is known to occur in at least three positions, leading to 4-hydroxy, 5-hydroxy and 6-hydroxyindole derivatives. In order to compare the GLC behaviour of positional isomers of hydroxyl-substituted N,N-dimethyltryptamines, the possible isomers were chromatographed directly and as the TMSi ethers. Two columns were employed (see

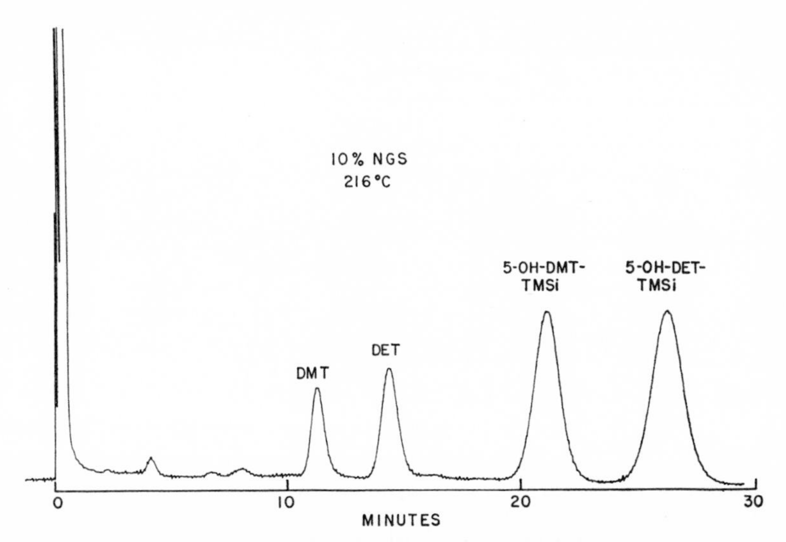

FIG. 9. Separation of N,N-dimethyltryptamine (DMT), N,N-diethyltryptamine (DET), 5-trimethylsilyloxy-N,N-dimethyltryptamine (5-OH-DMT-TMSi) and 5-trimethylsilyloxy-N,N-diethyltryptamine (5-OH-DET-TMSi). Conditions: 10% NGS on 100- to 120-mesh Gas Chrom P, 216°C, 19 psi; argon ionization detection system.

From HORNING *et al.*, *Analyt. Chem.* (1965).

Table 2). The order of elution of the position isomers (for the free phenolic amines) with both columns was found to be 4-, 7-, 5- and 6-substituted. When these amines were converted to TMSi ethers, the order of elution (with the F-60-Z column) was found to be 7-, 4-, 5- and 6-substituted (Fig. 10). The 4-substituted ether was relatively unstable, but could still be determined. Its parent compound psilocine is noted for its instability even under less stringent chemical conditions. The excellent separation powers of the method is apparent from Fig. 10 and this can be compared to Fig. 11 where a fluorescence analysis fails to distinguish between DMT + 5-OH-DMT + 5-HT in a synthetic mixture. The great advantage of gas chromatography in this case is that it allows the identification also of position isomers with identical molecular weight.

We then proceeded to the analysis of the *epená* extract by direct GLC separation. The results were those in Fig. 12 and Fig. 13, upper parts. The minor components had retention times corresponding to N,N-dimethyltryptamine and to bufotenine, but the major alkaloid did not correspond to reference substances which were at hand. The synthetic derivatives containing —$CH_2CH_2N(C_2H_5)_2$ side chains had much longer retention times than any of the components of the drug.

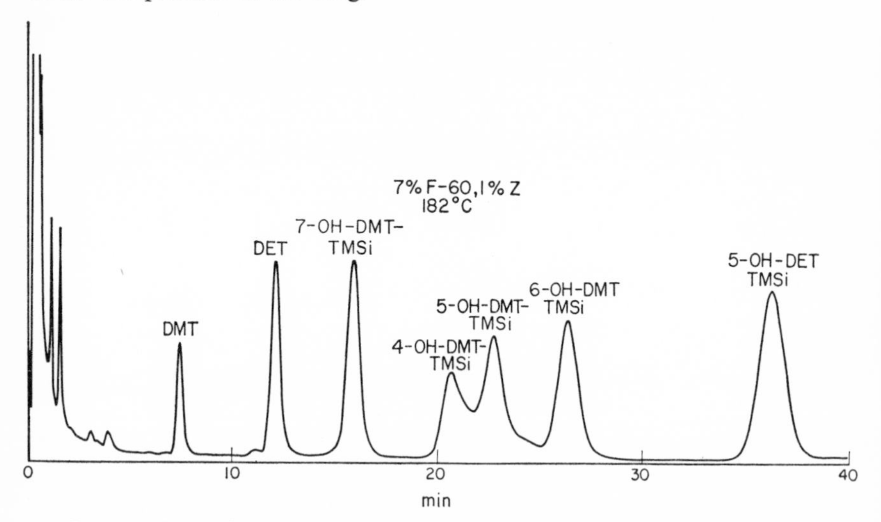

FIG. 10. Separation of tryptamine-related indole bases. The compounds are N,N-dimethyltryptamine (DMT), N,N-diethyltryptamine (DET), 7-trimethylsilyloxy-N,N-dimethyltryptamine (7-OH-DMT-TMSi), 4-trimethylsilyloxy-N,N-dimethyltryptamine (4-OH-DMT-TMSi), 5-trimethylsilyloxy-N,N-dimethyltryptamine (5-OH-DMT-TMSi), 6-trimethylsilyloxy-N,N-dimethyltryptamine (6-OH-DMT-TMSi), and 5-trimethylsilyloxy-N,N-diethyltryptamine (5-OH-DET-TMSi). Conditions: 7% F-60, 1% EGSS-Z, on 100- to 120-mesh Gas Chrom P, 182°C, 18 psi; argon ionization detection system.
From HOLMSTEDT, *Arch. Internat. Pharmacodyn.* (1965).

When the extract was treated with acetone, this did not bring about any change in the retention time, indicating the absence of a reactive primary amine group in the side chain. Again when the same extract was submitted to a trimethylsilylation with hexamethyldisilazane this did not change the position of the peaks, providing information that no phenolic group was present as had originally been suspected when previous analytical methods strongly indicated that 5-OH-DET was identical to fraction A. Inspection of the retention time data suggested that a methoxy-N,N-dimethyltryptamine structure was likely for the major component. 5-methoxy-N,N-dimethyltryptamine (5-MeO-DMT) had previously been investigated by Gessner and

Page (1962) pharmacologically, but we had had no opportunity to include it among our test compounds. A telephone call to Dr. Page's department brought us an authentic sample of the synthetic product within 24 hr. Identity was established by GLC techniques with the major component of the extract. A mixture of bases was made to correspond approximately to the

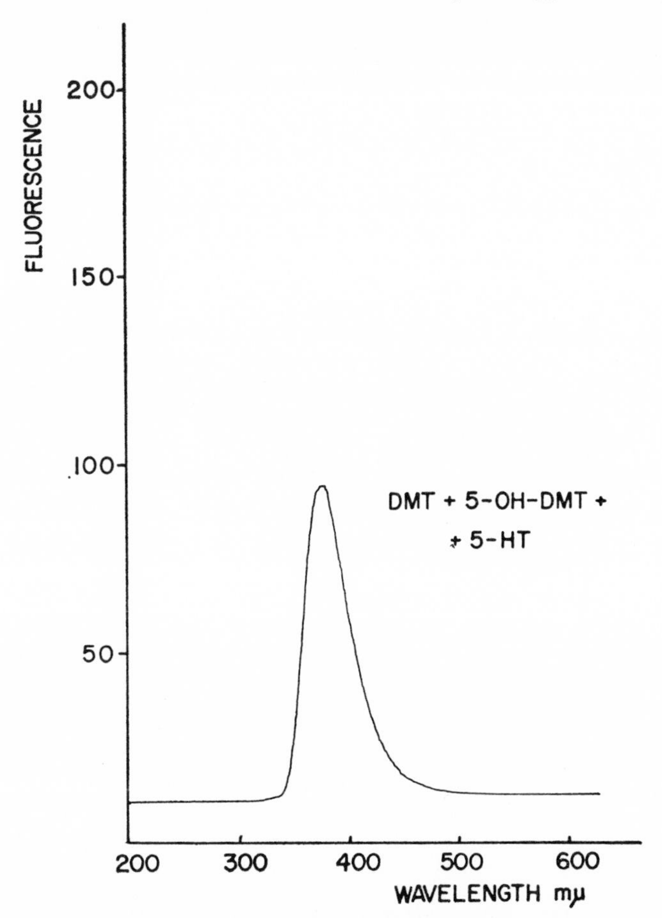

FIG. 11. Fluorescence spectrum of a mixture of N,N-dimethyltryptamine (DMT), 5-hydroxy-N,N-dimethyltryptamine (5-OH-DMT) and serotonine (5-HT). Activation at 290 mμ.

composition seen for the natural mixture of indole bases, and comparison of the GLC records for the two mixtures is demonstrated in Fig. 12 and Fig. 13.

Thus, we finally succeeded to prove that our original fraction A was not 5-hydroxy-N,N-diethyltryptamine but 5-methoxy-N,N-dimethyltryptamine or methylated bufotenine.

This exposition could be brought to a conclusion here, except for the fact that it appeared to me necessary to compare also with previously used methods 5-MeO-DMT and 5-OH-DET, even in the face of the overwhelming evidence that our original fraction A was identical with the former. Fluorescence spectra of the three and a bioassay of 5-MeO-DMT and 5-OH-DET were therefore made and are presented in Fig. 14 and Fig. 15. As seen, completely identical results were obtained which on the one hand provided a consolation for our previous mistake of 5-OH-DET being the compound identical with

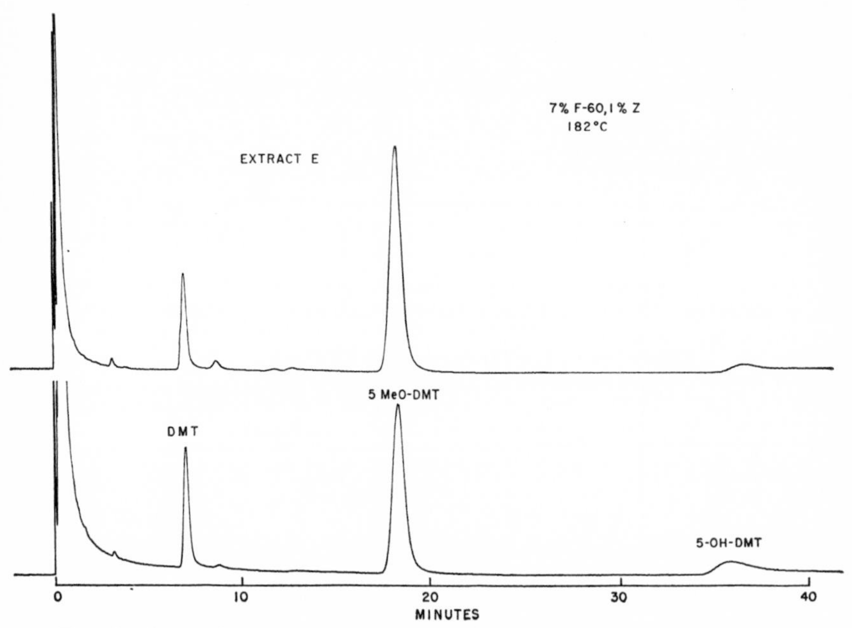

FIG. 12. Comparison of the gas chromatographic analysis of the indole base fraction of an extract of the South American snuff *epená* (EXTRACT E) with a gas chromatographic analysis of a synthetic mixture of N,N-dimethyltryptamine (DMT), 5-methoxy-N,N-dimethyltryptamine (5-MeO-DMT) and 5-hydroxy-N,N-dimethyltryptamine (5-OH-DMT). Column conditions: 6 ft × 4 mm glass column; 7% F-60 and 1% EGSS-Z on 80- to 100-mesh Gas Chrom P, 182°C, 18 psi.

From HOLMSTEDT *et al.*, *Analyt. Biochem.* (1964).

fraction A. On the other hand, it serves well to demonstrate that although fluorescence and bioassay at the moment are more sensitive than gas chromatography, their power to distinguish between compounds with the related structures is much lower than that of GLC. When the former methods are used with biological extracts, a mixture of compounds may be quantitated instead of a single component.

5-MeO-DMT is only one of the many indoles found in plants (Stowe, 1958; Cerletti, 1960). GLC provides the easiest and most rapid way of

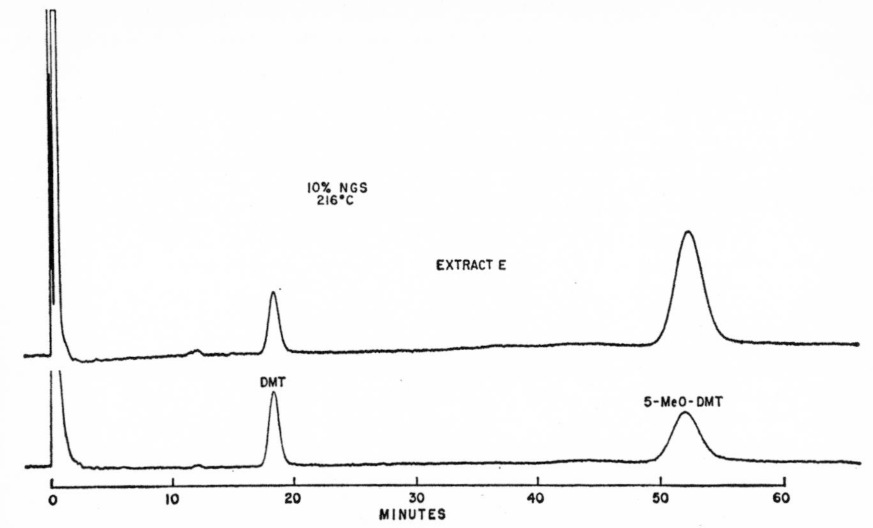

FIG. 13. Comparison of gas chromatographic separation of bases for: upper panel, extract (E) from *epená*, and, lower panel, mixture of reference samples of N,N-dimethyltryptamine (DMT) and 5-methoxy-N,N-dimethyltryptamine (5-MeO-DMT). Conditions: same as for Fig. 9.
From HORNING *et al.*, *Analyt. Chem.* (1964).

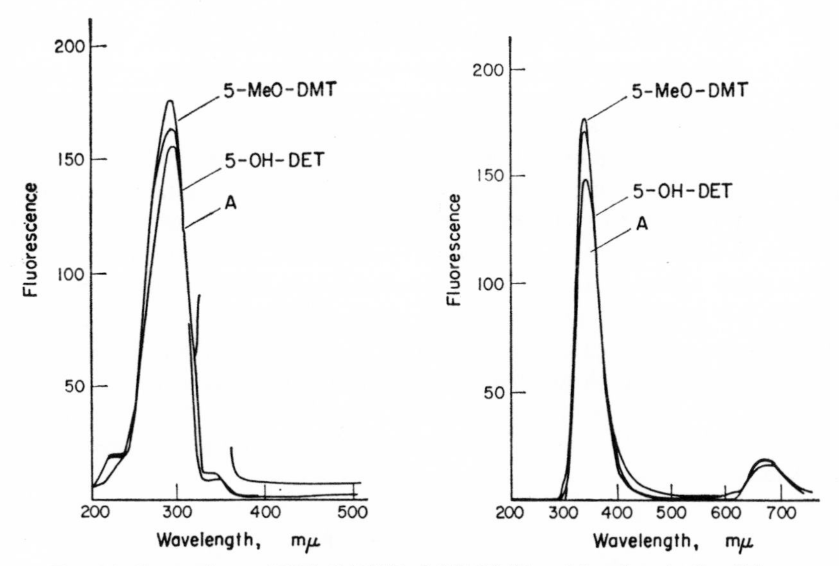

FIG. 14. Comparison of 5-MeO-DMT, 5-OH-DMT and fraction A. Conditions as in Fig. 5.
From HOLMSTEDT, *Arch. Internat. Pharmacodyn.* (1965).

determination of these compounds in various plant materials, and it can be expected to play a large role in the future for identification of hitherto unknown structures, especially since only small samples of the original material are needed. Work is at present on the way in our laboratory, where parts such as root, leaf, bark of reputed psychoactive plants are investigated. An example of this is the rapid identification of harmine derivatives in species of Banisteriopsis.

In my opinion, the experience gained by GLC analysis of indoles in plants will provide us with a very good background for future work with other

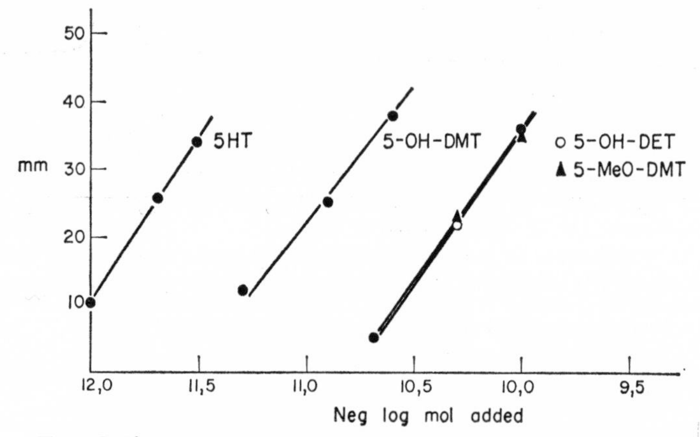

FIG. 15. Bioassay of tryptamine derivatives. Conditions as in Fig. 7. From HOLMSTEDT, *Arch. Internat. Pharmacodyn.* (1965).

sources of tryptamines such as urine and brain. For current analytical gas chromatography columns, only a very small volume may be applied (1–10 μl); hence, high indole concentrations must be achieved for suitable detection. This is in contrast to spectrophotofluorometric techniques whereby indoles may be detected at the 0·1 μg level in 1 ml of fluid. However, in situations where high concentrations can be obtained, gas liquid chromatography permits not only qualitative resolution, but quantitative estimation as well. A final outstanding feature which I hope has been well documented is the ability for gas liquid chromatography to resolve closely related compounds.

Along with the development of better extraction and concentration procedures an increasing sensitivity of the gas chromatographic systems may be expected.

ACKNOWLEDGMENT

This work has been supported by the Swedish Medical Research Council, Project No. 40X–677–01 and by Stiftelsen Thérèse och Johan Anderssons Minne.

REFERENCES

BECHER, H. (1960) *Die Surára und Pakidái, zwei Yanonámi-Stämme in Nordwestbrasilien*, Hamburg, Kommisionsverlag Cram, De Gruyter & Co. (133 pp.)

BROCHMANN-HANSSEN, E. and BAERHEIM SVENDSEN, A. (1962) Separation and identification of sympathomimetic amines by gas–liquid chromatography, *J. Pharmaceut. Sciences*, **51,** 938–41.

BURCHFIELD, H. P. and STORRS, E. E. (1962) *Biochemical Applications of Gaschromatography*, New York, Academic Press.

BÖSZÖRMÉNYI, Z. and GRUNECKER, G. (1957) *Dimethyltryptamine* (*DMT*) *Experiments with Psychotics. Psychotropic Drugs*, ed. by S. Garattini and V. Ghetti, Milano (580 pp.).

CERLETTI, A. (1960) *Über Vorkommen und Bedeutung der Indolstruktur in der Medizin und Biologie. Fortschritte der Arzneimittelforschung*, **II,** 228–49, Basel und Stuttgart, Birkhäuser Verlag.

FALES, H. M. and PISANO, J. J. (1964) *The Gas Chromatography of Amines, Alkaloids, and Amino Acids. Biochemical Applications of Gas Chromatography*. Based on lectures presented during the Fifth Annual Gas Chromatography Institute at Canisius College, Buffalo, New York, 1963, ed. by H. A. Szymanski, Plenum Press, New York.

FISH, M. S., JOHNSON, N. M. and HORNING, E. C. (1955) Piptadenia alkaloids. Indole bases of *P. peregrina* (L.) Benth. and related species, *J. Am. Chem. Soc.* **77,** 5892–5.

FISH, M. S. and HORNING, E. C. (1956) Studies on hallucinogenic snuffs, *J. Nervous and Mental Disease*, **124,** 33–7.

GESSNER, P. K. and PAGE, L. H. (1962) Behavioral effects of 5-methoxy-N:N-dimethyltryptamine, other tryptamines and LSD, *Am. J. Physiol.* **203,** 167–72.

HANSON, A. (1965) *Chemical Analysis of Indolealkylamines and Related Compounds. Heffter-Heubner Handbuch der experimentellen Pharmakologie*, Vol. **XIX.**

HOLMSTEDT, B., VANDENHEUVEL, W. J. A., GARDINER, W. L. and HORNING, E. C. (1964) The separation and identification of tryptamine-related indole bases by gas chromatographic methods, *Analyt. Biochem.* **8,** 151–7.

HOLMSTEDT, B. (1965) Tryptamine derivatives in epená, an intoxicating snuff used by some South American Indian tribes, *Arch. Internat. de Pharmacodyn. et de Thér.*, **156,** 285–306.

HORNING, E. C., HORNING, M. G., VANDENHEUVEL, W. J. A., KNOX, K. L., HOLMSTEDT, B. and BROOKS, C. J. W. (1964) (Gas chromatographic studies of catecholamines, tryptamines, and other biological amines). Part II. Tryptamine-related amines and catecholamines, *Analyt. Chem.* **36,** 1546–9.

JACKSON, M., DULANEY, E. L., PUTTER, I., SHAFER, H. M., WOLF, F. J. and WOODRUFF, H. B. (1962) Transethylation in antibiotic biosynthesis, *Biochimica and Biophysica Acta*, **62,** 616–19.

LUUKAINEN, T., VANDENHEUVEL, W. J. A., HAAHTI, E. O. A. and HORNING, E. C. (1961) Gas-chromatographic behavior of trimethylsilyl ethers of steroids, *Biochimica and Biophysica Acta*, **52,** 599–601.

SCHULTES, R. E. (1954) A new narcotic snuff from the Northwest Amazon, *Botanical Museum Leaflets, Harvard University*, **16,** 241–60.

STOWE, B. B. (1958) Occurrence and metabolism of simple indoles in plants, *Fortschritte der Chemie organischer Naturstoffe* (Herausgegeben von L. Zechmeister), **16,** 248–97, Wien, Springer Verlag.

STROMBERG, V. L. (1954) The isolation of bufotenine from Piptadenia peregrina, *J. Am. Chem. Soc.* **76,** 1707.

SZARA, S. (1957) The comparison of the psychotic effect of tryptamine derivatives with the effects of mescaline and LSD-25 in self-experiments, *Psychotropic Drugs*, ed. by S. Garattini and V. Ghetti, Milano, 460.

SZARA, S. (1961) Hallucinogenic effects and metabolism of tryptamine derivatives in man, *Fed. Proc.* **20,** 885–8.

SZARA, S. and HEART, E. (1961) The 6-hydroxylation of tryptamine derivatives: A way of producing psychoactive metabolites. To be included in the monograph *Some Biological Aspects of Schizophrenic Behavior* to be published by the New York Academy of Sciences.

SZARA, S. and ROCKLAND, L. H. (1961) Psychological effects and metabolism of N,N-diethyltryptamine, an hallucinogenic drug. Presented at the III. World Congress of Psychiatry, Montreal, Canada, June.

SZYMANSKI, H. A. (1964) Editor. *Biomedical Applications of Gas Chromatography*. Based on lectures presented during the Fifth (1963) Annual Gas Chromatography Institute at Canisius College, Buffalo. New York, Plenum Press.

UDENFRIEND, S. (1962) *Fluorescence Assay in Biology and Medicine*, New York; London, Academic Press.

VANE, J. R. (1957) A sensitive method for the assay of 5-hydroxytryptamine, *British Journal of Pharmacology*, **12,** 344–9.

VANE, J. R. (1959) The relative activities of some tryptamine analogues on the isolated stomach strip preparation, *British Journal of Pharmacology*, **14,** 87–98.

WASSÉN, S. H. and HOLMSTEDT, B. (1963) The use of paricà, an ethnological and pharmacological review, *Ethnos*, **28,** 5–45.

ZERRIES, O. (1964) *Waika, Die kulturgeschichtliche Stellung der Waika-Indianer des oberen Orinoco im Rahmen der Völkerkunde Südamerikas*. Klaus Renner Verlag, München (Ergebnisse der Frobenius-Expedition 1954/55 nach Südost-Venezuela. Band I. Waika).

TRYPTOPHAN METABOLISM IN MENTAL ILLNESS

DEREK RICHTER

Medical Research Council Neuropsychiatric Research Unit, Carshalton, Surrey

IN THE search for biochemical abnormalities in mental illness, several lines of inquiry have suggested the possible involvement of derivatives of tryptophan. The indole nucleus of tryptophan is present in lysergic acid diethylamide, psilocybin and a number of other drugs with hallucinogenic or psychotomimetic actions: it is present also in adrenochrome, which is formed by oxidation of adrenaline (Green and Richter, 1937). Tryptamine and 5-hydroxytryptamine (5-HT), which occur normally in the urine, are reported to be present in the rat brain (Hess and Doepfner, 1961); and mental symptoms can be produced in man by administering tryptophan either alone or together with a monoamine oxidase inhibitor, so that the levels of these amines in the body are increased (Lauer *et al.*, 1958; Oates and Sjoerdsma, 1960; Pollin *et al.*, 1961; Smith and Prockop, 1962). Clearly there are many other factors, including the catecholamines, which may influence the mental state, but circumstantial evidence suggesting a link between tryptophan metabolites and mental state is particularly strong. What then are the normal physiological functions of the amines derived from tryptophan, and what evidence is there of any disorder of tryptophan metabolism in patients who are mentally ill?

1. ACTIONS OF TRYPTAMINE AND 5-HT

5-HT was first recognized as a peripheral vasoconstrictor and a substance which causes various smooth muscles to contract. Its presence in considerable amounts in blood platelets, skin and intestine indicates that its actions in the body are not confined to the nervous system. There is good evidence that 5-HT acts as a transmitter of nervous impulses in the ganglia of some invertebrates and it is likely that 5-HT released from the enterochromaffin cells when the gut is distended modifies the activity of the nervous netwok of the vertebrate intestine (Bülbring, 1958). It has also been shown to exert a modifying action on the transmission of nervous impulses in the superior cervical ganglion (Trendelenburg, 1956). The occurrence of 5-HT in considerable amounts in the diencephalon of higher as well as lower vertebrates suggests that it may have a similar role in the mammalian brain, where it is present in relatively high concentration in the "old" cortex of the limbic lobe and related subcortical structures including the septal nuclei, amygdala and hypothalamus (Welch, 1964; Paasonen *et al.*, 1957). These regions contain some of the main autonomic centres concerned in regulating the vegetative functions of the body and also centres concerned in the behavioural expression of emotion. There is evidence that 5-HT may have special functions in the vertebrate eye (Welch, 1964) and in the pineal organ (Quay, 1964), but in general the distribution of 5-HT in the brain is consistent with the view that it may play a part in the mechanisms controlling autonomic activity and affective state.

Among the central actions attributed to 5-HT is an apparent sedative effect which may follow an initial excitatory action. It has been suggested that the sedation produced by reserpine may be due to release of 5-HT rather than catecholamines, since reserpine produces neither release of 5-HT nor sedation in animals that have previously been stressed (Brodie *et al.*, 1960). Evidence of a central depressant action of 5-HT in the chicken brain has been reported by Dewhurst and Marley (1964) who found, however, that tryptamine acts mainly as an excitant. A central excitant action of tryptamine was previously observed by Tedeschi *et al.* (1959), who showed that it reverses reserpine sedation and acts as a convulsant in the rat. Comparison of tryptamine with 5-HT is complicated by the fact that both amines are biphasic in action. There is also evidence that there are species differences in the actions of amines at different centres in the brain; and any one amine may have different actions at different receptor sites. It has been shown, for example, that dopamine has central excitatory effects at some receptor sites in the rabbit brain, while it also appears to have inhibitory effects at other sites (Vogt, 1965): but the central actions of adrenaline and noradrenaline are predominantly inhibitory (Dewhurst and Marley, 1964). 5-HT does not readily cross the blood–brain barrier system whereas tryptamine, which is lipid-soluble, passes more freely from the blood into the brain. The brain contains an enzyme which forms tryptamine directly from tryptophan (Lovenberg, *et al.*, 1962), but it may also be affected by tryptamine formed in other organs, including the gut.

The level of 5-HT in the brain can be raised by administering its immediate precursor, 5-hydroxytrptophan, together with a monoamine oxidase inhibitor; but this raises the level of 5-HT in other organs at the same time and the central actions may be masked by the severe effects due to contraction of smooth muscle in the periphery: the symptoms include diarrhoea, nausea, hypertension and visceral cramps (Bogdanski *et al.*, 1958). Further, there is evidence from animal experiments with the rat that the exogenous 5-HT appearing in the brain under these conditions is distributed differently and may be situated in a different metabolic pool from the 5-HT normally formed in the brain from tryptophan (Green and Sawyer, 1964; Sharman, 1965). It has been noted in animal experiments that the behavioural changes induced by treatment with amine precursors and a monoamine oxidase inhibitor do not correlate very closely with the increase in indolylamines in the brain (Hess and Doepfner, 1961); but a close quantitative relationship is hardly to be expected if the amines are partly free and partly bound, and can occur in different metabolic pools.

The symptoms produced by administering tryptophan to human subjects are especially informative, since tryptophan is the normal source of the indolylamines found in the tissues, and only in man can we study the effects on mood. The effects of tryptophan are more marked if a monoamine oxidase inhibitor is given at the same time, but Smith and Prockop (1962) found that tryptophan alone in doses up to 90 mg/kg can produce a striking change of mood in normal subjects. The reactions included on the one hand brief phases of excitement indicated by hyperactivity, uninhibited behaviour, inappropriate laughter and euphoria, and on the other hand marked drowsiness, yawning and sleep. The drowsiness, which has been reported to coincide with a rise of 5-hydroxyindoles in the blood (Dewhurst, 1965), may reasonably be attributed to a central action of 5-HT. Independent evidence of an effect of tryptophan metabolites on sleep mechanisms has come from the recent observation of Oswald (1965) that in many subjects administration of tryptophan hastens the change from normal sleep to "deep sleep" or "REM sleep", as indicated by the continuously recorded EEG. Animal experiments have shown that the onset of sleep coincides with a marked rise in the 5-HT level in the hamster brain (Matussek and Patschke, 1964). Evidence has also been obtained that 5-HT is implicated in the sleep mechanisms operating in the chicken (Spooner, 1965) and in the cat (Koella and Csicman, 1965). This may also be the function of the 5-HT released from the pineal gland of the rat (Quay, 1964). The distribution of tryptamine receptors in the central nervous system has not yet been fully explored, but they appear to be widely distributed, since local electrical responses to substituted tryptamines can be recorded from electrodes in cerebral cortex, thalamus, brain stem and spinal cord (Collier *et al.*, 1961). It is to be expected that amines such as tryptamine and 5-HT, which differ in lipid solubility and other properties, will have a different distribution in the storage granules and at the receptor sites; and therefore they will differ to some extent in their physiological actions.

2. METABOLIC FACTORS IN DEPRESSION

It is generally recognized that there are physiological changes in depressive illness which form a part of the clinical picture: but the nature of the metabolic accompaniments of depression, and the extent to which they are causal or secondary results of the mental state, are not yet clear. Some of the metabolic

TABLE 1. METABOLIC CHANGES REPORTED IN SEVERELY DEPRESSED PATIENTS

	Mean change from normal (%)	$P<$	
Body weight reduced	−19	0·01	Pryce (1958)
CSF "5-hydroxyindoles" reduced	−60	0·001	Ashcroft and Sharman (1960)
Urinary corticoids increased	—	—	Ferguson *et al.* (1964)
Plasma corticoids increased	+120	0·001	Gibbons and McHugh (1962)
Androgen excretion low	—	—	Ferguson *et al.* (1964)
Serum cholinesterase raised	+28	0·01	Richter and Lee (1942a)
Na^+ transport across BBB reduced	−29	0·001	Coppen (1960)
Glucose tolerance low	−32	0·001	Pryce (1958)
Plasma acetoin raised	+48	0·002	Anderson and Dawson (1962)
Intracellular Na^+ high	+48	0·001	Coppen and Shaw (1963)
Intracellular K^+ low	−19	0·001	Shaw and Coppen (1966)
Urinary tryptamine low	−55	0·001	Rodnight (1961); Coppen *et al.* (1965b)
$^{14}CO_2$ from 5-H [^{14}C] TP reduced	−50	—	Coppen *et al.* (1965a)
Urinary xanthurenic acid high	+101	0·05	Cazzullo *et al.* (1966)
Extracellular fluid decreased	−3	0·01	Coppen and Shaw (1963)

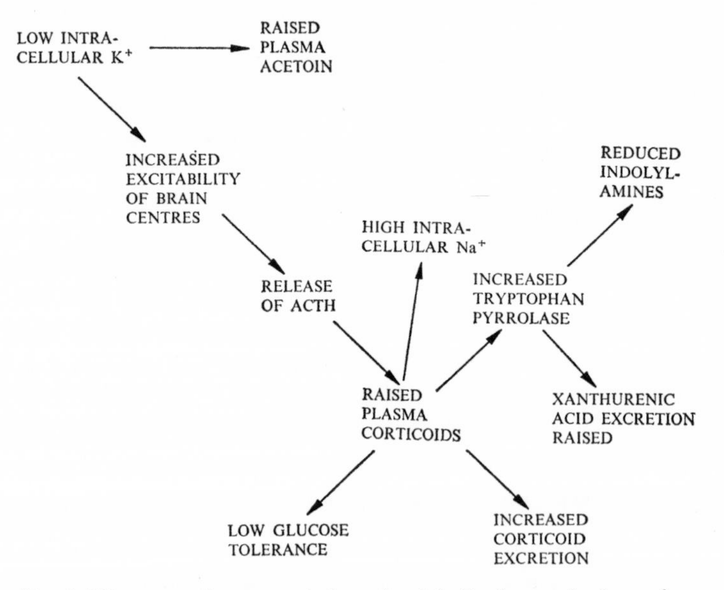

FIG. 1. Diagrammatic representation of metabolic changes in depression.

changes reported to occur in depression are of little significance since they disappear if dietary and other incidental factors are controlled, but there are other changes which appear to be more closely connected with the depressive state. A number of these are listed in Table 1. The mechanisms operating in the development of a depressive psychosis are still unknown and caution is needed in attributing a causal role to any factor which might equally be a secondary effect: but it is unlikely that the various abnormalities found to occur in depressive states are entirely unrelated and it may be useful to consider the kind of way in which they may be linked (Fig. 1). It should be emphasized that the suggested relationships are based on very little experimental evidence and they are therefore largely speculative, but it would appear that with the gradual accumulation of new data a general pattern of biochemical change in depression is now beginning to emerge.

The genetic evidence indicates that depression commonly occurs in individuals who have a genetically determined constitutional predisposition to a depressive type of illness. Any biochemical abnormalities found to persist in patients who have recovered from a depressive illness are likely to be constitutional in nature and different in kind from the temporary changes observed only during phases of depression. Abnormalities reported to persist after recovery include a low intracellular K^+ (Shaw and Coppen, 1966) and an apparent deficiency in certain androgenic steroids (Ferguson *et al.*, 1964). Cade (1964) found the plasma Mg^{++} level abnormally high in depressive patients before and after recovery, but the significance of this finding is doubtful since the diet of his patients was not controlled. The increase in plasma corticoids, and in excretion of steroid metabolites, gives evidence of a generalized stress reaction, which is a frequent if not invariable feature of severe depression. If it is taken that constitutional endocrine factors giving a low intracellular K^+ lead to increased excitability of certain centres of the brain (Woodbury, 1958), this could result in a relative instability under conditions of stress and lead to release of ACTH. A rise in plasma corticoids is known to occur as an unspecific stress response in anxiety and other affective disorders, and it might account for the increase in intracellular Na^+, which has been observed to occur also in manic states and other conditions of stress (Coppen *et al.*, 1966). It may be noted that in a depressive patient this response has the elements of a vicious circle, since an increase in intracellular Na^+ would be expected to increase the irritability of neurons of the central nervous system and so add to the excitatory effects of a low intracellular K^+. In this connection it is of interest that lithium, which affects the mood in mania, changes the distribution of Na^+ and also the EEG response to stimulation, so that the cortical recovery cycle resembles that seen in depression (Shagass and Schwarz, 1962; Coppen *et al.*, 1965). The raised serum cholinesterase level may also be an unspecific stress response, since it is found also in anxiety states (Richter and Lee, 1942b).

Decrease in weight in depression is often severe, but this is apparently not related to the reduction in glucose tolerance, which is probably due to a reduced sensitivity to insulin (Pryce, 1958). The raised plasma acetoin, which is a form of ketosis found also in diabetes, may depend in part on the low intracellular K^+ in depression, since it has been shown that a low K^+ level favours the formation of acetoin from glucose in brain tissue slices incubated *in vitro* (Dawson and Bone, 1963). It is of interest to compare the biochemical changes found in depression with the stress responses described by Engel (1951) as occurring as a result of trauma in animals and in man: "Negative nitrogen balance, an impairment of carbohydrate metabolism with a decreased sensitivity to insulin, an increased mobilization of fat from the periphery to the liver with a tendency to fasting ketosis and changes in electrolyte balance with a negative potassium balance."

It is of interest that four of the physiological changes reported in patients with severe depression (Table 1) relate to the metabolism of tryptophan. A possible relationship between tryptophan metabolism and depression was suggested by a report of Ashcroft and Sharman (1960) that the level of "5-hydroxyindoles" estimated fluorimetrically in the cerebrospinal fluid was significantly lower in nine patients with depressive psychoses than in a control series of ten neurological patients who were not depressed. It has been reported that there is a reduced excretion of 5-hydroxyindolylacetic acid in depressed patients who respond favourably to treatment with iproniazid (Pare and Sandler, 1959; Praag and Leijnse, 1963) and recently it has been found that the excretion of tryptamine (39 μg/24 hr) in patients suffering from depression is considerably less than in the same patients after recovery (66 μ/24 hr, $P<0{\cdot}001$) (Coppen *et al.*, 1965b). This agrees with a previous observation of Rodnight (1961) who found the excretion of tryptamine, estimated by a specific chromatographic method, significantly lower in patients who were depressed (34 μg/24 hr, $P<0{\cdot}05$) than in schizophrenics or normal subjects (61 μg/24 hr).

Tryptophan can be metabolized in a number of different ways and whereas in depression the excretion of tryptamine is reduced, the excretion of xanthurenic acid has been found to be increased (Cazzullo *et al.*, 1966). This suggests that during depression tryptophan is metabolized to a greater extent along the kynurenine pathway. It is significant that cortisone induces the formation of the enzyme tryptophan pyrrolase which effects the oxidation of tryptophan by this route. These observations suggest a possible modification of the metabolism of tryptophan leading to a reduced level of indolylamines in the tissues in patients suffering from depression. Indolylamines are formed from tryptophan by decarboxylation either of tryptophan or of 5-hydroxytryptophan. Measurements of the ^{14}C content of the expired air after administration of carboxy-labelled 5-hydroxy[1-^{14}C]tryptophan were carried out by Coppen *et al.* (1965a) in a small group of patients before and after recovery from depression. The result showed that in some patients the rate of liberation of $^{14}CO_2$ from labelled 5-hydroxytryptophan was considerably reduced during depression. This gave independent evidence of a modification of tryptophan metabolism which might lead to a reduced formation of indolylamines in patients suffering from depression.

The interpretation of the mechanism of drug actions *in vivo* is notoriously difficult, but it is significant that reserpine and α-methyldopa, both of which decrease the level of biogenic amines in the brain, tend to cause depression in human subjects and may precipitate a depressive illness. Conversely drugs such as amphetamine, imipramine and the monoamine oxidase inhibitors, which increase the level of amines or cause a direct stimulation of central tryptamine receptors, produce euphoria or elevation of mood. Kline and Sacks (1963) claimed that they could produce rapid alleviation of depression by injection of 5-hydroxytryptophan, which is the precursor of 5-HT. However, this result might have been influenced by the unpleasant side-effects —nausea, vomiting and abdominal pain. Pare and Sandler (1959) failed to observe any alleviation of depressive symptoms in patients treated with 5-hydroxytryptophan and iproniazid; and a more recent report of Kline *et al.* (1964) throws doubt on the beneficial effects of this treatment. In this connection it is relevant that treatment with antidepressant monoamine oxidase inhibitors is reported to raise the levels of tryptamine and 5-HT in the rat brain, and the rise is greatly increased by concurrent administration of their common precursor, tryptophan (Hess and Doepfner, 1961). In a carefully controlled clinical trial with patients suffering from depression it was found that treatment with tryptophan together with tranylcypromine produced a striking alleviation of the symptoms of depression (Coppen *et al.*, 1963).

Patients on tryptamine commonly reported their first good night's sleep for weeks and the general improvement in the trial group treated in this way persisted after the period of the trial. These observations were confirmed by Pare (1963) who also obtained alleviation of depression by administering tryptophan and iproniazid. Clearly other factors, including catecholamines, electrolytes and endocrine balance, must also play a part; but Pare and Sandler (1959) were unable to relieve the symptoms of depression by administering DOPA together with iproniazid and their finding was confirmed by Klerman *et al.* (1963). This suggests that dopamine may be less important than amines derived from tryptophan in determining the symptoms of patients who are depressed. The role of catecholamines in depression has been the subject of speculation for many years, but the catecholamine hypothesis of affective disorders is based largely on animal experiments in which sedation and alerting in animals have been taken to correspond to depression of mood and euphoria in man. Earlier reports of changes in catecholamine metabolites in depression have not been confirmed by later work, and there is little evidence of any consistent abnormality of catecholamine metabolism in depressive states in man. If it is established that in severe depression the metabolism of tryptophan is in some way deranged, this might offer an explanation for a number of clinical observations including perhaps the frequently seen disturbance of the normal cycle of sleep, which apparently depends on a mechanism involving 5-HT in the tissues (Oswald, 1965; Koella and Csicman, 1965).

3. BIOCHEMICAL CHANGES IN MANIA

The relation between mania and depression is clearly very close, both from a genetic viewpoint and in clinical experience, for the same patient may swing from one extreme to the other within a short space of time. There is a relative lack of information about the metabolism of patients in the manic state and this is not surprising in view of the practical difficulties in dealing experimentally with patients of this kind.

Manic patients differ from depressives in being generally above the average in weight (Kallmann, 1950), which suggests a difference in constitutional endocrine factors. Cade (1964) reported that manic patients differed from depressives in that the plasma Mg^{++} was not raised: it remained at a normal level before and after remission.

The recent finding of Coppen *et al.* (1966) that the intracellular Na^{+} level is raised in mania, as in depression, supports the view that depression of mood does not depend only on the change in Na^{+} distribution, although this might determine the lability which is common to both conditions. Depression of mood is likely to be determined rather by the pattern of distribution of all the biogenic amines and electrolytes at different centres in the brain.

4. TRYPTOPHAN METABOLISM IN SCHIZOPHRENIA

It is widely recognized that genetic factors play an important part in influencing the predisposition to a schizophrenic psychosis. The evidence suggests a multifactorial type of inheritance, or the operation of a single intermediate gene producing a psychosis in all the homozygous and about 26% of the heterozygous carriers (Slater, 1961). To say that a condition is genetically determined is to imply that it is biochemically determined, since genetic factors operate through biochemical mechanisms. Biochemical abnormalities have been reported from time to time in individual cases, or in special subgroups of schizophrenics, and several biochemical hypotheses of the causation of schizophrenia have been proposed; but no clear evidence of a general mechanism of causation has hitherto been recognized.

In looking for biochemical factors that might be concerned in determining a constitutional predisposition to schizophrenia, there is evidence that schizophrenics as a group differ from the normal mean in body-build: they tend to have a more immature or female type of habitus. In this connection interest attaches to a recent chance finding that male schizophrenics have a habitually low excretion of Δ^{16}-androstenol (Brooksbank, 1962). It has also been reported that schizophrenics differ significantly ($P<0{\cdot}001$) from normal controls in their excretion of kynurenine derivatives after a loading dose of tryptophan (Benassi *et al.*, 1961).

The observations of Pollin *et al.* (1961) have drawn attention to the possibility of an abnormality of tryptophan metabolism in schizophrenia, since they found that administration of tryptophan together with a monoamine oxidase inhibitor produced an apparent activation of affective behaviour in some patients. There is now a considerable literature on the excretion by schizophrenics of urinary metabolites of tryptophan. Earlier workers reported abnormal excretion of 5-hydroxyindolylacetic acid and xanthurenic acid by schizophrenics, but later investigators questioned these findings and they were unable to agree on any consistent excretion pattern characteristic of schizophrenia. It became clear that the urinary excretion of tryptophan metabolites depends on a number of variables which need to be carefully controlled if consistent values are to be obtained. The pattern of excretion is influenced by diet, pyridoxine deficiency, intestinal flora, drugs and incidental physical disorders. The indole metabolites excreted after a loading dose of tryptophan correspond to only a small part (1–2%) of the dose administered and they appear to indicate metabolic processes occurring in the body as a whole rather than processes occurring only in the brain (Sjoerdsma *et al.*, 1959). Nevertheless, the 24-hr urinary excretion pattern can give information about certain aspects of the metabolism of patients if the various dietary and other factors are controlled.

The problem was considerably clarified, and some of the conflicting reports in the literature were explained, by the observation of Brune and Himwich (1963) that some schizophrenics showed a striking increase in excretion of tryptamine and other tryptophan metabolites during outbursts of psychotic behaviour. The results showed no correlation between the urinary excretion of indole derivatives and the diagnosis of schizophrenia: excretion was normal in schizophrenics in whom the psychosis was apparently inactive, but high values were obtained in patients showing "exacerbations of schizophrenic activity in terms of aggravations of hallucinatory and delusional experiences as well as aggressiveness and hostility". Large increases in the excretion of tryptamine were accompanied by smaller increases in indolylacetic acid, 5-hydroxyindolylacetic acid and creatinine. The rise in creatinine excretion, and the observation that behavioural worsening was invariably accompanied by motor restlessness, suggested the behavioural change might be due to the release of tryptophan and methionine associated with an increased breakdown of muscle protein: the possible formation of a psychoactive methylated indolylamine was also considered (Brune and Himwich, 1963). An outburst of psychotic activity is commonly associated with a change of mood, and in interpreting these findings it is of interest to compare them with the observations on the excretion of tryptophan metabolites in affective states. Tryptamine and 5-HT are normally oxidized in the body almost completely to indolylacetic and hydroxyindolylacetic acids, and excreted in this form. An increased excretion of tryptamine does not necessarily imply that the formation of tryptamine in the body is increased. It means rather that a slightly higher proportion of the tryptamine has escaped oxidation by the monoamine oxidase. This could occur if the transport of amines to the enzyme is reduced, or if the active centres of the enzyme are occupied competitively by other amines such as phenylethylamine which have a relatively high affinity for the enzyme. In the patients studied by Brune and Himwich both factors appear to operate, since the increased excretion of tryptamine was accompanied by a moderate increase in indolylacetic acid. The evidence is consistent with an increased formation of amines due to increased catabolism of endogenous protein, such as might result from release of ACTH as an acute stress response.

SUMMARY

1. The distribution of 5-HT in the limbic cortex and associated subcortical structures suggests that it may play a part in the mechanisms controlling autonomic activity and affective state.

2. Tryptamine and 5-HT are both biphasic in action. The central actions of tryptamine are predominantly excitatory.

3. Drugs such as reserpine and α-methyldopa which reduce the levels of amines at central receptor sites may cause depression. Drugs such as monoamine oxidase inhibitors, which cause a stimulation of central amine receptors, may have anti-depressant action.

4. The findings of a reduced level of hydroxyindoles in the cerebro-spinal fluid, increased excretion of xanthurenic acid, reduced excretion of tryptamine and reduced liberation of $^{14}CO_2$ from 5-hydroxy[1-^{14}C]tryptophan, suggest a disturbance of tryptophan metabolism in patients who are severely depressed. The further experimental finding that depression can be relieved by measures which raise the level of indolylamines suggests that metabolites of tryptophan may play a part in determining the changes in depression.

5. Other biochemical factors related to mental changes in manic-depressive and schizophrenic patients are discussed.

REFERENCES

Anderson, W. M. and Dawson, J. (1962) The clinical manifestations of depressive illness with abnormal acetylmethlcarbinol metabolism, *Journal of Mental Science*, **108**, 80–7.

Ashcroft, G. W. and Sharman, D. F. (1960) 5-Hydroxyindoles in human cerebrospinal fluids, *Nature* (*London*), **186**, 1050–1.

Benassi, C. A., Benassi, P., Allegri, G. and Ballarin, P. (1961) Tryptophan metabolism in schizophrenic patients, *Journal of Neurochemistry*, **7**, 264–70.

BOGDANSKI, D. F., WEISSBACH, H. and UDENFRIEND, S. (1958) Pharmacological studies with the serotonin precursor, 5-hydroxytryptophan, *Journal of Pharmacology and Experimental Therapeutics*, **122,** 182–94.

BRODIE, B. B., FINGER, K. F., ORLANS, F. B., QUINN, G. P. and SULZER, R. (1960) Evidence that the tranquillizing action of reserpine is associated with change in brain serotonin and not in brain norepinephrine, *Journal of Pharmacology and Experimental Therapeutics*, **129,** 250–6.

BROOKSBANK, B. W. L. and PRYSE-PHILLIPS, W. (1964) Urinary androstenol, 17-oxosteroids and mental illness, *British Medical Journal*, **1,** 1602–6.

BRUNE, G. G. and HIMWICH, H. E. (1963) Biogenic amines and behaviour in schizophrenic patients, *Recent Advances in Biological Psychiatry*, **5,** 144–60.

BÜLBRING, E. (1958) Physiology and pharmacology of intestinal smooth muscle, *Lectures on the Scientific Basis of Medicine*, **7,** 374–97.

CADE, J. F. J. (1964) A significant elevation of plasma magnesium levels in schizophrenia and depressive states, *The Medical Journal of Australia*, **1,** 195–6.

CAZZULLO, C. L., MANGONI, A. and MASCHERPA, G. (1966) Some aspects of tryptophan metabolism in affective psychoses, *British Journal of Psychiatry*, **112,** 157–62.

COLLIER, H. O. J., CORNE, S. J., MARLEY, E. and BRADLEY, P. B. (1961) Tryptamine receptors in central nervous system, *Nature (London)*, **191,** 1069–9.

COPPEN, A. J. (1960) Abnormality of the blood-cerebrospinal fluid barrier of patients suffering from a depressive illness, *Journal of Neurology, Neurosurgery and Psychiatry*, **23,** 156–61.

COPPEN, A., MALLESON, A. and SHAW, D. M. (1965) The effects of lithium carbonate on electrolyte distribution in man, *Lancet*, **1,** 682–5.

COPPEN, A. and SHAW, D. M. (1963) Mineral metabolism in melancholia, *British Medical Journal*, **2,** 1439–44.

COPPEN, A., SHAW, D. M. and FARRELL, J. P. (1963) Potentiation of the antidepressive effect of a monoamine-oxidase inhibitor by tryptophan, *Lancet*, **1,** 79–81.

COPPEN, A., SHAW, D. M. and MALLESON, A. G. (1965a) Changes in 5-hydroxytryptophan metabolism in depression, *British Journal of Psychiatry*, **111,** 105–7.

COPPEN, A. J., SHAW, D. M., MALLESON, A. and COSTAIN, R. (1966) Mineral metabolism in mania *British Medical Journal*, **1,** 71–5.

COPPEN, A., SHAW, D. M., MALLESON, A., ECCLESTON, E. and GUNDY, G. (1965b) Tryptamine metabolism in depression, *British Journal of Psychiatry*, **111,** 993–8.

DAWSON, J. and BONE, A. (1963) The effect of alterations in tissue K^+ concentration on the production of 3-hydroxybutan-2-one by brain slices, *Journal of Neurochemistry*, **10,** 537–40.

DEWHURST, W. G. (1965) The biochemical basis of mood, *Journal of Psychosomatic Research*, **9,** 115–27.

DEWHURST, W. G. and MARLEY, E. (1964) The differential effect of sympathomimetic amines in the central nervous system, H. Steinberg, A. V. S. de Reuck and J. Knight, Editors. *Ciba Foundation Symposium on Animal Behaviour and Drug Action*, London, J. & A. Churchill Ltd.

ENGEL, F. L. (1951) A consideration of the roles of the adrenal cortex and stress in the regulation of protein metabolism, *Recent Progress in Hormone Research*, **6,** 277–313.

FERGUSON, H. C., BARTRAM, A. C. G., FOWLIE, H. C., CATHRO, D. M., BIRCHALL, K. and MITCHELL, F. L. (1964) A preliminary investigation of steroid excretion in depressed patients before and after electro-convulsive therapy, *Acta Endocrinologica*, **47,** 58–68.

GIBBONS, J. L. and MCHUGH, P. R. (1962) Plasma cortisol in depressive illness, *Journal of Psychiatric Reseach*, **1,** 162–71.

GREEN, D. E. and RICHTER, D. (1937) Adrenaline and adrenochrome, *Biochemical Journal*, **31,** 596–616.

GREEN, H. and SAWYER, J. L. (1964) Biochemical-pharmacological studies with 5-hydroxytryptophan, precursor of serotonin, H. E. Himwich, and W. A. Himwich, Editors. *Biochemical Amines*, Amsterdam, Elsevier Publishing Company (pp. 150–67).

HESS, S. M. and DOEPFNER, W. (1961) Behavioural effects and brain amine contents in rats, *Archives internationales de Pharmacodynamics*, **134,** 89–99.

KALLMAN, F. J. (1950) The genetics of psychoses, *American Journal of Human Genetics*, **2,** 385–90.

KLERMAN, G. L. SCHILDKRAUT, J. J., HASENBUSH, L. L., GREENBLATT, M. and FRIEND, D. G. (1963) Clinical experience with dihydroxyphenylalanine (DOPA) in depression, *Journal of Psychiatric Research*, **1,** 289–97.

KLINE, N. and SACKS, W. (1963) Relief of depression within one day using an MAO inhibitor and intravenous 5-HTP, *American Journal of Psychiatry*, **120,** 274–5.

KLINE, N., SACKS, W. and SIMPSON, G. M. (1964) Further studies on one-day treatment of depression with 5-HTP (25–50 mg I/V), *American Journal of Psychiatry*, **121,** 379–81.

KOELLA, W. P. and CSICMAN, J. S. (1965) The area postrema as a possible receptor site for EEG synchronization by 5-HT, *Federation Proceedings*, **24,** 646–7.

LAUER, J. W., INSKIP, W. M., BERNSOHN, J. and ZELLER, E. A. (1958) Observations on schizophrenic patients after iproniazid and tryptophan, *Archives of Neurology and Psychiatry*, **80,** 122–30.

LOVENBERG, W., WEISSBACH, H. and UDENFRIEND, S. (1962) Aromatic L-amino acid decarboxylase, *Journal of Biological Chemistry*, **237,** 89–93.

MATUSSEK, N. and PATSCHKE, U. (1964) Beziehungen des Schlaf- und Wachrhythmus zum Noradrenalin- und Serotoningehalt in Zentralnervensystem von Hamstern, *Medicina Experimentalis*, **11,** 81–7.

OATES, J. A. (1961) Urinary tryptamine, tyramine and serotonin, *Methods in Medical Research*, **9,** 169–74.

OATES, J. A. and SJOERDSMA, A. (1960) Neurological effects of tryptophan in patients receiving a monoamine oxidase inhibitor, *Neurology* (*Minneapolis*), **10,** 1076–8.

OSWALD, I. (1965) *Journal of Psychosomatic Research*, **9,** 111–12

PAASONEN, M. K., MACLEAN, P. D. and GIARMAN, N. J. (1957) 5-Hydroxytryptamine (serotonin, anteramine) content of structures of the limbic system, *Journal of Neurochemistry*, **1,** 326–33.

PARE, C. M. B. (1963) Potentiation of monoamine oxidase inhibitors by tryptophan, *Lancet*, **2,** 527–8.

PARE, C. M. B. and SANDLER, M. (1959) A clinical and biochemical study of a trial of iproniazid in the treatment of depression, *Journal of Neurology, Neurosurgery and Psychiatry*, **22,** 247–51.

POLLIN, W., CARDON, P. U. and KETY, S. S. (1961) Effects of amino acid feedings in schizophrenic patients treated with iproniazid, *Science*, **133,** 104–5.

PRAAG, H. M. VAN and LEIJNSE, B. (1963) Die Bedeutung der Monoaminoxydase-hemmung als antidepressives Princip, *Psychopharmacologia*, **4,** 1–14.

PRYCE, I. G. (1958) Melancholia, glucose tolerance and body weight, *Journal of Mental Science*, **104,** 421–7.

QUAY, W. B. (1964) Circadian and estrous rhythms in pineal and brain serotonin, H. E. Himwich and W. A. Himwich, Editors, *Biogenic Amines*, Amsterdam, Elsevier Publishing Company (pp. 61–3).

RICHTER, D. and LEE, M. (1942a) Serum choline esterase and depression, *Journal of Mental Science*, **88,** 435–9.

RICHTER, D. and LEE, M. (1942b) Serum choline esterase and anxiety, *Journal of Mental Science*, **88,** 428–34.

RODNIGHT, R. (1961) Body fluid indoles in mental illness, *International Review of Neurobiology*, **3,** 251–92.

SHAGASS, C. and SCHWARTZ, M. (1962) Cerebral cortical reactivity in psychotic depressions, *Archives of General Psychiatry*, **6,** 235–42.

SHARMAN, D. F. (1965) Metabolism of tryptamine and related compounds in the central nervous system, *British Medical Bulletin*, **21,** 62–5.

SHAW, D. M. and COPPEN, A. (1966) Potassium and water distribution in depression. *British Journal of Psychiatry*, **112,** 269–76.

SJOERDSMA, A., OATES, J. A., ZALTSMAN, P. and UDENFRIEND, S. (1959) Identification and assay of urinary tryptamine: Application as an index of monoamine oxidase inhibition in man, *Journal of Pharmacology and Experimental Therapeutics*, **126,** 217–22.

SLATER, E. T. O. (1961) Heredity of mental diseases, A. Jones, Editor, *Clinical Aspects of Genetics*, London, Pitman Medical Publishing Company (pp. 23–9).

SMITH, B., and PROCKOP, D. J. (1962) Central-nervous system effects of injection of L-tryptophan by normal subjects, *New England Journal of Medicine*, **267**, 1338–41.

SPOONER, C. E. (1965) Comparison of averaged auditory evoked responses during spontaneous and monoamine induced states of wakefulness and sleep in the chick, *Federation Proceedings*, **24**, 135–6.

TEDESCHI, D. H., TEDESCHI, R. E. and FELLOWS, E. J. (1959) The effects of tryptamine on the central nervous system, *Journal of Pharmacology and Experimental Therapeutics*, **126**, 223–32.

TRENDELENBURG, U. (1956) The action of 5-hydroxytryptamine on the nictitating membrane and on the superior cervical ganglion of the cat, *British Journal of Pharmacology*, **11**, 74–80.

VOGT, M. (1965) Effect of drugs on metabolism of catecholamines in the brain, *British Medical Bulletin*, **21**, 57–61.

WELCH, J. H. (1964) The quantitative distribution of 5-hydroxytryptamine in the nervous system, eyes and other organs of some vertebrates. In *Comparative Neurochemistry*, D. Richter, Editor, Oxford, Pergamon Press (pp. 353–77).

WOODBURY, D. M. (1958) Relation between the adrenal cortex and the central nervous system, *Pharmacological Reviews*, **10**, 275–357.

HALLUCINOGENIC AMINES AND SCHIZOPHRENIA (WITH A BRIEF ADDENDUM ON N-DIMETHYLTRYPTAMINE)

STEPHEN SZARA

Clinical Neuropharmacology Research Center, NIMH,
Saint Elizabeth's Hospital, Washington, D.C.

SEVERAL simple alkyl derivatives of tryptamine, like α-methyltryptamine, N,N-dimethyltryptamine (DMT), N,N-diethyltryptamine (DET), psilocybin, and psilocin, produce abnormal psychological symptoms similar to LSD-25 or mescaline (Szara, 1957; Murphree *et al.*, 1961; Hofmann *et al.*, 1958).

The symptom complex produced has often been called a schizophrenia-like model psychosis because of the more or less pronounced similarity to symptoms present in schizophrenia. It is significant, however, that the clinical diagnosis of schizophrenia is based not on a single symptom or set of symptoms but, rather, on the entire set of longitudinal and momentarily observable symptom complex. The general consensus of opinion today is that if we take all these factors into consideration the drug-induced states and schizophrenia are two distinctly different entities although some overlap of symptoms exists (Bleuler, 1959; Hollister, 1962; Hoch and Hoff, 1964).

Drug-induced models in animals, however, could be of use as research tools if we first establish what component of the human symptom complex is reproducible in animals and then apply the result to that particular component of the symptom complex in humans (Hoch and Hoff, 1964).

At the outset our interest in the dysleptic drugs was nourished by the apparent similarities between schizophrenia and the drug-induced states and by the eventual possibility that the endogenous psychoses might be explained on the basis of an erroneous metabolism producing a simple toxic derivative of tryptamine. We studied the metabolism of these compounds and found that 6-hydroxylation plays a role in the psychodysleptic action (Szara, 1961). The identity of the actually active metabolite is still unsettled but it is significant that if we prevent the 6-hydroxylation by substituting the 6-position of the indole ring with fluorine, the resulting compound, 6-fluoro N,N-diethyltryptamine (6-FDET), is found to be an active placebo, i.e. produces some autonomic changes without the characteristic psychodysleptic effect in man (Kalir and Szara, 1963).

All attempts so far to find DMT or its metabolites in schizophrenics' urine have failed and there is no evidence that this metabolite is *the* "toxic agent" presumably related to schizophrenia. The reports of Himwich and his group, however, finding large amounts of tryptamine in the urine of patients at the time of increased mental disturbances keep interest alive in the theory that the two phenomena might be causally related and we must therefore continue our search for new, thus far unknown, metabolites of tryptamine as potential toxic agents related to schizophrenia (Himwich *et al.*, 1964; Himwich 1958).

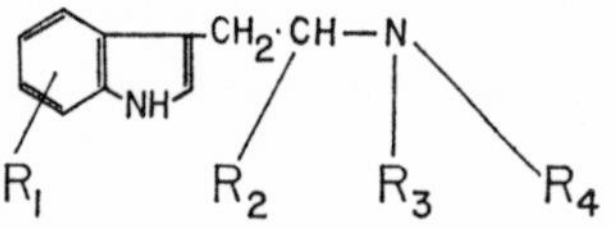

Compound	R_1	R_2	R_3	R_4
DMT	-H	-H	$-CH_3$	$-CH_3$
DET	-H	-H	$-C_2H_5$	$-C_2H_5$
SEROTONIN	5-HO-	-H	-H	-H
BUFOTENIN	5-HO-	-H	$-CH_3$	$-CH_3$
dl-αMT	-H	$-CH_3$	-H	-H
PSYLOCYBIN	$4\text{-}OPO_3H_2$	-H	$-CH_3$	$-CH_3$
4-HDMT (Psilocin)	4-HO-	-H	$-CH_3$	$-CH_3$

(General structure in header: indole ring with R_1, NH, side chain $CH_2 \cdot CH(R_2)-N(R_3)(R_4)$)

FIG. 1. Chemical structures of simple derivatives of tryptamine with reported psychotropic activity.

Until we find the elusive "toxin", we felt it was worth while to keep on studying the mechanism of action of these powerful drugs, using the drugs as tools in elucidating the normal and pathological functions of the central nervous system (CNS), in the hope that eventually they might shed some light on the enigma of schizophrenia. Furthermore, these drugs are potentially valuable as aids in psychotherapy but we will have to learn more about their interaction with the functions of the CNS before we can do more than just grope in the dark.

Following is an outline of our research strategy in which we make use of the dysleptic drugs as tools on several levels of approach within a unifying theoretical framework.

I. THE THEORETICAL MODEL

A theoretical model of brain function has been developed from several "precursors" in order to accommodate both the subjective, phenomenological, and objective behavioral aspects of the CNS functions which might be influenced by drugs.

Kety presented a simple model for information processing brain functions some time ago in which he described how the sensory information is encoded and stored in memory tapes and how a built-in "computer" makes a decision on which behavioral program to use in a particular situation (Kety, 1961). He admitted, however, that he was unable to introduce into his model a physical-chemical mechanism for feeling and consciousness. I would like to propose now a model of brain function which might offer physico-chemical substrate for consciousness using the information processing language as Kety did, retaining the idea of the "behavioral programmers", but omitting the power supply since, as he pointed out, "it takes just as much oxygen to think an irrational thought as it does to think a rational one".

Before presenting the information-flow chart for the central processes in the nervous system we should get acquainted with the notion of the Turing machine (Turing, 1936).

Briefly, a Turing machine is a finite automaton A, together with a potentially infinite tape (which at any moment contains only a finite number of non-blank symbols) divided lengthwise into squares (each square being a blank or bearing one symbol) and a device connected to the finite automaton and capable of functioning as:

1. Tape scanner (reading one square of tape at one moment of time).
2. A printer and eraser mechanism capable of erasing the symbol and/or printing a new symbol on the square actually scanned.
3. Tape mover.

We will regard the finite automaton A as a "black box", meaning that irrespective of its internal structure it has the following functional characteristics:

1. It can accept any of a finite number of inputs.
2. It has a finite number of internal states.
3. It can emit any of a finite number of outputs.

We assume, furthermore, that the input and state at time t determine the output and state at time $t+1$.

Any Turing machine is completely described by a *machine table* which consists of detailed instructions for operating the scanning device.

The notion of a Turing machine is also subject to generalization of various sorts as shown by Davis (1958) and we will take full advantage of this.

It should be mentioned that Turing machines are capable of doing anything that any computing machine (of whatever kind) can do. This follows from Turing's original hypothesis based on Church's thesis, i.e. an effective procedure for calculating the sequences of symbols exists if the function to be computed is recursively enumerable (Arbib, 1964).

Although the idea of the single-tape Turing machine as a generalized model of finite automaton adequately describes the logical functions of digital computers, it is an adequate model for brain functions. This inadequacy is most prominent if we try to apply it to solve the puzzle of privacy, the phenomena of subjective experience, or, in general, the problem of consciousness. Putnam has examined this problem and came to the conclusion that the mental states and "impressions" of human beings do not form a causally closed system to the extent to which the "configurations", i.e. logical states, of a Turing machine do (Putnam, 1960).

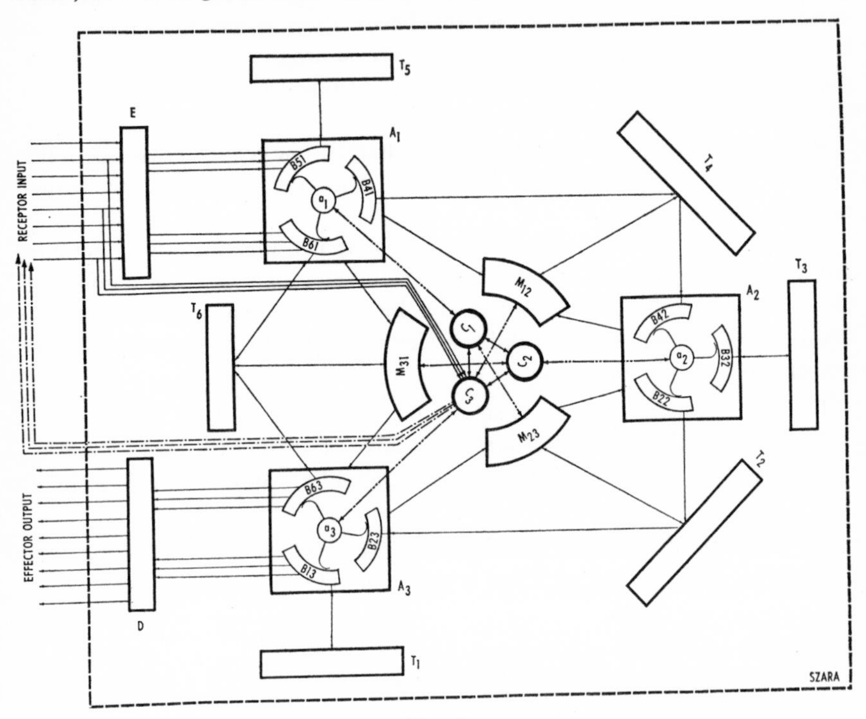

Fig. 2

The logical limit for the finite deterministic automaton are set by the basic incompleteness theorem of Gödel (for formal discussion see Arbib, 1964). If we have two or more tapes in the automaton they have to be read alternately one at a time in order to operate effectively. If both tapes are read simultaneously the correspondence problem is not effectively solvable and as a matter of fact all hope of any constructive decision processes is lost (Rabin and Scott, 1959). In other words, Turing machines with two or more tapes are inherently non-deterministic, i.e. it is impossible to predict their state at any time of $t+1$ even if all the relevant information is available at time t.

Now we are ready for the model which is shown in Fig. 2.

FIG. 2. INFORMATION-FLOW CHART FOR THE CENTRAL PROCESSES IN THE NERVOUS SYSTEM

Symbol	Function	Tentative functional identification
E	Encoder for sensory input	Geniculate bodies Sensory nuclei of cranial nerves in the brain stem
D	Decoder for effector output	Pontobulbar and spinal motor mechanism
A_1	Sensory recognizer system (automaton)	Thalamic system
a_1	Scanning center for A_1 (tape mover)	Non-specific thalamic nuclei
B_{51} B_{41} B_{61}	Banks for the scanning center connecting to adjacent structures (Read-write heads for tapes T_5, T_4, and T_6, resp.)	Specific thalamic nuclei Limbic nuclei of thalamus Sensory nuclei of medulla Certain cerebellar nuclei
A_2	Comparator organizer system	Hippocampal limbic system
a_2	Scanning center for A_2	Septal nuclei
B_{42} B_{32} B_{22}	Banks for the scanning center a_2	Hippocampus and dentate gyrus
A_3	Motor effector system	Pyramidal and extrapyramidal motor system
a_3	Scanning center for A_3	Motor reticular nuclei of brain stem
B_{23} B_{13} B_{63}	Banks for the scanning center a_3	Basal ganglia Certain thalamic nuclei (A.M., A.V.) Nucleus ruber Certain cerebellar nuclei (dentate *n*)
M_{12}	Feedback center regulating the functional relationship between A_1 and A_2; biased by C_3	Mammillary body
M_{23}	Feedback center between A_2 and A_3; biased by C_1	Amygdala
M_{31}	Feedback center between A_1 and A_3; biased by C_2. Also provides shortcut (reflex) pathway between sensory input and motor output	Certain pontine and mesencephalic nuclei. (Sup. and inf. colliculi; dorsal tegmental nuclei; subst. nigra.)
C_1	"Anxiety" center; ergotropic system (Hess; Brodie)	Adrenergic nuclei of hypothalamus
C_2	"Pleasure" center; trophotropic system (Hess; Brodie)	Serotoninergic areas of hypothalamus
C_3	"Arousal" center	Amine modulated areas of midbrain reticular formation
T_5	Storage of primary sensory data	Granulous type cortex (Konio cortex, Economo). Areas 17, 41, 42, 26, 27 (Brodmann)
T_4	Storage of complex sensory data (sensory association)	Polar type cortex (Ec.) Areas 18, 19, 11, 12 (Br.)
T_3	Storage of complex symbols	Parietal type cortex (Ec.) Areas 39, 40, 22, 36, 37, 10 (Br.)
T_2	Storage of goals, goal-directed behavior patterns (motor association)	Frontal type cortex (Ec.) Areas 7, 89, 44, 45, 46, 47, 40, 31, 23, 20, 21, 38 (Br.)
T_1	Storage of subgoals, methods	Agranular pyramidal motor cortex (Ec.) Areas 3–1–2 (Br.)
T_6	Sensory-motor association (coordination)	Cerebellar cortex

Solid arrows: specific pathways.
Broken arrows: non-specific pathways.
Association pathways (interconnecting links between tapes T_1 through T_6) were omitted for the sake of clearness of figure.

We visualize the information flow in the CNS as being processed by three Turing machines (A_1, A_2, and A_3) each having its own "private" tape (T_5, T_3, and T_1) and interconnected in a specific way by common tapes (T_4, T_2, and T_6), feedback units (M_{12}, M_{23}, and M_{31}) and central regulating units (C_1, C_2, and C_3).

Each automaton has read-write heads interconnected with the tapes (B units), the banks of which are activated periodically by a scanning mechanism (a_1, a_2, and a_3).

We assume that each Turing machine is capable of reading one tape at a time (i.e. it functions deterministically) only after certain regulators are set. These regulators would be primarily C_1, C_2, and C_3, which are responsible for the scanning speeds of the individual automaton and are also interconnected (i.e. they are not independent). The functions of these units are enumerated in the legend for Fig. 2 and their potential anatomical identifications on a functional basis are noted—but it should be strongly emphasized that the identifications are highly tentative, open for change, correction, and further specifications on the basis of further experimental data.

It would be impossible to justify the anatomical identifications listed within this given space and I am sure somebody could come up with better guesses than I. My sole purpose was to show that the information processing functions presented in the chart are more or less consistent with present-day anatomical physiological pictures, but the elements of the model are not necessarily anatomical structures. For example, the cortex, with its various types of short and long-axoned cells, specific and association afferent and efferent connections, seemed to be a likely candidate for the function of a tape (Lorente de Nó, 1949). Information processing and storing ability of self-organizing nets with structures similar to that of cortex is being studied widely and discussed by engineers (Rosenblatt, 1962; Greene, 1962, 1964) and neurophysiologists alike (Jung, 1961; Penfield and Perot, 1961). At the other end, the reticular system with its short-axoned network, non-specific connections, and spontaneously firing units seemed to be a logical candidate for scanning, i.e. firing off periodically connecting specific units. Such function has already been suggested by neurophysiologists (Moruzzi and Magoun, 1949; Magoun, 1958; Hernández-Peón, 1961).

Without further elaboration of anatomical, physiological, or biochemical correlates let us follow the main pathway of sensory information as processed by the three automata (Fig. 2):

1. A_1 compares the specially coded (through E encoder) sensory input with primary sensory symbols (stored in T_5) and with sensory motor association symbols (stored in T_6) and sends the information to T_4 for further association with complex symbols on command from the feedback unit M_{12}.

2. A_2 "reads" the information on T_4 and compares it with stored complex memories (T_3) and makes a decision if action has to be taken. Based on the information about the need of the system and on available methods (M_{23}) a command is transmitted to T_2 where the goal directed motor patterns (behavioral programs) are stored.

3. A_3 "reads" the behavioral pattern to be followed (from T_2), selects the appropriate methods from T_1, assesses the data on current situation (from T_6) and on command from M_{31} sends out the proper codes through the decoder (D) to the effector system.

You may be able to recognize in this model several more "precursors" like the information-flow model of MacKay (1956), the idea of a concentric nervous system built around biased homeostats (Pribram, 1960), the organization of receptor and effector processes in human skill (Crossman, 1964), the essentially statistical character of notation employed by the mixed digital–analog functioning nervous system (von Neumann, 1958), and the idea of plastic correlation between perceptual and motor processes (Holst, 1954; Held, 1960).

II. THE EFFECT OF HALLUCINOGENIC DRUGS

Radioactive DMT and some of its basic metabolites penetrate the blood brain barrier in mice and reach high levels in the first 10 min, the neocortex showing larger quantities than others. After this, there is at first a sharp, then a gradual, decline in all areas except the hippocampus which seems to retain this drug in greater quantities than other areas. This distinct difference in distribution at the early and later periods might be related to the behavioral changes observed in the animals.

The normal exploratory behavior of the mice (broken line in Fig. 4) is significantly affected by supressing the hyperactivity in the first 30 min, and after this period in causing a hyperactivity when compared to the behavior of control (non-treated) animals in the same situation.

Adey and his collaborators have found that hippocampal tissue exhibited a greater susceptibility to LSD and psilocybin than subcortical and cortical areas examined (Adey, 1963). These investigators have found also that these drugs produced abnormal seizure-like discharges in the hippocampus of cats which were closely related to the deteriorated performance of a learned discriminative task (Adey *et al.*, 1962). These seizure-like episodes seemed critically dependent on reduction of visual and auditory sensory influences. Similar close relationship between the effect of these drugs on electrical activity of the brain and sensory inputs was noted by Bradley and Elkes in cats although these authors claim the main effect was at the site of afferent sensory collaterals impinging upon the brain stem reticular formation (Bradley and

Elkes, 1957). De Baran *et al.* (1963) working on rabbits have placed the site of action of LSD-25 into the hippocampus again.

In our attempt to find regional differences in the metabolic effects of hallucinogenic tryptamine derivatives which might be relevant to the specific dysleptic effect, we studied the effects of the hallucinogenic DET and the non-hallucinogenic 6-fluoro analog (6-FDET) on the metabolism of C^{14}-labeled precursor of serotonin in small areas of mice brain. The method is reported at the meeting of the Federation of American Societies for Experimental Biology (Szara, 1965).

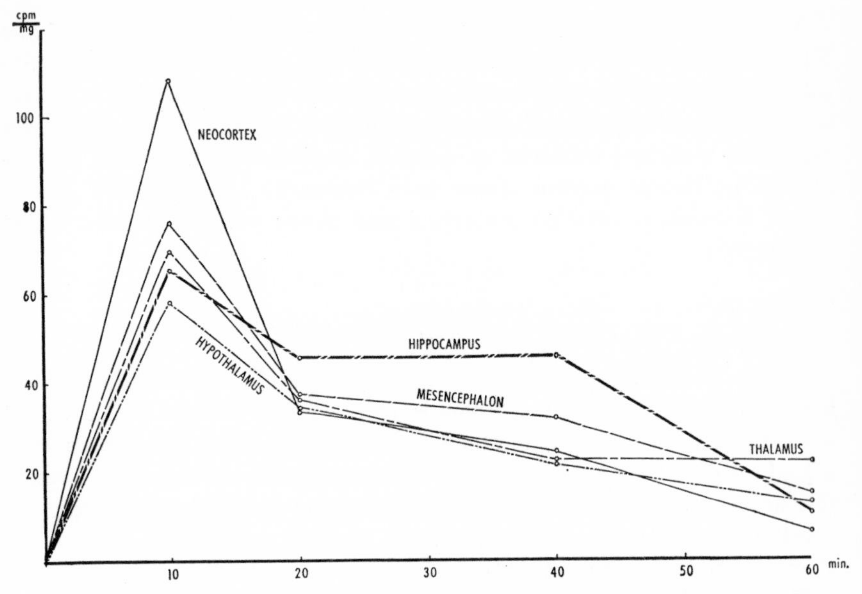

FIG. 3. Levels of combined basic metabolites of DMT-H^3 in various regions of the mouse brain. Injected amount: 250 μg of DMT-H^3 (specific activity 109 mC/mM) intraperitoneally corresponding to 10 mg/kg dose. Found values expressed in counts per min per mg of wet brain tissue. Counting efficiency of technique used: 3·7%.

The highlights of this report are shown on Fig. 5. The results show that the levels of C^{14}-serotonin (5-HT-C^{14}) in the different regions of the brain are not affected equally by the drugs tested. The maximal relative changes were found in the thalamus of the animals after both DET and 6-FDET. But this change, since it occurred after both the hallucinogenic and non-hallucinogenic drugs, cannot be related to the hallucinogenic action of DET. In other areas, however, there were significant differences in the shift of C^{14}-serotonin level due to these two drugs. In the anterior hypothalamus there was a highly significant increase after DET, but the increase after 6-FDET was much smaller and not significant statistically. On the other hand, in the posterior hypothalamus and, to a smaller extent, in the hippocampus, we found a statistically significant increase after 6-FDET only, but not after DET. In other areas of the brain, both drugs changed the serotonin levels to approximately equal degree. The 6-hydroxy metabolite of DET (6-HDET) did not change the C^{14}-serotonin levels significantly when compared to the control levels.

We cannot go into a detailed analysis of the remainder of the data here, but it suffices to say that the uptake of 5-hydroxytryptophane (5-HTP-C^{14}) into the brain was not influenced by either DET or 6-FDET, and we found a

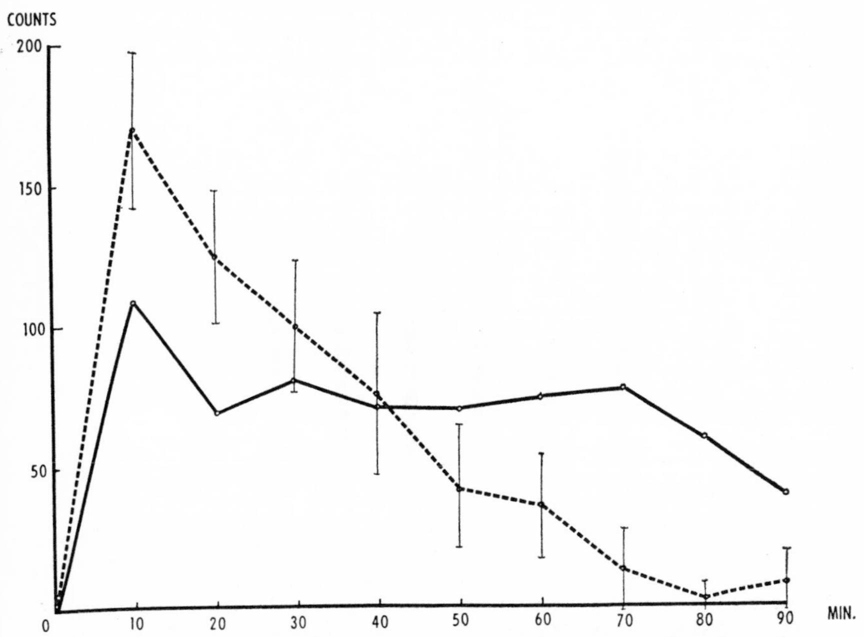

FIG. 4. Effect of DMT (20 mg/kg) on mice in activity cage. Number of crossing of light path in a round activity cage by four animals in a cage. Average of three experiments. Broken line: controls. Solid line: drug treated animals (Szara *et al.*, 1962).

decrease in the concentration of 5-hydroxyindoleacetic acid (5-HIAA-C^{14}), closely corresponding to the increases of 5-HT-C^{14}) concentration. This would point to a decreased function of monoamine oxidase (MAO) resulting from either a direct inhibitory action of the drug on the enzyme or from an indirect mechanism which increases the storage of 5-HT, thus preventing the action of MAO on serotonin.

But in a separate experiment we could see no difference in the activity of MAO prepared separately from the anterior and posterior part of the hypothalamus. Both enzymes were equally sensitive to the competitive inhibition by DET, even when the enzymes were prepared from DET pre-treated animals.

It seems unlikely then that the differential effect in the two parts of the hypothalamus (as seen in Fig. 5) would be a direct metabolic effect of DET. Unless we find a specific metabolite acting selectively in the anterior hypothalamus as an additional MAO inhibitor, or in the posterior hypothalamus as a "releaser" of 5-HT, we have to assume that this metabolic effect is an indirect

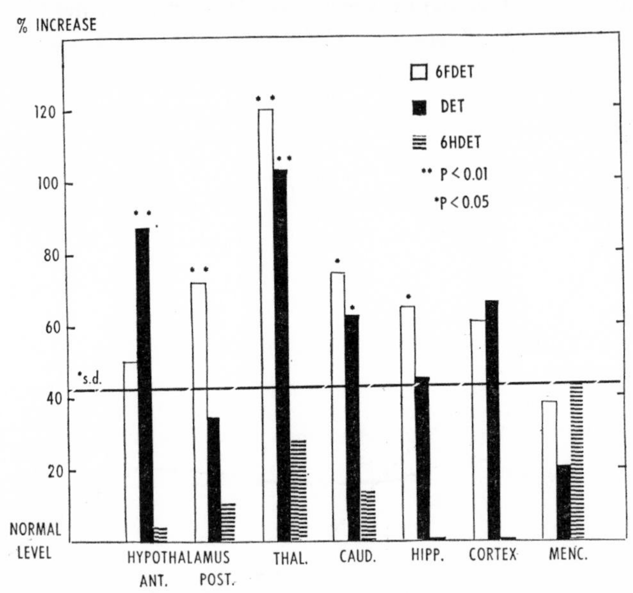

FIG. 5. Increase of 5-HT-C^{14} levels in various regions of mouse brain in the presence of tryptamine derivatives. For abbreviation of drugs see text. Normal levels of 5-HT-C^{14} obtained 30 min after the injection of 5-HTP-C^{14} (spec. act.: 2·64 mC/mM; 25 mg/kg intraperitoneally, equivalent to 8 μc/30 g animal) in the various areas (calculated as μg/g of wet tissue) were: hypothalamus anterior 0·37; posterior 0·44; thalamus 0·27; caudate nucleus 0·38; hippocampus 0·22; cortex 0·20; and mesencephalon 0·42. These are average values of five animals. S.D. = standard deviation of normal values.

physiological reflection of a more direct effect of the drug on hippocampal neurons.

On the basis of these data, we hypothesize that the specific dysleptic symptoms produced by these drugs are the result of a malfunction in the anatomically and functionally well-documented serotoninergic pathway running from hippocampus through the septum into the hypothalamus (Nauta and Kuypers, 1958; Green *et al.*, 1960; Heller *et al.*, 1962).

If we now recall the information-flow chart of the CNS, we can see that this pathway forms an important feedback loop between A_2 and A_1 running from the banks B_{42}, B_{32}, and B_{22} through a_2 into C_2 and C_1. Since we assigned the function of regulating the scanning speeds of A_1 and A_2 for this loop we might conclude that the dysleptic drugs disrupt the mechanism which regulates the scanning speeds of A_1 and A_2.

If we further assume that the proper ratio of scanning speeds determines the channel capacity between A_1 and A_2 (Miller, 1956), then we have a beautiful model to accommodate most of the psychological symptoms observed and experienced as the specific effects of dysleptic, hallucinogenic drugs. These symptoms are too numerous to elaborate on here but it will be attempted on another occasion. It is sufficient to point out here that the basis for this

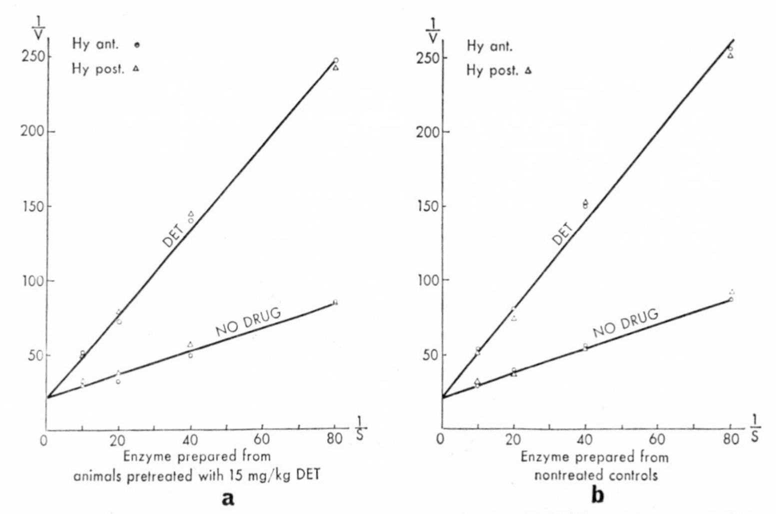

FIG. 6. Lineweaver–Burk plots showing competitive inhibition of monoamine-oxidase (MAO) prepared from the anterior and posterior part of the hypothalamus, pooled from several animals by N,N-diethyltryptamine (DET). Substrate for MAO was C^{14}-labeled tryptamine. Substrate disappearance technique was used for measuring 1/V. (a) Shows the plots obtained from enzyme prepared from animals pretreated with 15 mg/kg i.p. 15 min before decapitation. (b) Shows the results obtained with enzyme prepared from non-treated control animals.

particular symptom complex—I am referring here to the disruption of the regulating mechanism for the communication channel between A_1 and A_2—is stated in a language which can be transplated easily into the language of neurophysiology, behavioral psychology, as well as clinical psychology, so that appropriate working hypotheses can be stated and tested using usual research techniques and methods.

III. SCHIZOPHRENIA

In trying to relate the drug-induced symptom complex to that of schizophrenia we run into the problems mentioned in the introduction. It is significant, however, that the most important fundamental disturbance in schizophrenia, the loosening of association (Bleuler, 1934), can easily be conceived in our model as a result of a disturbance in setting the proper scanning speeds between automaton A_1 and A_2 so that the associative function of tape T_4 becomes indeterminate which is another way of saying that the association is "loose". It should be noted that T_4 is the main connecting link between A_1 and A_2 and its functional connections constitute the most important channel of communication between these two Turing machines.

The cross-section of the complex psychological deficit, recently summarized by Shakow (1963), points to a basic weakening of the control center that serves the integrating and organizing function of the central nervous system and provides for the establishment of what Shakow has called "generalized" or "major sets". He refers to the world of the schizophrenics as an inefficient, unmodulated system, full of "noise", and of indeterminate figure–ground relationships. Thus, it is very tempting to speculate that this control center Shakow is referring to is functionally equivalent to our C_1 and C_2 centers

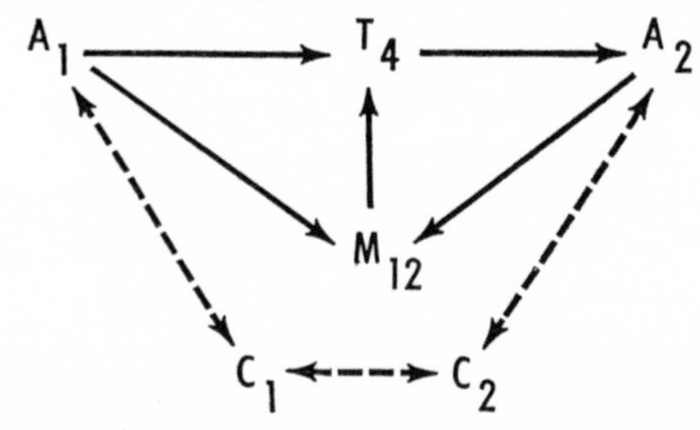

FIG. 7. The basic communication channel hypothesized to be involved in both schizophrenia and the hallucinogenic drug action. For explanation of symbols see legend for Fig. 2.

which in our model form a most important part of the feedback loop regulating the "communication channel" between A_1 and A_2. In this way, "noise" becomes more than just a figure of speech—it assumes specific meaning amenable to information—theoretical analysis and provides new approaches for experimental analysis of this basic schizophrenic disturbance.

We might conclude then that the same basic functional circuitry involved in the action of hallucinogenic drugs might also be involved in schizophrenia.

Each member of this circuitry is also a member of other circuits so that if a malfunction of any of these structures introduces noise it would not only limit the capacity of this channel but also interfere with the functions of the additional circuits to which its belongs. In the action of hallucinogenic drugs we blamed the connection $A_2 \leftrightarrow C_2$ for the basic disturbance. Of course, all the circuits of which A_2 and C_2 are members would also be disturbed at the same time. In schizophrenia the point of disturbance might be another member of this basic circuitry which would result in additional symptoms different from those observed in the case of dysleptic drugs. This might be an explanation for the discrepancies between the two-symptom complex referred to in the introduction. It is also a possibility that the primary point of attack is the same in both cases but that there are additional functional disturbances in schizophrenia due to attacks of a hypothetical toxin on other points in the CNS. Schizophrenia might also be due to inherited or acquired functional inadequacies of the same circuit manifesting themselves in a different manner than in the case of the hallucinogenic drug effects.

A final word of caution seems to be in order. It is very easy to substitute psychological terms for the technical terms of information theory. Thus, inputs and outputs of a channel are easily and naturally translated into the stimuli and responses of the organism. Verbal recoding of this sort is not simply playing with words. It influences the choice of variables and the design of experiments (Frick, 1959). The variables, however, have to represent real measurable quantities and the network of influences among them have to be actually observed or specifically assumed in order to arrive at valid conclusions (Toch and Hastorf, 1955).

In our theoretical model we used parameters, variables and functions (like anxiety, pleasure, arousal, disturbance of function, etc.) not always quantifiable very easily. Such an analog description of function, however, matches most people's ordinary modes of thought better and is, therefore, likely to facilitate interaction between theory and experiment. As theory develops much more precision of statement and formalization of assumptions on the basis of experimental data will be in order. To accomplish this it would seem we have a lifetime program ahead of us.

ACKNOWLEDGMENT

The expert technical assistance of Arliene Aikens is gratefully acknowledged.

SUMMARY

I. An information-flow map for the central processes in the nervous system is proposed. It is characterized by:

A. Three interconnected Turing machines (automata) which are capable of functioning both deterministically and indeterministically.

B. Cortical areas are hypothesized to function as "tapes" while the reticular formation is viewed as a scanning system equivalent to the function of "tape mover" and "tape scanner" of the automata.

C. The scanning speed of the individual Turing machines is assumed to be regulated by interdependent central reticular structures.

II. Literature data and results of our experiments indicate that the specific dysleptic symptoms produced by the hallucinogenic drugs might be the result of a malfunction in the serotoninergic pathway from hippocampus through the septum into the hypothalamus.

It is proposed that this pathway is the most important feedback loop regulating the relative scanning speeds between the sensory recognizer and comparator organizer system; malfunction of this pathway results in narrowing the capacity of the communication channel between the two systems.

III. The psychological deficit in schizophrenia is viewed as the result of a disturbance in the same basic circuitry subserving the communication channel between the sensory recognizer and comparator organizer system. The possible difference in the mechanism of disturbance could account for the discrepancies between the drug-induced symptom complex and schizophrenia.

ADDENDUM

A short review of the author's earlier work with hallucinogenic drugs follows.

Interest in the possible hallucinogenic activity of N,N-dimethyltryptamine (DMT) stems from the report by Fish, Horning and Johnson (*J. Am. Chem. Soc.* **77,** 5892, 1955) who found DMT, together with bufotenin, in snuff powder prepared by Haitian natives from *Piptadenia peregrina* seeds which the natives used in their religious ceremonies to produce mystical states of consciousness.

In 1956 the hallucinogenic action of bufotenin was reported by Fabing (*Am. J. Psychiat.* **113,** 409) but no information whether DMT had similar psychotropic activity was available. We prepared DMT by chemical synthesis and tested its activity on animals and humans. It was found that it produced mescaline- and LSD-like symptoms lasting for a surprisingly short period of time (45 min–1 hr) after intramuscular injection of about 1 mg/kg dose of the drug (Szara, *Experientia,* **12,** 441, 1956).

Because of the very short action of the drug, we turned our attention to the study of the metabolism of DMT in animals and in man. A new pathway —6-hydroxylation of the indole ring—was shown to be a major route for the metabolism of DMT and DET in animals (Szara and Axelrod, *Experientia,* **15,** 216, 1959; Szara and Hearst, *Ann. N.Y. Acad. Sci.* **96**/1, 134–41, 1962), but in human subjects only a small portion (5–15%) of the administered drug could be recovered from urine as 6-hydroxy metabolites (Szara and Rockland, *Proc. IIIrd World Cong., Psychiatry,* **I,** 670, 1961). In spite of this latter finding it was felt that the 6-hydroxylation pathway is pharmacologically important for two reasons. First, a strong correlation was found between the individual ability of a subject to hydroxylate DET and the LSD-like symptoms (perceptual distortion, paranoid ideation, etc.) produced by a 1 mg/kg dose of the drug (Szara, Rockland, Rosenthal and Handlon, submitted for publication). The second reason, mentioned also in the formal paper given in this symposium, is that if 6-hydroxylation is prevented by a substitution of the 6-position of the indole ring by a fluoro-atom, the resulting derivative, 6-fluoro-N,N-diethyltryptamine, is not hallucinogenic any more although it retains some of its non-specific, autonomic effects in man.

It might be of interest to mention here that Axelrod has found an enzyme in mammalian organisms which can methylate serotonin and tryptamine to psychotomimetic bufotenin and DMT (*Science*, **134**, 343, 1961). But, as we already mentioned in the formal paper, all attempts to find bufotenin or DMT in schizophrenics' urine have failed. This is not discouraging, however, since DMT, if it would be formed, would be metabolized so very fast that chances of finding it unchanged in the urine would be slim.

Research is under way to explore the metabolic fate of these tryptamine derivatives in the hope that among the unknown metabolites we may find perhaps some which will prove more useful in understanding the mechanism of the hallucinogenic action and thus possibly help us to understand the etiology of schizophrenia.

REFERENCES

ADEY, W. R. (1963) Computer analysis of hippocampal EEG activity and impedance in approach learning, *Biochemical Pharmacology*, **12,** suppl., 269.

ADEY, W. R., BELL, F. R. and DENNIS, B. J. (1962) Effects of LSD-25, psilocybin and psiolocin on temporal lobe EEG patterns and learned behavior in the cat, *Neurology*, **12,** 591–602.

ARBIB, M. A. (1964) *Brains, Machines and Mathematics*, New York, McGraw-Hill.

BLEULER, E. (1934) *Textbook of Psychiatry*, New York, MacMillan Co.

BLEULER, M. (1959) Discussion: comparison of drug-induced and endogenous psychoses in man. In *Neuro-Psychopharmacology*, P. B. Bradley, P. Deniker and C. Radouco-Thomas, Editors, Amsterdam, Elsevier.

BRADLEY, P. B. and ELKES, J. (1957) The effects of some drugs on the electrical activity of the brain, *Brain*, **80,** 77–117.

BRODIE, B. B. (1957) Serotonin and norepinephrine as antagonistic chemical mediators regulating the central autonomic nervous system. In *Neuropharmacology*, Vol. III H. A. Abramson, Editor, New York, Josiah Macy, Jr. Foundation.

CROSSMANN, E. R. F. W. (1964) Information processes in human skill, *British Medical Bulletin*, **20,** 32–7.

DAVIS, M. (1958) *Computability and Unsolvability*, New York, McGraw-Hill.

DE BARAN, L., GOGOLAK, G., LONGO, V. G. and STUMPF, C. (1963) The action of tryptamine upon the electrical activity of single hippocampal neurons, *Journal of Pharmacology and Experimental Therapeutics*, **139,** 337–44.

FRICK, F. C. (1959) Information theory. In *Psychology; A Study of a Science*, **2,** pp. 611–40, New York, McGraw-Hill.

GREEN, J. D., MAXWELL, D. S., SCHINDLER, W. J. and STUMPF, C. (1960) Rabbit EEG theta rhythm; its anatomical source and its relation to activity in single neurons, *Journal of Neurophysiology*, **23,** 403–20.

GREENE, P. H. (1962) On the representation of information by neural net models. In *Self Organizing Systems*, M. C. Yovits, *et al.*, Editors, Baltimore, Spartan Books, pp. 551–63.

GREENE, P. H. (1964) New problems in adaptive control. In *Computer and Information Sciences*, J. T. Tou and R. H. Wilcox, Editors, Washington, Spartan Books, pp. 410–56.

HELD, R. (1960) Exposure-history as a factor in maintaining stability of perception and coordination, *Journal of Nervous and Mental Diseases*, **132,** 26–32.

HELLER, A., HARVEY, J. A. and MOORE, R. Y. (1962) A demonstration of a fall in brain 5 HT following central nervous system lesions in the rat, *Biochemical Pharmacology*, **11,** 859–66.

HERNÁNDEZ-PEÓN, R. (1961) Reticular mechanisms of sensory control. In *Sensory Communication*, Walter A. Rosenblith, Editor, M.I.T. Press, pp. 497–520.

HESS, W. R. (1954) Diencephalon: Autonomic and extrapyramidal functions. Monograph in *Biology and Medicine*, Vol. III, New York, Grune and Stratton, Inc.

HIMWICH, H. E. (1958) Biochemical and neurophysiological action of psychoactive drugs, *Science*, **127,** 59–72.

HIMWICH, H. E., BERLET, H. H. and SPAIDE, J. K. (1964) Paper presented at the IV International Meeting of CINP in Birmingham, England, 31 Aug.–3 Sept.

HOCH, PAUL and HOFF, H. (1964) General discussion and summing up at the end of the IV International Meeting of CINP in Birmingham, England, 3 Sept.

HOFMANN, A., HEIM, R., BRACK, A. and KOBEL, H. (1958) Psilocybin ein psychotroper Wirkstoff aus dem mexikanischen Rauschpilz Psilocybe mexicana Heim, *Experientia*, **14,** 107–9.

HOLLISTER, L. E. (1962) Drug-induced psychoses and schizophrenic reactions: A critical comparison, *Annals of the New York Academy of Sciences*, **96,** 80–8.

HOLST, E. V. (1954) Relations between the central nervous system and the peripheral organs, *British Journal of Animal Behavior*, **2,** 89–94.

JUNG, R. (1961) Neuronal integration in the visual cortex and its significance for visual information. In *Sensory Communication*, Walter A. Rosenblith, Editor, M.I.T. Press, pp. 627–74.

KALIR, A. and SZARA, S. (1963) Synthesis and pharmacological activity of fluorinated tryptamine derivatives, *Journal of Medicinal Chemistry*, **6,** 716–19.

KETY, S. S. (1961) Chemical boundaries of psychopharmacology. In *Control of the Mind*, S. M. Farber and R. H. L. Wilson, Editors, New York, McGraw-Hill, pp. 79–91.

LORENTE DE NÓ, R. (1949) The structure of the cerebral cortex. In *Physiology of the Nervous System*, John F. Fulton, Editor, Oxford Med. Publications, New York, 3rd ed.

MACKAY, D. M. (1956) Towards an information-flow model of human behavior, *British Journal of Psychology*, **47,** 30–44.

MAGOUN, H. W. (1958) *The Waking Brain*, Springfield, Illinois, Charles C. Thomas.

MILLER, G. (1956) The magical number seven plus or minus two: Some limits on our capacity for processing information, *Psychological Reviews*, **63,** 81–97.

MORUZZI, G. and MAGOUN, H. W. (1949) Brain stem reticular formation and activation of the EEG, *Electroencephalography and Clinical Neurophysiology*, **1,** 455–73.

MURPHREE, H. B., DIPPY, R. H., JENNEY, E. H. and PFEIFFER, C. C. (1961) Effects in normal man of α-methyltryptamine and α-ethyltryptamine, *Clinical Pharmacology and Therapeutics*, **2,** 722–6.

NAUTA, J. H. and KUYPERS, A. J. M. (1958) Some ascending pathways in the brainstem reticular formation. In *Reticular Formation of the Brain*, H. H. Jasper, *et al.*, Editors, Boston, Little Brown & Co., pp. 3–30.

PENFIELD, W. and PEROT, P. (1961) Activation of the brain's record of experience—the interpretive cortex, *Proceedings of Third World Congress of Psychiatry*, Vol. 1, pp. 128–33.

PRIBRAM, K. H. (1960) A review of theory in physiological psychology, *Annual Review of Psychology*, Vol. II, pp. 1–40.

PUTNAM, H. (1960) Minds and Machines. In *Dimensions of Mind*, Sidney Hook, Editor, New York, New York University Press, pp. 148–79.

RABIN, M. O. and SCOTT, D. (1959) Finite automata and their decision problems, *IBM Journal of Research and Development*, Vol. 3, No. 2, pp. 114–25.

ROSENBLATT, F. (1962) *Principles of Neurodynamics; Perceptions and the Theory of Brain Mechanisms*, Washington, Spartan Books.

SHAKOW, D. (1963) Psychological deficit in schizophrenia, *Behavioral Science*, **8,** 275–305.

SZARA, S. (1957) The comparison of the psychotic effect of tryptamine derivatives with the effects of mescaline and LSD_{25} in self experiments. In *Psychotropic Drugs*, S. Garattini and V. Ghetti, Editors, Amsterdam, Elsevier, pp. 460–7.

SZARA, S. (1961) Hallucinogenic effects and metabolism of tryptamine derivatives in man, *Federation Proceedings*, **20,** 885–8.

SZARA, S., HEARST, E. and PUTNEY, F. (1962) Metabolism and behavioral action of psychotropic tryptamine homologues, *International Journal of Neuropharmacology*, **1,** 111–17.

SZARA, S. (1965) Serotonin metabolism in the brain: Regional changes by a short-acting hallucinogen, *Federation Proceedings*, **24/2,** 194.

TOCH, H. H. and HASTORF, A. H. (1955) Homeostatic psychology, *Psychiatry*, **18,** 81–91.

TURING, A. M. (1936) On computable numbers, with an application to the Entscheidungs problem, *Proceedings of the London Mathematical Society*, **42,** 230–65.

VON NEUMANN, J. (1958) *The Computer and the Brain*, New Haven, Yale University Press.

FACTORS INFLUENCING S-ADENOSYLMETHIONINE LEVELS IN MAMMALIAN TISSUES

ROSS J. BALDESSARINI

Laboratory of Clinical Science,
National Institute of Mental Health, Public Health Service,
U.S. Department of Health, Education and Welfare, Bethesda, Maryland

THIRTEEN years ago there appeared (Osmond and Smythies, 1952) an idea of Harley-Mason's that abnormal transmethylation of a catecholamine might produce a compound like mescaline of importance in schizophrenia.

Later, schizophrenic patients given amino acids (most notably, methionine) and a monoamine oxidase inhibitor suffered a striking exacerbation of psychosis, not produced by either agent alone (Pollin *et al.*, 1961). Rather similar results were obtained in a repeat study of the phenomenon done in 1963 (Park *et al.*, 1965), and other investigators have generally supported this finding (Brune and Himwich, 1962; Alexander *et al.*, 1963).

A closely related structural analog of mescaline, 3,4-dimethoxyphenylethylamine (Fig. 1), has been found more often in the urine of schizophrenic patients than in normal controls (Friedhoff and Van Winkle, 1962). Subsequently, this finding has been variously confirmed and denied (Takesada *et al.*, 1963; Kuehl *et al.*, 1964; Perry *et al.*, 1964; Sen and McGeer, 1964), with reported absence of the compound in urine of patients given plant-free diets (Perry *et al.*, 1964; Gjessing, 1964). A summary of the available data will be found in another report (Park *et al.*, 1965).

It is a striking fact that many compounds either known to be hallucinogens or which, for other reasons, have been implicated in schizophrenia, are structurally related methylated amines (Fig. 2).

Transmethylation is the major known catabolic alternative to oxidation of amines by monoaminoxidase (MAO), especially when MAO is inhibited (Axelrod, 1959, 1962a, 1962b; Kopin and Gordon, 1963). S-adenosylmethionine (SAMe) is the active methyl donor involved in transmethylation of amines (Axelrod, 1959). Methionine, the precursor of this methyl donor, reacts with adenosine triphosphate (ATP) and a liver activating enzyme to form SAMe (Cantoni, 1953).

The above findings can be unified into a single "transmethylation hypothesis" (Fig. 3). The inhibition of MAO would be expected to promote transmethylation, and methionine might help by stimulating the production of active methyl donor (SAMe). Thus, an abnormal methylated amine might

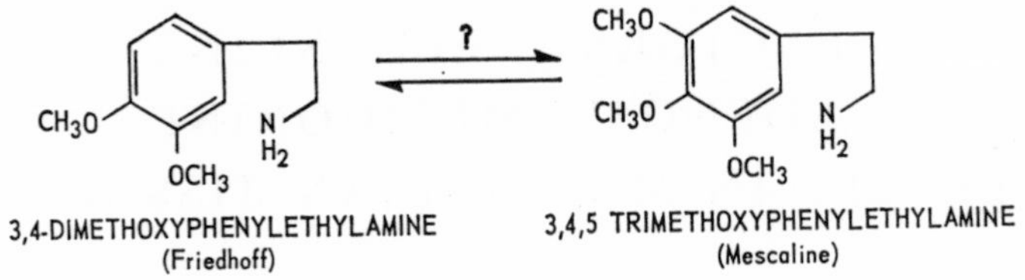

3,4-DIMETHOXYPHENYLETHYLAMINE (Friedhoff) 3,4,5 TRIMETHOXYPHENYLETHYLAMINE (Mescaline)

FIG. 1. Hypothetical relationship between mescaline and Friedhoff's compound, 3,4-dimethoxyphenylethylamine.

MESCALINE TRIMETHOXYAMPHETAMINE ADRENOCHROME (?)

BUFOTENINE (?) DIMETHYLTRYPTAMINE PSILOCYBIN

HARMINE

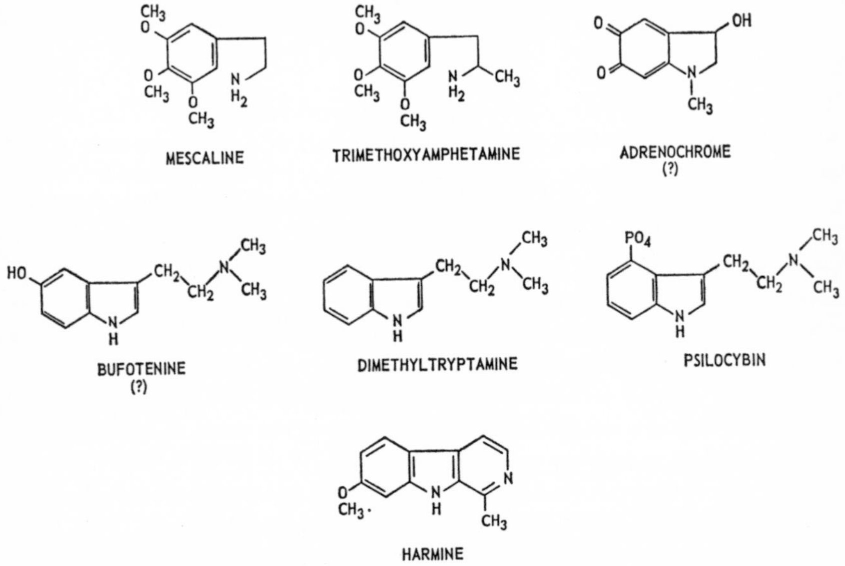

FIG. 2. Methylated amines known or suspected to be hallucinogenic (adrenochrome's significance is still controversial).

occur and influence some aspects of the complex diagnostic cluster, schizophrenia. In addition, MAO inhibition might decrease the destruction of the hypothetical psychotogenic methylated amine.

In order to investigate this hypothesis, the process of biological transmethylation is under study. Tissue levels of SAMe can be assayed using a double label, isotope dilution method (Baldessarini, 1963; Baldessarini and Kopin, 1963) of reacting N-acetyl serotonin-H^3 (NAS) with SAMe-C^{14} in the presence of hydroxyindole-O-methyl transferase (HIOMT) to make melatonin-H^3-C^{14} (Axelrod, 1960) as the only labeled product extracted and counted to determine the radioactivity ratio, H^3:C^{14}. In general, tissue extract with unlabeled endogenous SAMe reduces the specific activity (radioactivity per mole) of the SAMe-C^{14} and thus produces melatonin with an increased H^3:C^{14} ratio. The change in this ratio has been shown mathematically and experimentally to bear a linear relationship to the amount of tissue SAMe added to the incubation mixture, and thus to provide a sensitive, specific, quantitative assay method (Fig. 4). The SAMe assay has been applied to a variety of experimental conditions. Publication of the

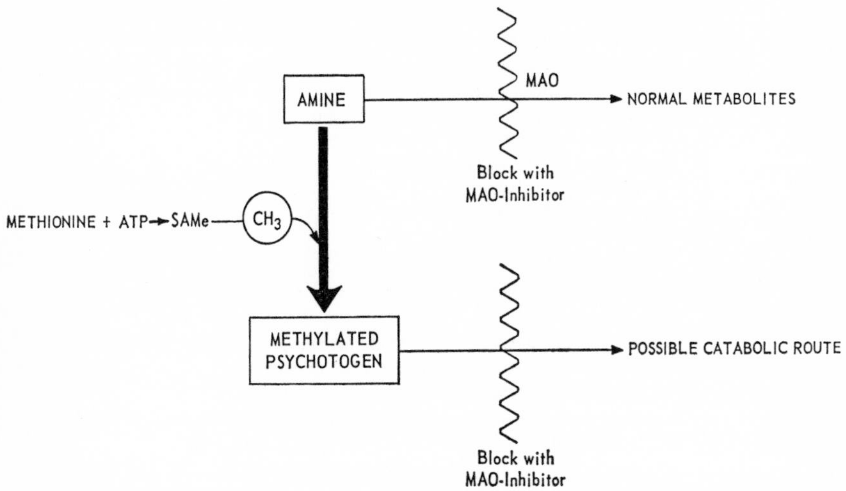

FIG. 3. An attempt to summarize available data into a transmethylation hypothesis related to schizophrenia.

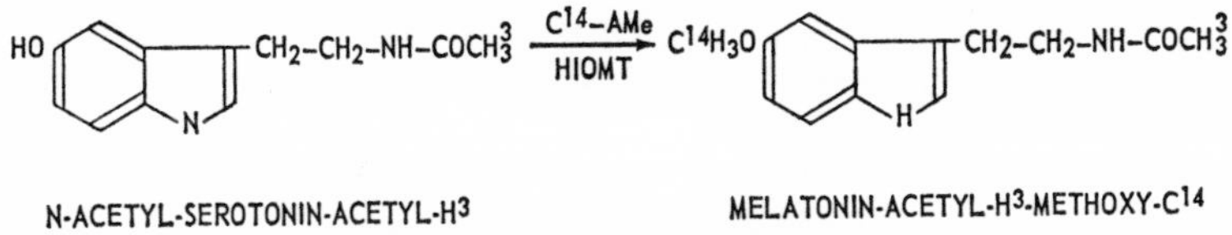

$$HO\text{-indole-}CH_2\text{-}CH_2\text{-}NH\text{-}COCH_3^3 \xrightarrow[\text{HIOMT}]{C^{14}\text{-AMe}} C^{14}H_3O\text{-indole-}CH_2\text{-}CH_2\text{-}NH\text{-}COCH_3^3$$

N-ACETYL-SEROTONIN-ACETYL-H^3 MELATONIN-ACETYL-H^3-METHOXY-C^{14}

FIG. 4. Reaction used in the assay of S-adenosylmethionine (SAMe). (HIOMT = hydroxyindole-O-methyl transferase.)

experimental details of the results is in progress and the findings will only be summarized here.

Normal values of methyl donor levels in rat tissues (about 10–50 μg/g) have been reported (Baldessarini and Kopin, 1963), along with demonstrated elevations of tissue SAMe levels after methionine administration, a finding consistent with the transmethylation hypothesis (Fig. 3). Centrifuged human white blood cells (Baldessarini and Carbone, 1965) have measurable levels of SAMe (about 2 μg/g), suggesting that blood may be a convenient biopsy material. Several experimental conditions have been found not to have significant effects on rat liver and brain levels of SAMe (Table 1).

Preliminary studies of regional differences of SAMe levels in the brains of rat, rabbit, and cat suggest that there are no striking differences among cerebrum, basal ganglia, brain stem, and cerebellum.

Maturation appears to be important, and a gradual fall in SAMe levels in rat brain and liver with maturation has been demonstrated (Table 2).

TABLE 1. SUMMARY OF EXPERIMENTAL CONDITIONS NOT SIGNIFICANTLY AFFECTING RAT LIVER AND BRAIN LEVELS OF SAMe

1. Normal saline injections.
2. Osborne–Mendel vs. Sprague–Dawley strains of the same sex.
3. Male vs. female rats of the same strain.
4. Overnight exposure to 0°C cold room.
5. Four days of thyroxin injections.
6. Nicotinamide infusions.
7. Amphetamine injections.
8. Pentobarbital injections.
9. Reserpine, c̄ or s̄ pheniprazine.

TABLE 2. SUMMARY OF EFFECTS ON RAT TISSUE S-ADENOSYL METHIONINE LEVELS
(+) = elevated (−) = lowered

Variable	Alteration in SAMe
1. MATURATION	(−)
2. METHIONINE	(markedly +)
3. MAO INHIBITION	(−)
4. METHIONINE + MAOI	(less +)
5. METHYL ACCEPTORS	(−)
6. THORAZINE	(−)
7. IMIPRAMINE	(−) (brain)
8. ECK FISTULA	(−) (liver)

Data obtained in a study of Sprague-Dawley female rat brains is presented (Fig. 5).

Nicotinamide, although it can be N-methylated in the rat (Cantoni, 1951), had no effect on SAMe levels (Table 1), but other compounds likely to accept methyl groups (pyrogallol, tropolone, purpurogallin) lowered tissue methyl donor. A representative study of pyrogallol's (1,2,3-polyphenol) effects is included (Fig. 6). Pyrogallol is a known methyl acceptor (Archer *et al.*, 1960). Pyrogallol and tropolone are inhibitors of methyl transferases (Carlsson, 1964) and might function partly by accepting methyl groups and lowering methyl donor levels.

On the assumption that MAO inhibition would favor methyl transfer systems, a series of MAO inhibitors were tested for their effects on SAMe. The results of this survey have been compiled (Fig. 7; Table 2). Pargyline, a potent non-hydrazine, clearly produced a decrease in liver and brain SAMe. A study of MAO inhibition with the MAO assay method of Wurtman and Axelrod (1963) revealed that pargyline depressed MAO activity to less than 1% of control in liver and brain, while pheniprazine, which did not significantly depress SAMe levels, was six to seven times less effective in doses used to survey the effects on SAMe. Methionine loads tended to protect tissues against SAMe depletion after MAO inhibition with pargyline (Fig. 8;

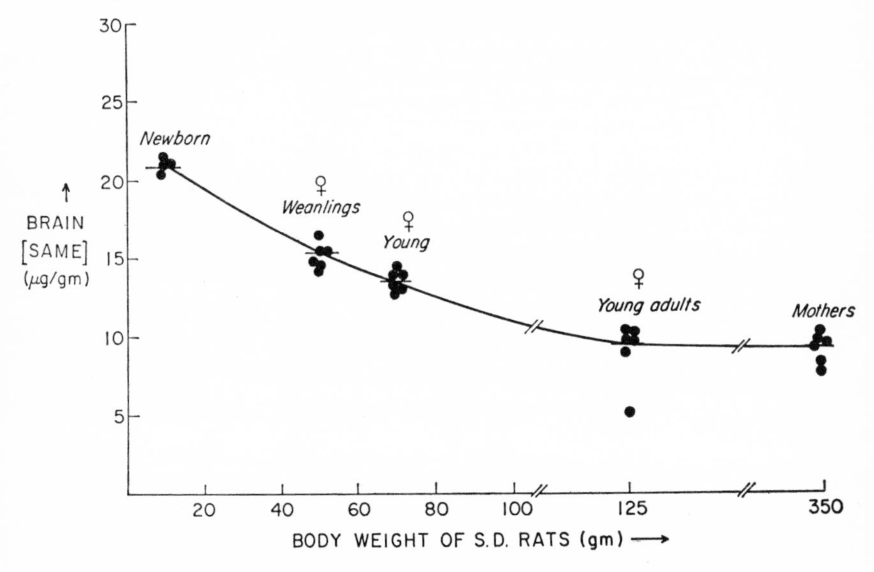

FIG. 5. Gradual decline in SAMe levels in Sprague-Dawley (S.D.) rat brain with age.

Table 2). These results are consistent with the proposal that MAO inhibition, coupled with methionine loading, favors transmethylation.

Other drugs known to produce striking effects on mood have been investigated. Chlorpromazine lowered rat liver and brain SAMe levels, but appears to be more effective in immature animals. It has been suggested that chlorpromazine may decrease ATP utilization (Grenell, 1955), and so it might lower SAMe by decreasing its synthesis by the methionine activating enzyme system (Cantoni, 1953).

Imipramine produced inconsistent results in rat liver, but consistently lowered brain SAMe levels (Table 2). It might act by decreasing catecholamine (Axelrod, 1964) and other amine uptake, exposing them to methyl transferases more than to intracellular oxidases, and thus increasing utilization of SAMe.

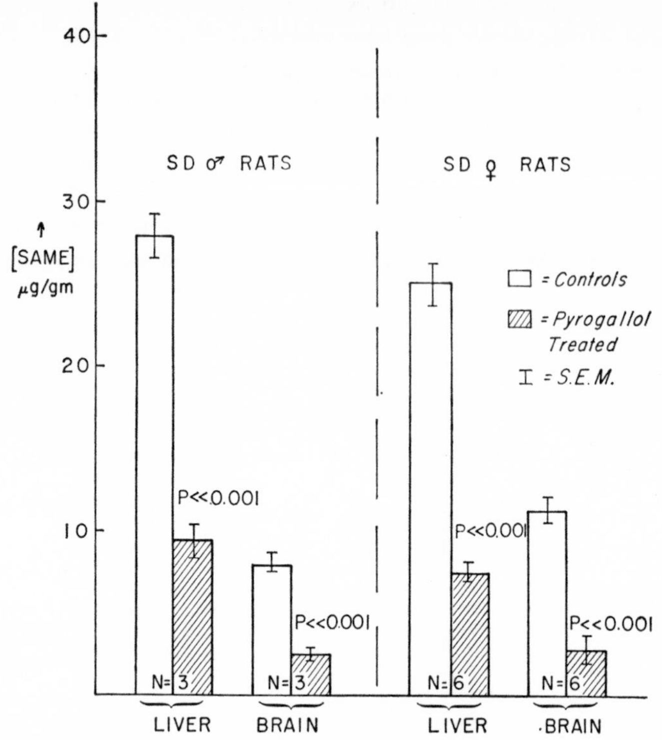

FIG. 6. Decrease in tissue SAMe by a methyl acceptor, and methyl transferase inhibitor, pyrogallol.

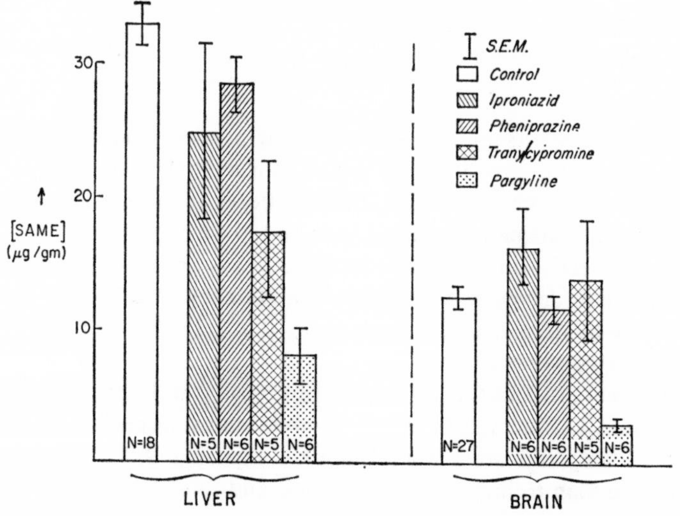

FIG. 7. Effects of a series of MAO inhibitors on rat tissue methyl donor.

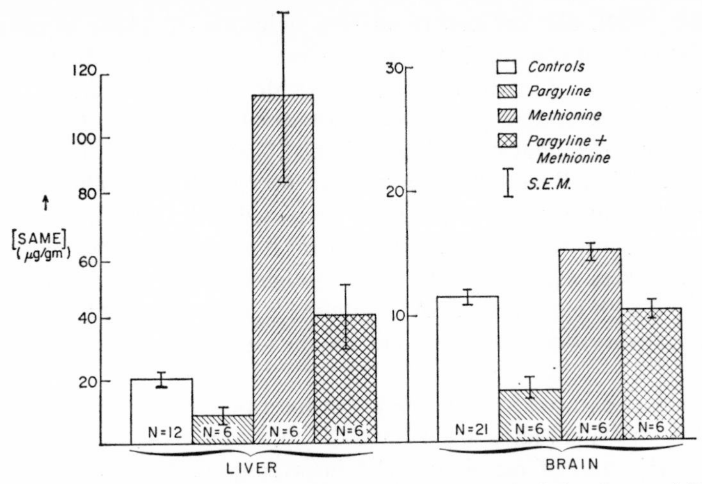

FIG. 8. Protective effect of methionine against SAMe depletion by an MAO inhibitor.

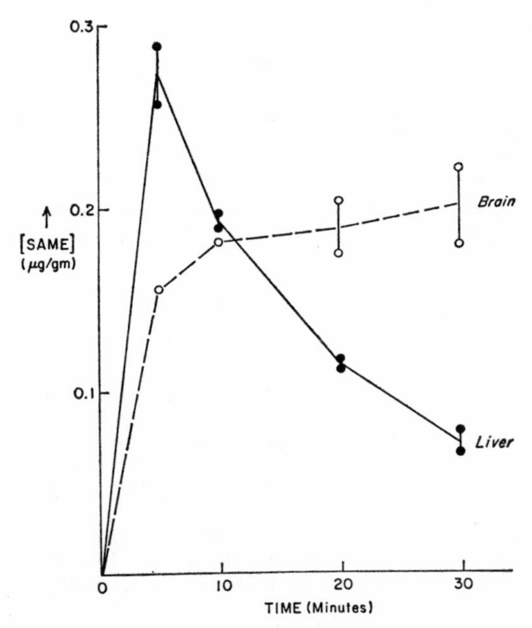

FIG. 9. Formation of SAMe-C^{14} in rat tissues after I.V. administration of methionine-C^{14}.

Reserpine, known to release and to inhibit uptake of biogenic amines (Axelrod, 1964), did not lead to striking reduction of SAMe in rat tissue, produced only an equivocal synergistic effect on SAMe reduction by pheniprazine, and did not inhibit elevation of SAMe by methionine.

Rats with Eck fistulae (end-to-side portacaval shunts) had striking reduction of liver SAMe, but normal brain levels (Baldessarini and Fischer, 1966) (Table 2). This fall may be due more to decreased availability of dietary methionine from portal blood than to decreased activating enzyme activity. That the former is the more important factor is suggested by the findings that post-shunt livers were able to respond to high oral and parenteral doses of methionine with elevation of SAMe almost as well as control animals, and further that short-term fasting alone may in some circumstances lower liver SAMe.

Preliminary data are available (Fig. 9) concerning the turnover of SAMe as studied by assaying radioactive SAMe-C^{14} formed in tissues at time intervals after the injection of methionine-C^{14} intravenously. This study suggests a rapid formation of SAMe from methionine in rat liver and brain, with a rapid turnover of SAMe in liver. The kinetics of SAMe turnover are currently being investigated.

SUMMARY

S-adenosylmethionine, an important metabolic intermediate (the major methyl donor in mammalian transmethylation reactions), has been assayed. Its alterations under a variety of physiologic and pharmacologic conditions have been presented, and the kinetics of its metabolism are under study. Its significance in a transmethylation hypothesis for schizophrenia is indicated.

REFERENCES

ALEXANDER, F., CURTIS, G. C., SPRINCE, H. and CROSLEY, A. P. (1963) L-methionine and l-tryptophan feedings in non-psychotic and schizophrenic patients with and without tranylcypromine, *Journal of Nervous and Mental Disease*, **137**, 135–42.

ARCHER, S., ARNOLD, A., KULLING, R. K. and WYLIE, D. W. (1960) Methylation of polyphenols, *Archives of Biochemistry and Biophysics*, **87**, 153.

AXELROD, J. (1959) Metabolism of epinephrine and other sympathomimetic amines, *Physiological Reviews*, **39**, 751–76.

AXELROD, J. (1962a) The enzymatic N-methylation of serotonin and other amines, *Journal of Pharmacology and Experimental Therapeutics*, **138**, 28–33.

AXELROD, J. (1962b) Factors affecting the metabolism of epinephrine and other amines, *Ultrastructural and Metabolism of the Nervous System*, Vol. XL, Research Publications, ARNMD, Baltimore, Williams and Wilkins Co. (pp. 280–6).

AXELROD, J. (1964) The uptake and release of catecholamines and the effects of drugs, *Progress in Brain Research*, H. E. and W. A. Himwich, Eds., Amsterdam, Elsevier Publishing Co. (pp. 81–9).

AXELROD, J. and WEISSBACH, H. (1960) Enzymatic O-methylation of N-acetylserotonin to melatonin, *Science*, **131**, 1312.

BALDESSARINI, R. J. (1963) Assay of S-adenosylmethionine, *Federation Proceedings*, **22,** 635.

BALDESSARINI, R. J. and KOPIN, I. J. (1963) Assay of tissue levels of S-adenosylmethionine, *Analytical Biochemistry*, **6,** 289–92.

BALDESSARINI, R. J. and CARBONE, P. (1965) *Science*, **149,** 644–5.

BALDESSARINI, R. J. and FISCHER, J. E. (1966) in preparation.

BRUNE, G. G. and HIMWICH, H. E. (1962) Effects of methionine loading on the behavior of schizophrenic patients, *Journal of Nervous and Mental Disease*, **134,** 447–50.

CANTONI, G. L. (1951) Methylation of nicotinamide with a soluble enzyme system from rat liver, *Journal of Biological Chemistry*, **189,** 203–16.

CANTONI, G. L. (1953) S-adenosylmethionine: A new intermediate formed enzymatically from L-methionine and adenosine-triphosphate, *Journal of Biological Chemistry*, **204,** 403–16.

CARLSSON, A. (1964) Functional significance of drug-induced changes in brain monoamine levels, *Progress in Brain Research*, H. E. and W. A. Himwich, Eds., Amsterdam, Elsevier Publishing Co. (pp. 9–27).

FRIEDHOFF, A. J. and VAN WINKLE, E. (1962) The characteristics of an amine formed in the urine of schizophrenic patients, *Journal of Nervous and Mental Disease*, **135,** 550–5.

GJESSING, L. R. (1964) personal communication.

GRENELL, R. G. (1955) Effect of chlorpromazine on brain metabolism, *AMA Archives of Neurology and Psychiatry*, **73,** 347–51.

KOPIN, I. J. and GORDON, E. K. (1963) Metabolism of administered and drug-released norepinephrine-7-H^3 in the rat, *Journal of Pharmacology and Experimental Therapeutics*, **140,** 207–16.

KUEHL, F. A., Jr., HICKENS, M., ORMOND, R. E., MEISINGER, M. A. P., GALE, P., CIRILLO, V. T. and BRINK, N. G. (1964) *p*-O-methylation of dopamine in schizophrenic patients, *Nature*, **203,** 154–5.

OSMOND, H. and SMYTHIES, J. (1952) Schizophrenia: A new approach, *Journal of Mental Science*, **98,** 309–15.

PARK, L., BALDESSARINI, R. J. and KETY, S. S. (1965) Effects of methionine ingestion in chronic schizophrenic patients treated with monoamine oxidase inhibitors, *Archives of General Psychiatry*, **12,** 346–51.

PERRY, T. L., HANSEN, S. and MACINTYRE, L. (1964) Failure to detect 3,4-dimethoxyphenylethylamine in the urine of schizophrenics, *Nature*, **202,** 519–20.

POLLIN, W., CARDON, P. V. and KETY, S. S. (1961) Effects of amino acid feedings in schizophrenic patients treated with iproniazid, *Science*, **133,** 104–5.

SEN, N. P. and MCGEER, P. L. (1964) 3-4-Dimethoxyphenylethylamine in human urine, *Biochemical Biophysics Research Communications*, **14,** No. 3.

TAKESADA, M., KAKIMOTO, Y., SANO, I. and KANEKO, Z. (1963) 3,4-Dimethoxyphenylethylamine and other amines in the urine of schizophrenic patients, *Nature*, **195,** 203–4.

WURTMAN, R. J. and AXELROD, J. (1963) A sensitive and specific assay for the estimation of monoamine oxidase, *Biochemical Pharmacology*, **12,** 1439.

GENERAL DISCUSSION[1]

UNFORTUNATELY, the tape recorder failed us during the discussion of the papers of H. E. Himwich, B. Holmstedt, D. Richter and S. Szara. However, the discussions were to some extent repaired by the kind cooperation of individuals whose remarks have been added subsequently.

DISCUSSION AFTER DR. HIMWICH'S PAPER

RICHTER: In your presentation you seem to be taking the attitude that norepinephrine and serotonin may act as neurotransmitters in the brain. Can you clarify your position in this matter?

HIMWICH: On this question I have been influenced by the work of the Swedish school led by Hillarp of Stockholm, Carlsson of Goteborg and Falck of Lund. In April 1964 I spent 2 weeks in the laboratory of Bengt Falck in order to gain familiarity with the powerful new method of fluorescence microscopy. By ultraviolet light I saw the bright yellow fluorescent particles of norepinephrine in the axons of the autonomic nervous system situated in the heart, iris, submaxillary gland and vas deferens, organs innervated by the terminals of the autonomic nervous system. Similarly in the brain, for example, in the hypothalamus, the yellow particles are seen in fibers which seem to terminate in synaptic arrangements. Green fluorescent particles of serotonin are also observed in the brain. Using such methods we may obtain additional evidence to explain the contrasting actions of imipramine and chlorpromazine on the nictitating membrane of the cat. Direct stimulation at the cervical sympathetic or the injection of serotonin, norepinephrine or epinephrine cause contractions of the membrane. The degree of contraction is increased by imipramine but decreased by chlorpromazine. It was concluded that imipramine decreases the permeability of the neuronal membrane. Thus the amines emitted from the cell did not return and instead accumulated in extraneuronal sites. Chlorpromazine also has such an action. Again both imipramine and chlorpromazine probably block alpha-adrenergic-receptors. The experiments on the nictitating membrane reveal that *in vivo* imipramine is prepotent in preventing return of the monoamine, thus enhancing effects on receptor sites, while chlorpromazine is more effective in blocking the receptor and therefore in decreasing the contractility of the membrane.

But we must remember that reserpine is a tranquilizer similar to the phenothiazines while the iminodibenzyls share antidepressant activities with MAO inhibitors. Reserpine depletes the monoamines especially in the granules by preventing the binding of the amines in these subcellular structures, thus exposing the monoamines to the activity of the MAO enzyme, decreasing their cellular concentrations and leaving fewer amines available for the process of transmission at receptor sites. MAO inhibitors in contrast increase monoamines in the cells, making more available at those sites. Using these observations on psychotropic drugs as a basis, Dr. Arvid Carlsson has suggested a paradigm for an autonomic synapse presented in Fig. 1. (For further documentation and discussion, see Himwich, H. E., *Folia Neurologica Psychiatric Japonica*, Vol. **19**, 1965, from which Fig. 1 and the accompanying legend are taken.)

STRAUGHAN: Dr. Himwich, those results of yours are very interesting. I should like to take issue with you, however, on a point you made in your discussion. You are probably right that those neurones which show monoamines by fluorescent microscopy have these substances as transmitters. However, I should like just to add the cautionary note that the necessary criteria for a postulated transmitter substance are not fully satisfied merely by

[1] The discussion refers to the papers of Drs. Himwich, Holmstedt, Richter, Szara and Baldessarini.

finding it histochemically in the nerve cell bodies or terminals. In intact brain an important point is to show that the substance is release in a chemically identifiable form by synaptic activation. This criterion still needs to be fulfilled for 5-HT and NA. Though I do agree with Anden and his colleagues' demonstration of 5-HT and NA release from the spinal cord agrees well with histochemical observations of 5-HT and NA in bulbospinal pathways.

The other important criterion which needs to be fulfilled is that the postulated transmitter substance should reproduce exactly the effects of activation of appropriate synaptic pathways. This, of course, has been the big stumbling-block in accepting glutamate and GABA

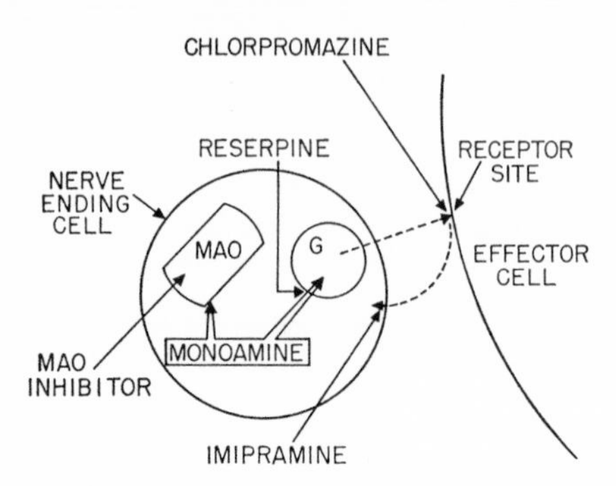

FIG. 1. Sites of action of representatives of four groups of psychotropic drugs. This figure is the schematic representation of a cell of a *sympathetic* nerve-ending, an effector organ and the gap between these two structures through which the monoamine, noradrenaline, is released from the nerve-ending, following a nerve impulse. The structure of the mitochondria is intimately bound with the monoamine oxidase activity of that enzyme. Monoamines are stored in granules (G) in a labile form. Noradrenaline liberated from the labile fraction may be utilized in four ways: (1) incorporation into a stable form, (2) after the nerve impulse the monoamine is released into the gap (straight dotted line), *and stimulates the effector cell at the receptor site* (3) once outside the nerve cell noradrenaline may also be transformed to normetadrenaline by COMT enzyme or (4) may re-enter the nerve ending (curved dotted line). Inside the cell the free monoamine may be oxidized by the MAO enzyme. Reserpine and chlorpromazine diminish the effectiveness of the response of the effector organ to nerve stimulation: reserpine blocks the incorporation of the monoamine into the labile form and thus diminishes the amount of available monoamine. Chlorpromazine has a similar effect but in another way, for that drug blocks the receptor site so that the monoamine cannot contact it. This blocking action is similar to that of atropine in regard to acetylcholine. The MAO inhibitor prevents the MAO enzyme from oxidizing noradrenaline and therefore increases its concentration. Imipramine accomplishes the same purpose by preventing the return of the free monoamine into the cell, thus raising the level of noradrenaline available to react with the receptor site. (*This figure is reproduced with the permission of Prof. Arvid Carlsson*).

as general excitatory and inhibitory transmitters in mammalian brain. It is also important to show that both the effects of the drug applied by iontophoresis and of synaptic activation are similarly affected by peripheral 5-HT and NA blocking agents.

To the best of my knowledge only Salmoiraghi's group have provided this sort of evidence —in the rabbit olfactory bulb. They have shown that NA and the inhibition produced by lateral olfactory stimulation are both blocked in a fairly substantial manner by alpha-adrenergic blocking agents.

HIMWICH: Dr. Straughan, you are entirely correct in calling for direct evidence rather than that of the circumstantial type before acceptance of a neurotransmitter function for the non-cholinergic substances I have mentioned. You do, however, point to the results of Anden and co-workers who have demonstrated the simultaneous increase of serotonin and noradrenaline in the spinal cord as well as its suspending medium following nerve stimulation. Though gravimetric measurements were not made, yet these substances were chemically identified. In regard to the second point, namely that the postulated neurotransmitter substances should produce exactly the effects of activation of appropriate synaptic pathways, we have additional evidence from Carlsson's laboratory (Anden, N. E., Jukes, M. G. M. and Lundberg, A., *Nature*, **202,** 1222, 1964; Anden, N. E., Jukes M. G. M., Lundberg, A. and Vyklick, L., *ibid.* **202,** 1344, 1964; Carlsson, A., Folkow, B. and Haggendal, J., *Life Sciences*, **3,** 1335, 1964; Anden, N. E., Carlsson, A., Hillarp, N. A. and Magnusson, T., *ibid.* **4,** 129, 1965) that the injection of serotonin into the spinal cat enhances spinal reflex activity. Stimulation of the raphe region of the medulla oblongata also increases spinal reflex activity and this effect is abolished by reserpine pretreatment with its depleting action on monoamines. Further evidence in favor of a neurotransmitter action is afforded by the effects of DOPA to inhibit transmission from the flexor reflex afferent to the primary afferents, motoneurones and ascending pathways, which are blocked by the alpha-adrenergic-blockers, phenoxybenzamine and chlorpromazine, but not by the beta-blocker nethalide. I am the first to admit, however, that only the accumulation of a large amount of direct evidence afforded acceptance by many investigators of the neurotransmitter action of acetylcholine though such activity in the brain is still doubted by some. Similarly only a continued accumulation of direct data can gain credence for neurotransmitter roles of these non-cholinergic substances.

MANDELL: The very interesting work by Dr. Himwich implicating the medulla and perhaps peripheral input to the medulla in the EEG arousal produced by dimethylated indole psychotogens, LSD congeners, and dimethoxyphenylethylamine brings up a basic issue relative to the singularity of arousal as a physiological parameter. Munroe and Heath (*J. Neuropsychiat.* **3,** 75, 1961) and Adey *et al.* (*Neurology*, **12,** 591, 1962; *EEG Clin. Neurophysiol.* **18,** 25, 1965; *Pharmacology of Conditioning, Learning and Retention*, Proc. 2nd Internat. Pharm. Meeting, Prague, 1963) have shown that hippocampal structures are most sensitive to the acute effects of these kinds of psychotogens. Using regularization of approach learning induced hippocampal theta, Adey demonstrated changes following acute administration of the 4-OH indoles. These changes were not as marked in the mesencephalic reticular formation or the neighboring pyriform cortex. The sensitivity of hippocampale tissue to drug and metabolic effects is well known (Meyer in *Modern Trends in Neurology*, D. William, Ed., Butterworth, London, p. 301, 1957) and one could argue that the observed changes in this structure are non-specific and unrelated to the brain stem-dependent phenomenon reported by Himwich. On the other hand, the predictable occurrence of theta in the hippocampus associated with "arousal" has been reported numerous times (Green and Arduini, *J. Neurophysiol.* **17,** 533, 1954) and important brain stem–hippocampal connections have been known since Herrick (*Proc. Natl. Acad. Sci.* **19,** 7, 1933). Kawamura *et al.* (*Japan J. Physiol.* **11,** 564, 1961) have shown that this hippocampal theta can be induced by stimulation of the brain stem reticular formation even when a number of the structures of the Papez circuit have been destroyed. It appears possible, therefore, that both the medullary-dependent changes reported by Dr. Himwich and those changes in the hippocampus reported by Adey are two different reflections of the same general nervous system event.

On the other hand, the gradual particularization of brain stem reticular formation structures resulting from recent work (Battini *et al.*, *Arch. Ital. Biol.* **97,** 26, 1959; Cordeau *et al.*, *EEG Clin. Neurophysiol.* **11,** 551, 1959) and experimental differentiation of various "arousal" states (Anokhin in *Brain and Behavior*, Vol. 1, M. Brazier, Ed., Am. Inst. Biol. Sci., Washington, 1961) suggests the possibility that there may be multiple arousal systems, each more or less activated by a variety of drug, electrical, and metabolic stimuli. If one subscribes to the amine hypothesis of the action of psychotogens (Brodie and Costa, *Psychopharmacol. Serv. Bull. Washington*, Part 5, 1962) a similarity of response of both brain stem and hippocampal structures would be expected in that both areas have high indoleamine content (Paasonen *et al.*, *J. Neurochem.* **1,** 326, 1957).

The suggestion of the importance of peripheral input in the phenomenology of the action of psychotogens is another exciting aspect of Dr. Himwich's work. It suggests work in the area of a systematic psychophysiological study of the effect of these substances; this is work which can be done in man.

HIMWICH: I want to thank you, Dr. Mandell, for re-emphasizing some of the points that could not be extensively discussed in a short presentation, for example, the part played by the peripheral input in the mechanism of the psychotogenic amines. In addition I am grateful to you for bringing to our attention the elegant observations of Munroe and Heath on the great sensitivity of the hippocampus, a sensitivity that appears to be specific from the observations of Adey *et al.* on the discriminative task performance of cats exposed to LSD. It is well known that the hippocampal theta is part and parcel of the EEG arousal reaction. Our earliest work disclosed that the hippocampal theta rhythm with spontaneous arousal following the administration of LSD had different characteristics from the theta accompanying the evoked arousal whether with or without LSD. The difference consisted in the waxing and waning of the theta wave amplitude with the psychotomimetic agent (Himwich, Van Meter and Owens, *Neuropsychopharmacology*, Bradley *et al.*, Eds., Elsevier, Amsterdam–New York, p. 329, 1959). After mescaline, the evoked alerting following sensory stimulation includes a hippocampal theta of 5-7/sec while the theta with the spontaneous altering after the agent appears at a lower rate, from 3-5/sec. In view of the fact that stimulation of the reticular formation can evoke both EEG arousal and hippocampal theta rhythms while stimulation of the posterior hypothalamus can also cause EEG alerting it would seem that these two processes are closely related phenomena.

DISCUSSION AFTER DR. RICHTER'S PAPER

STRAUGHAN: Several points occur to me, Dr. Richter, on looking at your data on disturbed ion transport in manic-depressive psychosis. First, these electrolyte changes are similar to those which would be found if there was an abnormality or deficiency in aldosterone secretion. It is of interest in this connection to remember that the pineal gland used to be assigned a role as the source of glomerulotrophin. Further, the pineal gland contains large amounts of 5-HT and O-methyl-N-acetyl 5-HT.

It would be interesting to know whether there are changes in aldosterone metabolism in depression and if these are secondary to changes in the pineal.

Secondly, a similar electrolyte pattern to that seen in depression would occur if there were an inhibition of the sodium-potassium activated adenosine triphosphatase. Now, cardiac glycosides also inhibit this enzyme; do you know if digoxin given therapeutically in congestive cardiac failure produces any effects on the mode of depressed patients?

FORREST: We had two patients with manic-depressive psychosis who showed signs of digitalis toxicity. This seemed to induce a manic change which regressed on modifying the therapy.

In connection with Dr. Straughan's remark on the NA ATPase, it is of interest that lithium has been used in the treatment of the manic phase of depression. This ion, of course, is not handled by the sodium pump mechanism and accumulates intracellularly. Is it possible that the changes in 5-HT metabolism occur secondarily to changes in the intra-cellular levels of sodium and potassium?

RICHTER: Mental changes have been observed in a number of conditions in which the electrolyte balance is disturbed: cerebral symptoms produced by digitalis include headache, drowsiness, disorientation, mental confusion and occasionally delirium. Lithium treatment produces a profound change in the sodium distribution and it can also influence the mental state in mania, but I do not think there is a direct relation between the intracellular sodium level and elevation of mood. The evidence suggests rather that an increase in intracellular sodium is an unspecific stress response that can occur in manic as well as depressive states.

The possibility that aldosterone metabolism is changed in depression has also occurred to us. Aldosterone secretion rates are unfortunately difficult to measure, but attempts that we have made to treat patients suffering from depression with DOCA and with aldosterone have not given encouraging results. Our experience of these treatments contrasts with the striking improvement obtained with MAO inhibitors and tryptophan.

SNYDER: The findings which you describe of altered CO_2 formation from radioactive 5-hydroxytryptophan in depressed patients is indeed intriguing. To establish whether this is specifically related to serotonin formation you might give other carboxyl-labelled amino acids and measure respired CO_2.

SPRINCE: The increased plasma acetoin levels in depression (Anderson and Dawson, *J. Ment. Sci.* **108,** 80, 1962) noted in Dr. Richter's Fig. 1 dealing with stress response in depression raises an interesting question. The immediate precursor of acetoin, otherwise known as acetyl methyl carbinol (AMC), has been shown to be pyruvate (Dawson and Hullin, *Biochem. J.* **57,** 177, 1954). Pyruvate is known to be increased after the administration of MAO inhibitors (Pletscher, *Deut. Med. Wochenschr.* **86,** 647, 1961: see also translation in *Psychopharmacology Service Center Bulletin*, **2,** 11, 1963). This suggests that MAO inhibitors may inhibit the formation of AMC from pyruvate. Thus it might be of interest to study pyruvate–AMC ratios after administration of MAO inhibitors just as tryptamine–indoleacetic acid ratios have been studied under similar circumstances (LaBrosse *et al.*, *J. Psychiat. Res.* **2,** 185, 1964). This might reveal a new type of metabolic activity for MAO inhibitors.

SCHILDKRAUT: Dr. Richter has presented some very interesting data suggesting that alterations in indoleamine metabolism may be of consequence in the affective disorders. Without disputing the possible importance of the indoleamines in this regard, I should, however, like to comment briefly on some of the evidence relating changes in catecholamine metabolism to the pathophysiology and pharmacotherapy of the affective disorders.

Psychopharmacological studies, while demonstrating changes in serotonin levels, as Dr. Richter has indicated, have shown an even more consistent relationship between the effects of these drugs on catecholamines, particularly norepinephrine, and affective or behavioral states (Schildkraut, J. J., *Am. J. Psychiat.* **122,** 509, 1965). Reserpine and tetrabenazine, both of which produce sedation and sometimes clinical depression, cause depletion of brain catecholamines as well as depletion of indoleamines in animals. Several investigators, however, have demonstrated that administration of the catecholamine precursor dihydroxyphenylalanine (DOPA) will reverse reserpine sedation and restore normal behavior in animals, while administration of the indoleamine precursor 5-hydroxytryptophan does not (Carlsson, Lindgvist and Magnusson, *Nature*, **180,** 1200, 1957).

There is, moreover, a considerable body of data suggesting that the anti-depressant actions of both the major classes of antidepressant agents, the monoamine oxidase inhibitors and the imipramine-like drugs, may be mediated by the catecholamines. Spector *et al.* (*Int. J. Neuropharmacol.* **2,** 81, 1963) have shown that the behavioral excitation following administration of monoamine oxidase inhibitors bears a better temporal relationship to the rise in brain norepinephrine than to the increase in brain serotonin. Monoamine oxidase inhibitors by decreasing the intracellular deamination and inactivation of norepinephrine are thought to cause spillover of free norepinephrine on to adrenergic receptor sites.

Imipramine, which inhibits neither of the enzymes (monoamine oxidase or catechol-O-methyl transferase) involved in norepinephrine metabolism, none the less potentiates the effects of norepinephrine in a variety of physiological test systems. Axelrod's group, moreover, has demonstrated that imipramine inhibits the uptake of norepinephrine both in peripheral sympathetic nervous tissue (Hertting, Axelrod and Whitby, *J. Pharmacol. Exp. Therap.* **134,** 146, 1961) and in the brain (Glowinski and Axelrod, *Nature*, **204,** 1318, 1964). Since cellular reuptake is an important mechanism for the physiological inactivation of free norepinephrine, this inhibition of uptake may account for the potentiation of the effects of norepinephrine by imipramine.

It is well known that the monoamine oxidase inhibitors will prevent or reverse reserpine-induced sedation in animals. Pretreatment with imipramine will also prevent the sedative effects of reserpine, and Sulser *et al.* (*Ann. N.Y. Acad. Sci.* **96,** 279, 1962) have demonstrated that this phenonomen is dependent upon the availablity of catecholamine stores. In animals partially depleted of catecholamines by α-methylmetatyrosine imipramine will not prevent reserpine sedation (Sulser, Bickel and Brodie, *J. Pharmacol. Exp. Therap.* **144,** 321, 1964).

In studies of urinary catecholamine metabolites in depressed patients treated with either monoamine oxidase inhibitors or imipramine, some years ago at the Massachusetts Health Center, we found that both of these agents decreased the excretion of 3-methoxy-4-hydroxmandelic acid (VMA), the major urinary metabolite of norepinephrine (Schildkraut *et al.*, *J. Psychiat. Res.* **2,** 257, 1964). Most VMA is believed to derive from norepinephrine which is synthesized in the nerve cell, but which is deaminated intracellularly by mitochondrial monoamine oxidase and thereby inactivated without necessarily having been utilized. The decrease in VMA in patients pretreated with monoamine oxidase inhibitors, therefore, presumably resulted from the chemical inhibition of the enzyme. The findings with impramine, however, were more difficult to explain. The inhibition of cellular reuptake of norepinephrine by impramine, reported in Axelrod's group, suggested that imipramine decreased membrane permeability to norepinephrine. We, therefore, hypothesized that imipramine, through such a decrease in membrane permeability, might limit the access of norepinephrine to mitochondrial monoamine oxidase, in part by inhibiting the intracellular release of norepinephrine from granules, and thereby decrease the intracellular deamination of norepinephrine.

More recently in a longitudinal study of depressed patients at the National Institute of Mental Health, in collaboration with Dr. Jack Durell, the finding of a decrease in VMA excretion during treatment with imipramine has been confirmed. Moreover, preliminary results from this study suggest that there is a gradual rise in noremetanephrine during the period of definitive clinical improvement in depressed patients treated with imipramine (Schildkraut *et al.*, *J. Psychiat, Res.*, in press). This may, in part, directly reflect the inhibition by impramine of the process of cellular reuptake of norepinephrine. With this pathway for the inactivation of norepinephrine inhibited, a larger fraction of norepinephrine may thus be metabolized to normetanephrine.

Since normetanephrine, the O-methylated metabolite, is believed to derive from norepinephrine which is released from the nerve in active form, however, the increase in normetanephrine excretion further suggests that there may be an increase in adrenergic activity during the period of clinical improvement in depressed patients treated with imipramine. By inhibiting the inactivation of norepinephrine by cellular reuptake, imipramine may potentiate the effects of norepinephrine centrally and thereby cause an increase in central adrenergic activity. This could then cause a secondary increase in peripheral adrenergic activity.

Preliminary results further indicate that there is an increase in normetanephrine excretion in some patients with retarded depression after successful treatment with imipramine, when values obtained under pretreatment and post-treatment placebo conditions are compared. In one of these patients during a subsequent hypomanic episode, which occurred without drug administration, there was an even greater rise in normetanephrine. Since there is no general agreement among investigators regarding the various chemical methods utilized to determine normetanephrine, and there is considerable disparity in the range of values reported by different investigators, all such data on normetanephrine excretion must be considered tentative. The finding of an increase in normetanephrine with mood elevation in patients with retarded depression is consistent, however, with the earlier finding of Strom-Olson and Weil-Malherbe (*J. Ment. Sci.* **104,** 696, 1958) that norepinephrine excretion was decreased in depression and increased in mania.

Caution must be exercised in interpreting such data on the urinary excretion of norepinephrine and metabolites to imply central changes specifically related to alterations in mood. Factors other than affective state, including muscular activity, postural changes or anxiety, have also been found to be associated with changes in the excretion of catecholamines and their metabolities. Moreover, a blood brain barrier to normetanephrine similar to that known to exist for norepinephrine has recently been described in animals by Glowinski *et al.* (*J. Neurochem.* **12,** 25, 1965). It is, therefore, not unlikely that only a small fraction of urinary norepinephrine or normetanephrine derives from the brain. Nonetheless, such data on the urinary excretion of norepinephrine and metabolites are of interest since changes in catecholamine metabolism in the periphery may reflect similar changes occurring centrally and, as we have already indicated, an increase in peripheral sympathetic activity may reflect increased central adrenergic activity.

In reference to the very interesting finding reported by Dr. Richter, that depressed patients have a decreased rate of liberation of ^{14}C from carboxy-labeled 5-hydroxy (1-^{14}C) tryptophan it should be noted that the same enzyme which decarboxylates 5-hydroxytryptophan also decarboxylates DOPA and that this finding may not, therefore, be specific for the indoleamine precursor.

In summary, then, there is reasonable data compatible with the hypotheses that some if not all depressions may be associated with a decrease in catecholamines, particularly norepinephrine, at central adrenergic receptor sites, and that the antidepressant agents may act by increasing or potentiating norepinephrine at such sites. Clearly, however, as Dr. Richter has indicated, the actions of the indoles and other biogenic amines, the hormones, and ionic changes will all have to be included in any comprehensive formulation of the biochemistry of the affective disorders.

PERRY: In a careful search by sophisticated chromatographic procedures I have failed to detect any tryptamine in the brain (Perry *et al.*, *J. Neurochem.* **12**, 397, 1965) Most or all of the tryptamine excreted in human urine is of intestinal bacterial origin, since the mammalian liver and kidney enzyme which decarboxylates DOPA and 5-HT has no activity for tryptophan. I therefore question whether tryptamine plays any role in the etiology of psychoses, and even whether tryptamine is present in the brain.

RICHTER: I have seen your paper in the *Journal of Neurochemistry* and I wonder if your method of estimating amines after anesthetizing and perfusing the brain with saline really gives reliable evidence of the normal levels *in vivo?* Perfusion with saline causes edema and can break down the normal separation of substrates and enzymes so that low values are obtained. In my experience it is desirable to use a rapid fixation method such as freezing with liquid air; then perhaps one can draw some conclusions about normal levels.

If you are right that the tryptamine excreted in the urine is of bacterial origin, that does not worry me at all: the important thing is that tryptamine is present in our patients. Any excess of tryptamine will be quickly broken down in any case by the amine oxidase, but the Michaelis constant of the enzyme is such that a low concentration will remain a long time in the tissues. If tryptamine is circulating in the body, even in small amounts, it is likely to be taken up and accumulated in the storage vesicles in the brain, just as they will take up octopamine and other circulating amines. The evidence suggests that the storage vesicles are relatively unspecific in this respect.

I must question your conclusion that the tryptamine in the body is all of bacterial origin, for Lowenberg, Weissbach and Udenfriend (*J. Biol. Chem.* **237**, 89, 1962) showed that an enzyme which forms tryptamine from tryptophan is present in many mammalian tissues including brain. If enzyme and substrate are present in the same tissue, it is reasonable to believe that some tryptamine will be formed there too.

DISCUSSION AFTER DR. HOLMSTEDT'S PAPER

SNYDER: I certainly agree with the implications of your elegant work indicating the necessity for care in identification of indolic compounds. We had been impressed with the non-specificity of the conventional assay techniques for serotonin, since fluorescence in strong acid is characteristic for all 5-hydroxy or 5-methoxy indoles. We have utilized the fluorescent reaction of serotonin with ninhydrin (Vanable, *Analyt. Biochem.* **6**, 393, 1963) to develop an assay for tissue serotonin which is highly specific and will not react with any indolic compound other than serotonin. It is also about ten times as sensitive as the conventional fluorescent assay for serotonin of Bogdanski (*J. Pharmacol. Exper. Therap.* **117**, 82, 1956).

DISCUSSION AFTER DR. BALDESSARINI'S PAPER

HORWITT: Dr. Baldessarini should be highly complimented on the way he went through this program. I am not surprised by the fact that young and old animals show differences because all of us who have tried to put things into the brain of animals have run into this distinction. After myelinization is finished the brain seems to be more fixed with respect to changes that can be made by dietary means. What were the constituents of the diet you used?

BALDESSARINI: I do not have specific data on the quantities of components of the diet. It is a standard Purina Laboratory rat chow, supposedly a balanced normal diet.

HORWITT: It so happens that many people who use casein are not aware that they might be feeding methionine-deficient diet.

BALDESSARINI: Except in the work where we showed that starving rats for 24 hr could have an effect in lowering SAMe in some strains, all the rats were starved (overnight) to the same degree and thus brought to an approximate dietary basal point. I attempted to show in other experiments that when rats are fed right up to the time assay, their SAMe levels are elevated, showing that diet does in fact have a SAMe elevating effect. It is well that the rats were starved to the same point.

HORWITT: Methionine is very tricky, as I indicated yesterday. We get a lot of effects with it which we cannot explain but have nothing to do with what we are discussing here today. As I say, the crucial point will be to show that this is a specific effect of this amino acid that does not happen with other amino-acid complexes.

HIMWICH: May I ask if you did it on dry-weight basis or wet weight?

BALDESSARINI: Wet weight was used. The tissues were chilled on ice and weighed as quickly as possible after sacrifice of the animals.

SPRINCE: Inositol phosphatides are found in appreciable quantities in the brain. Have you considered using inositol or inositol phosphatides as a methyl acceptor? It may be that the free hydroxyl groups of inositol could be transformed to methoxy groups.

I have one other question. Do you have any explanation for this lack of effect of nicotinamide?

BALDESSARINI: This is puzzling. Cantoni showed that nicotinamide is very easily methylated by rat liver and so the methyl donor might be exposed to decrease (Cantoni, G. L., *J. Biol. Chem.* **189,** 203, 1951). However, one can only speculate about the lack of decrease in SAMe until the kinetics of nicotinamide methylation and SAMe formation and utilization are certain.

SPRINCE: One wonders whether you are not getting the same effect that Waisman got with excess phenylalanine fed to rats and monkeys in his work with experimental phenylketonuria. Excess phenylalanine resulted in a marked decrease in phenylalanine hydroxylase activity due, perhaps, to metabolic overloading with substrate (Waisman, H. A. and Harlow, H. F., *Science*, **147,** 685, 1965). It is possible that a similar situation might develop here where metabolic overloading with nicotinamide as substrate may inhibit the methylating enzyme. However, in some preliminary, unpublished experiments of our own, we have found that urinary N^1-methylnicotinamide is markedly increased in rats after nicotinamide load by intraperitoneal injection. This would argue against the above explanation. It may be that the usual methyl donors are not decreased by nicotinamide load simply because body protein may be capable of supplying enough endogenous methionine to act as the necessary methyl donor for this reaction.

FRIEDHOFF: Dr. Baldessarini's work is a very nice next step in the attempt to understand methionine loading experiments. I think it has also demonstrated how often basic research follows clinical research rather than the other way around. I wonder, though, if you have had an opportunity yet to obtain any direct evidence that you are in fact increasing the amount of methylated metabolites. . . .

BALDESSARINI: That is the "$64 question"! This is the sort of thing that needs to be done next.

FRIEDHOFF: Secondly, don't your starvation data disagree somewhat with Cantoni's findings that you could increase levels of S-adenosylmethionine by methionine feeding but not decrease them by methionine deprivation?

BALDESSARINI: Cantoni did not measure tissue S-adenosylmethionine. This is the first time I know of that it has been measured sensitively in tissues.

FRIEDHOFF: Yes, I think I am wrong about that, but I believe he did determine the effects of methionine feeding on methionine stores, therefore indirectly on S-adenosylmethionine. He came to his conclusion some way though I am afraid I do not know how.

BALDESSARINI: I am not aware of this effect of diet to which you refer.

EFRON: Do you have some estimation of the action of pyrogallol?

BALDESSARINI: There are two possibilities—for the action of pyrogallol and I really do not want to say that one is more important than the other. It is quite possible that pyrogallol attaches to COMT and is methylated like a catechol (it is a sort of double catechol), and it may thus be an ordinary enzyme inhibitor. Alternatively it may deplete the methyl donor so as to make it unavailable for methylating other substrates.

KETY: I can, in all modesty, compliment Dr. Baldessarini on his work because I had nothing to do with it except perhaps to prod Dr. Kopin to think a bit about the transmethylation hypothesis. He was fortunate enough to get Dr. Baldessarini to work with him and I think that the results they have obtained in this basic process are quite remarkable. In fact it was very interesting that there was not a method for S-adenosylmethionine before they began working. As a matter of fact, one knew very little about what levels of this important compound existed in various tissues and how it was influenced. There are two results which you recorded, Dr. Baldessarini, which somehow seemed a little out of keeping with your expectations. One is the fact that neither amphetamine nor reserpine affected the SAMe levels. I wonder whether this is really surprising. Would one have expected the noradrenaline to be O-methylated in sufficient amounts to influence measurably the SAMe levels in the brain? With regard to reserpine, since it causes the release of substances which are quite rapidly oxidized, one wonders whether the competition with the monoamine oxidase might not have prevented them from being available as methyl acceptors.

BALDESSARINI: I think it may be a mistake to narrow our sights on what we happen to know about amines. Methylation is a very widely occurring process and SAMe is probably used for many methylations of which we have no knowledge. At this time, we are describing phenomena and their mechanisms need not be explained in terms of what we know about catechol transferase systems above.

KUEHL: If we are to assume that inhibition by tropolone is due to competition for the S-adenosylmethionine, how do you account for the fact that there is no methylatable phenolic group in tropolone?

BALDESSARINI: I am rather puzzled by the effect of tropolone to lower SAMe. Tropolone has a peculiar structure with a phenolic hydrocyl and a double-bonded oxygen. There may be enough resonance in such a structure to make it an "almost catechol". However, I have recently been unable to find any ability of rat liver extract to attach C^{14}-methyl of labelled SAMe to tropolones.

KUEHL: Have you tried any other inhibitors such as α-propyl dopa acetamide which are more potent inhibitors of COMT than pyrogallol?

BALDESSARINI: No.

SPRINCE: One should also consider the possibility that 3-hydroxykynurenine, 3-hydroxyanthranilic acid, xanthurenic acid with its phenolic hydroxyl group in position 8, and 5-hydroxytryptamine might also be capable of being methyl acceptors. Indeed, methoxy derivatives of the latter three compounds are known to occur as urinary metabolites. This raises the question as to whether methoxy derivatives of the tryptophan-nicotinic acid pathway could not act as metabolic feedback inhibitors of this pathway. It might also be of interest to test for an increase of such methoxy metabolites after a methionine load.

BERLET: May I mention briefly in this connection that some while ago we did the reverse of these experiments. We had a group of patients on a methionine-low diet for approximately 2 months and at the end of this period we loaded the patients for 2 days with a total of 4 g of nicotinamide. We measured adrenaline and noradrenaline and VMA along with 1-methylnicotinamide in the hope of finding a decrease of methylated catecholamines and of 1-methylnicotinamide as compared with nicotinamide by supposedly depleting the methyl groups. We were not able to find any reduction in the excretion rates of adrenaline or VMA or 1-methyl nicotinamide. In other words, there were still enough active methyl groups available to take care of metabolic transmethylations.

THE ACTIONS OF VARIOUS BIOLOGICAL AMINES ON SINGLE NEURONES IN THE LIMBIC SYSTEM

DONALD W. STRAUGHAN

University Department of Psychiatry, Royal Edinburgh Hospital,
Morningside Park, Edinburgh 10

INTRODUCTION: THE ROLE OF 5-HYDROXYTRYPTAMINE AND NORADRENALINE

RECENT researches have established the importance of the limbic system in the control of emotion, behavioural organization, memory and learning. Since it is these functions which are disturbed in psychotic states, the physiology and pharmacology of the limbic system are of great importance to the psychiatrist.

In the last decade neurochemical estimations have shown that there are generally relatively high levels of 5-hydroxytryptamine (5-HT) and moderate levels of noradrenaline in the limbic system, as well as the enzymes for their synthesis and destruction (Amin *et al.*, 1954; Vogt, 1954; Bogdanski *et al.*, 1957; Paasonen *et al.*, 1957; Kuntzmann *et al.*, 1961). Furthermore, the 5-HT content of limbic structures has been shown to differ in "emotional" and "non-emotional" strains of rats (Sudak and Maas, 1964). Also, psychotropic drugs such as reserpine and the monoamine oxidase inhibitors have been shown to produce large changes in the 5-HT and noradrenaline levels in the limbic system. While it is likely that 5-HT and noradrenaline, or closely related substances, could be either synaptic neurotransmitters or act locally as regulators of neuronal excitability, it is also possible that these substances play no direct part in the regulation of synaptic transmission but have some other, as yet undefined, metabolic role.

If 5-HT and noradrenaline are neurotransmitters, then it should be possible to show that they are released by nervous stimulation, e.g. as with ACh from the neocortex (MacIntosh and Oborin, 1953; Mitchell, 1961, 1963). So far the release of 5-HT or noradrenaline from limbic structures by nervous stimulation has not been demonstrated, though there is evidence for the release of 5-HT from the spinal cord following nervous stimulation (Andén *et al.*, 1964).

It is also important that the potential transmitter should have the right intracellular location, that is, it should be concentrated in the nerve terminals. In this connection abundant catechol amine-containing fine nerve terminals have been shown by a histochemical method in the hypothalamus and elsewhere in the limbic system (Carlsson *et al.*, 1962b). The cell bodies giving rise to these terminals in the hypothalamus, pyriform cortex and hippocampal formation lie in the midbrain (Dahlström *et al.*, 1964). In the amygdala, the 5-HT containing nerve terminals appear to be localized to the medial part (Carlsson *et al.*, 1962a).

Further, administration of the proposed transmitter should reproduce the effect of nerve stimulation. The force of this evidence is increased if a specific blocking agent can be found to prevent the effects of both the proposed transmitter substance and nerve stimulation. This present survey is concerned with the actions of 5-HT and noradrenaline on some single neurones in the limbic system, as steps towards satisfying these criteria.

MICROELECTROPHORESIS

There are several obvious difficulties associated with drug administration by conventional methods when the activity of single neurones is studied. With systemic injections there is the problem of whether the drug in fact traverses the various diffusion barriers to the region under study and reaches it without being altered. Further, any effects observed could well be brought about by general systemic changes, or, reflexly, by stimulation of peripheral sensory receptors or by actions on other parts of the brain with connections to the region under study. The microelectrophoretic method allows one or more drugs to be ejected in a controlled manner into the environment of single nerve cells with simultaneous recording of extracellular spike potentials. Also small amounts of peripheral blocking agents can be expelled into a restricted environment on repeated occasions, which avoids the hazard of tissue saturation. This occurs if blocking agents with a long duration of action are given systemically. The recovery of the cell from the drug may then be delayed for many hours.

In its present form the microelectrophoretic method was first used by Curtis and Eccles (1958) and a very comprehensive account has been given recently by Curtis (1964). For details of some important theoretical considerations the reader is referred to papers by Krnjević and Phillis (1963a) and Krnjević, Mitchell and Szerb (1963). Basically, the method utilizes five-barrelled glass micropipettes; the four outer barrels are symetrically arranged around and fused to the central barrel. The pipette assembly is then pulled in a machine similar to that described by Winsbury (1954). The tip is then broken back to a diameter of 4 to 10 μ and the electrodes filled by boiling in glass distilled water at atmospheric pressure. After cooling, the tips are checked for complete filling. The contents of each barrel are now aspirated and replaced by the required drug solution. The central barrel is filled with 2·7 M NaCl and one of the outer barrels is filled with 1 M sodium L-glutamate at pH 8·5 (British Drug Houses). The other barrels are filled with aqueous solutions of 0·05 M 5-HT creatinine sulphate (Burroughs Wellcome), 0·2 M 5-HT bimaleinate (Koch-Light Labs.), 0·5 M noradrenaline bitartrate (Koch-Light Labs.) and 0·5 M 3-hydroxytyramine (dopamine) hydrochloride (Koch-Light Labs.) all at an acid pH. The tips are then filled by centrifugation and the electrodes used in the next few hours.

Drugs can now be expelled by the passage of currents (between 5 and 200 mμA) through each barrel, the indifferent electrode being a silver-silver-chloride plate imbedded in the animal's neck. The actual amounts of drug ion expelled will vary with the tip dimensions and the transport number of the particular substance used, but is likely to be of the order of 4×10^{-15} mole/mμA-sec. The actual concentration of drug in the neighbourhood of the cell might be of the order of 10^{-4} M (Krnjević and Phillis, 1963a). With electrode tips of 5 to 10 μ diameter, and resistances of 20 to 40 MΩ spontaneous diffusion of drugs from the tips occurs (Krnjević, Laverty and Sharman, 1963; Krnjević, Mitchell and Szerb, 1963) but experience suggests that this may be effectively controlled by small 'braking' currents of opposite polarity to that used for ejection (del Castillo and Katz, 1955).

The central barrel of the micropipette is connected to the grid of a cathode follower valve, and the electrode is then mounted in a micromanipulator and inserted into the brain of an anaesthetized cat. Extracellular responses are amplified in a conventional manner and displayed on an oscilloscope screen. It is very convenient to count the firing rates of individual cells with a rate-meter, and then display the rates on a penwriter.

ACTIONS OF 5-HT

5-HT has been ejected into the environment of single cells in the pyriform cortex (Randić and Straughan, 1966; Legge *et al.*, 1966), amygdala (Straughan and Legge, 1965) and hippocampal cortex (Biscoe and Straughan, 1965, 66). The cells were detected either because they fired spontaneously or in response to afferent stimulation, or because they could be excited by L-glutamate discharged into their vicinity from an adjacent barrel of the micropipette by iontophoresis. The most usual effect observed was depression of cell firing (see Figs. 1 and 2). This was seen with both barbiturate and non-barbiturate anaesthetics. The majority of 5-HT sensitive cells in the hypothalamus are also depressed (Bloom *et al.*, 1963). These depressant effects could be distinguished from "anodal depression" (Curtis and Koizumi, 1961; Krnjević and Phillis, 1963a) by passing an equal current through a barrel containing only NaCl. The depressant action of 5-HT typically takes between 10 and 30 sec to develop, and it persists for up to several minutes after stopping the expelling current. This is very different from the depression seen with GABA, where the effect develops within several hundred milliseconds and recovers equally rapidly. 5-HT depression was also seen in the lateral complex of the amygdala even though 5-HT containing nerve terminals are not present in this region.

Though the usual effect of 5-HT applied iontophoretically to central neurones is depression, a few cells excited by 5-HT have been noted in the hypothalamus (Bloom *et al.*, 1963), neocortex (Krnjević and Phillis, 1963b) and hippocampal cortex (Biscoe and Straughan, 1966), while in the brain-stem 40% of the neurones are excited by 5-HT (Bradley and Wolstencroft, 1965).

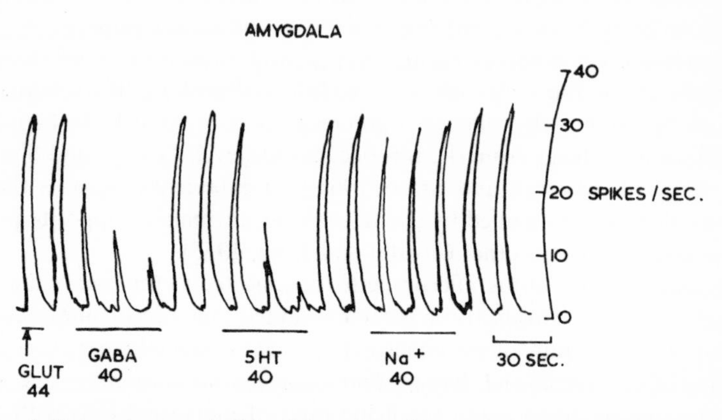

FIG. 1. Ratemeter record of the firing of a cell in the basomedial complex of the amygdala. The cell was quiescent and so was excited by the regular application of L-glutamate 44 nA for 5 sec in every 15 sec (only the first application is indicated at the ↑). A background application of GABA 40 nA was then applied from another barrel of the micropipette (indicated by bar below record). This caused a rapidly progressing block of the firing induced by L-glutamate. When 5-HT 40 nA was applied this also caused a depression of firing, but this developed more slowly than with GABA. At the extreme right of the record a control tip positive current of 40 nA was passed through the NaCl barrel (Na^+ 40) and indicated by the bar below the record. This had virtually no effect on cell firing. Scale at right shows the number of spikes counted per sec by the ratemeter. Cat anaesthetized with Dial compound. (This record taken from unpublished observations by Legge and Straughan.)

In the neocortex, though excitation only occurred when relatively large amounts of 5-HT were applied, it was seen with both the creatinine sulphate salt and the bimaleinate (Krnjević and Phillis, 1963a). Thus, it cannot be attributed to direct excitation by the creatinine moiety (Bradley and Wolstencroft, 1965). It has been suggested that the 5-HT excitation seen in the neocortex is due to a "non-specific disruptive effect" on the cell membrane (Krnjević and Phillis, 1963b). In the hippocampal cortex, however (Biscoe and Straughan, 1966), the excitation was seen even with small amounts of 5-HT.

The observed depression of these limbic system neurones by 5-HT is seen whether the units are activated synaptically or by direct stimulation of the postsynaptic membrane. This suggests that the effect is exerted directly on the postsynaptic membrane and not presynaptically, as in the lateral geniculate nucleus (Curtis and Davis, 1962). The explanation for the delayed effects seen with 5-HT is not known. The distance between the electrode tip and the cell is probably of the order 20 to 60 μ. Even over this short distance enzymic and diffusion barriers could be of importance, particularly in view of the relative absence of extracellular space in the brain, and the low permeability of 5-HT at the blood brain barrier interface.

Olds (1958) reported that 5-HT could antagonize the depressant effect of lysergic acid diethylamide (LSD 25) in self-stimulation studies in the prepyriform cortex of rats. More recently Bond and Guth (1964) have shown that LSD 25 and 5-HT are mutually antagonistic on the transcallosal response. In view of these observations and the known specific blockade of peripheral 5-HT receptors obtained with LSD 25 (Gaddum, 1953), it seemed of interest to see if the depressant effects of 5-HT on pyriform cortical neurones could be antagonized. The results (Legge *et al.*, 1965) were disappointing, for despite the passage of large iontophoretic currents of LSD 25, 2-brom lysergic acid diethylamide (BOL 148) and methysergide (UML 491) for several minutes no definite antagonism of 5-HT depression could be demonstrated. These lysergic acid derivatives have a powerful and prolonged depressant action of their own, which makes 5-HT antagonism more difficult to demonstrate. A similar direct depressant action of lysergic acid derivatives has been observed in the feline neocortex (Krnjević and Phillis, 1963b) and lateral geniculate nucleus (Curtis and Davis, 1962), and LSD 25 did not modify the action of 5-HT in these regions. These results have have been interpreted by Krnjević and Phillis (1963b) as meaning that specific 5-HT receptors (as seen in the periphery) are not present on these central neurones.

NORADRENALINE AND DOPAMINE

These substances have been applied iontophoretically to neurones in the pyriform cortex, amygdala and hippocampus. The only effect seen was that of depression (see Fig. 2). This is in marked contrast to the situation in the hypothalamus, where a quarter of all the sensitive cells are excited by noradrenaline (Bloom *et al.*, 1963). Dopamine was usually more potent than 5-HT, and noradrenaline less potent than 5-HT in the pyriform cortex. However, the time courses of noradrenaline and dopamine were similar, the effect of both was slow in onset and it persisted after stopping the iontophoretic current. The time course of the depression produced by noradrenaline and dopamine was shorter than that seen with 5-HT. In the lateral geniculate nucleus and neocortex these catechol amines are also depressant and have a slow time course. The depression appears to be postsynaptic since both L-glutamate and synaptic activation of units were similarly affected. These catecholamines do not impair the spike amplitude, as does LSD 25 in the neocortex (Krnjević and Phillis, 1963b). A similar action of 5-HT and noradrenaline in the hippocampus to that outlined here has been briefly reported by Stefanis (1964) and Herz and Nacimiento (1965).

There are marked regional differences in the response to these catecholamines—in the brain stem the effects of noradrenaline are predominantly excitant and dopamine is frequently either inactive or less potent on the same cells (Bradley and Wolstencroft, 1965).

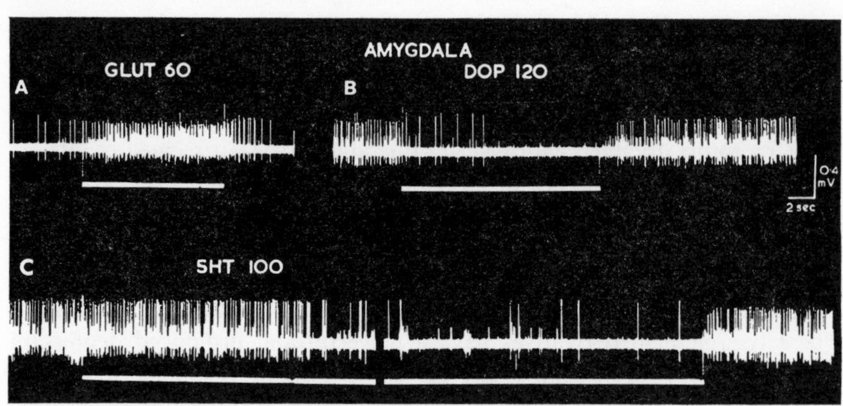

FIG. 2. Extracellular spike responses from two cells in the lateral complex of the amygdala. At (A) the cells were firing spontaneously at a low rate. The application of L-glutamate with a tip-negative current of 60 nA (GLUT 60 and indicated by the white bar beneath record) caused a characteristic increase in firing rate. At (B) the rate of cell firing was increased by the continuous background application of L-glutamate. When dopamine 120 nA (DOP 120) was now applied (indicated by the white bar beneath the record) it caused complete depression of cell firing. At (C) 5-hydroxytryptamine 100 nA (5-HT 100) was applied to the cells for 1 min (indicated by bar below record—note that the middle section of this drug application has been omitted); this caused a slowly developing depression of cell firing. Cat anaesthetized with chloralose and urethane. (This record taken from unpublished observations by Legge and Straughan.)

It seemed of interest to see if the depressant effects of noradrenaline could be specifically blocked by peripheral adrenergic blocking agents. It has recently been demonstrated by Salmoiraghi and his colleagues (Salmoiraghi *et al.*, 1964; Bloom *et al.*, 1964) that noradrenaline depression of olfactory bulb neurones and the inhibition which results from stimulation of the lateral olfactory tract can be antagonized by the local release of adrenergic blocking agents. Further, the duration of inhibition is significantly reduced by the selective depletion of local noradrenaline stores with α-methyl metatyrosine. In the pyriform cortex, however, we have been unable to antagonize the depressant effects of noradrenaline, despite the prolonged application of α and β adrenergic blocking agents. Similarly, Bradley, Dhawan and Wolstencroft (cited in Bradley and Wolstencroft, 1965) have failed to modify the effect of noradrenaline on brain stem neurones with adrenergic blocking agents; and in the neocortex adrenergic blocking agents do not appear to modify the inhibition evoked by epicortical stimulation or noradrenaline depression (Krnjević *et al.*, 1965). In view of the very prolonged applications of adrenergic blocking agents sometimes needed to block noradrenergic responses in the rabbit olfactory bulb, it is possible, though unlikely, that we have missed this effect because of the difficulty of holding units for very long periods.

In conclusion, therefore, it can be said that if 5-HT and catecholamines are released from limbic neurones then their effect could be expected to be predominantly depressant. There is still, however, insufficient evidence that these substances do in fact act as neurotransmitters or local regulators of neuronal excitability.

ACKNOWLEDGMENT

The experiments cited herein were done in conjunction with Dr. Mirjana Randić, Dr. T. J. Biscoe and Mr. K. F. Legge. I am grateful to the Schizophrenia Research Fund for their Rothschild Fellowship which has supported me.

REFERENCES

AMIN, A. H., CRAWFORD, T. B. B. and GADDUM, J. H. (1954) The distribution of substance P and 5-hydroxytryptamine in the central nervous system of the dog, *Journal of Physiology*, **126**, 596–618.

ANDÉN, N.-E., CARLSSON, Å., HILLARP, N.-Å. and MAGNUSSON, T. (1964) 5-Hydroxytryptamine release by nerve stimulation of the spinal cord, *Life Sciences*, **3**, 473–8.

BISCOE, T. J. and STRAUGHAN, D. W. (1965) The pharmacology of hippocampal neurones, *Journal of Pharmacy and Pharmacology*, **17**, 60–1.

BISCOE, T. J. and STRAUGHAN, D. W. (1966) Micro-electrophoretic studies of neurones in the cat hippocampus, *Journal of Phyisology*, **183**, 341–59.

BLOOM, F. E., COSTA, E. and SALMOIRAGHI, G. C. (1964) Analysis of individual rabbit olfactory bulb neuron responses to the microelectrophoresis of acetylcholine, norepinephrine and antagonists, *Journal of Pharmacology and Experimental Therapeutics*, **146**, 16–23.

BLOOM, F. E., OLIVER, A. P. and SALMOIRAGHI, G. C. (1963) The responsiveness of individual hypothalamic neurons to microelectrophoretically administered endogenous amines, *International Journal of Neuropharmacology*, **2**, 181–93.

BOGDANSKI, D. F., WEISSBACH, H. and UDENFRIEND, S. (1957) The distribution of serotonin 5-hydroxytryptophan decarboxylase and monoamine oxidase in brain, *Journal of Neurochemistry*, **1**, 272–8.

BOND, H. W. and GUTH, P. S. (1964) Interaction of 5-hydroxytryptamine and lysergic acid diethylamide in the central nervous system, *The Pharmacologist*, **6**, 171.

BRADLEY, P. B. and WOLSTENCROFT, J. W. (1965) Actions of drugs on single neurones in the brain-stem, *British Medical Bulletin*, **21**, 15–18.

CARLSSON, A., FALCK, B. and HILLARP, N.-Å. (1962a) Cellular localization of brain mono amines, *Acta Physiologica Scandinavica*, **56**, Supplement 196, 1–28.

CARLSSON, A., FALCK, B., HILLARP, N.-Å. and TORP, A. (1962b) Histochemical localization at the cellular level of hypothalamic noradrenaline, *Acta Physiologica Scandinavica*, **54**, 385–6.

CURTIS, D. R. (1964) "Microelectrophoresis" in *Physical Techniques in Biological Research*, Vol. V, Part A, Nastuk, W. L., Editor, Academic Press, New York and London (p. 144).

CURTIS, D. R. and DAVIS, R. (1962) Pharmacological studies upon neurones of the lateral geniculate nucleus of the cat, *British Journal of Pharmacology and Chemotherapy*, **18,** 217–46.

CURTIS, D. R. and ECCLES, R. M. (1958) The excitation of Renshaw cells by pharmacological agents applied electrophoretically, *Journal of Physiology*, **141,** 435–45.

CURTIS, D. R. and KOIZUMI, K. (1961) Chemical transmitter substances in brain stem of cat, *Journal of Neurophysiology*, **24,** 80–90.

DAHLSTRÖM, A., FUXE, K., OLSON, L. and UNGERSTEDT, U. (1964) Ascending systems of catecholamine neurones from the lower brain stem, *Acta Physiologica Scandinavica*, **62,** 485–6.

DEL CASTILLO, J. and KATZ, B. (1955) On the localization of acetylcholine receptors, *Journal of Physiology*, **128,** 157–81.

GADDUM, J. H. (1953) Antagonism between lysergic acid diethylamide and 5-hydroxytryptamine, *Journal of Physiology*, **121,** 15 P.

HERZ, A. and NACIMIENTO, A. (1965) Über die Wirkung von Pharmaka auf Neurone des Hippocampus nach mikroelektrophoretischer Verabfolgung. Naunyn-Schmiederberg's *Archiv für Experimentelle Pathologie und Pharmakologie*, **250,** 258–9.

KRNJEVIĆ, K., LAVERTY, R. and SHARMAN, D. F. (1963) Iontophoretic release of adrealine, noradrenaline and 5-hydroxytryptamine, *British Journal of Pharmacology and Chemotherapy*, **20,** 491–6.

KRNJEVIĆ, K., MITCHELL, J. F. and SZERB, J. C. (1963) Determination of iontophoretic release of acetylcholine from micropipettes, *Journal of Physiology*, **165,** 421–36.

KRNJEVIĆ, K. and PHILLIS, J. W. (1963a) Iontophoretic studies of neurones in the mammalian cerebral cortex, *Journal of Physiology*, **165,** 274–304.

KRNJEVIĆ, K. and PHILLIS, J. W. (1963b) Actions of certain amines on cerebral cortical neurones, *British Journal of Pharmacology and Chemotherapy*, **20,** 471–90.

KRNJEVIĆ, K., RANDIĆ, M. and STRAUGHAN, D. W. (1966) Pharmacology of cortical inhibition, *Journal of Physiology*, **184,** 78–105.

KUNTZMANN, R., SHORE, P. A., BOGDANSKI, D. and BRODIE, B. B. (1961) Microanalytical procedures for fluorometric assay of brain DOPA–5HTP decarboxylase, norepinephrine and serotonin, and a detailed mapping of decarboxylase activity in brain, *Journal of Neurochemistry*, **6,** 226–32.

LEGGE, K. F., RANDIĆ, M. and STRAUGHAN, D. W. (1966) The pharmacology of neurones in the pyriform cortex, *British Journal of Pharmacology and Chemotherapy*, **26,** 87–107.

MACINTOSH, F. C. and OBORIN, P. E. (1953) Release of acetylcholine from intact cerebral cortex, *Abstract XIX International Congress of Physiology*, pp. 580–1.

MITCHELL, J. F. (1961) Acetylcholine release from the cerebral cortex during stimulation, *Journal of Physiology*, **158,** 20–21 P.

MITCHELL, J. F. (1963) The spontaneous and evoked release of acetylcholine from the cerebral cortex, *Journal of Physiology*, **165,** 98–116.

OLDS, J. (1958) Self-stimulation of the brain, *Science* (*New York*), **127,** 315–24.

PAASONEN, M. K., MACLEAN, P. D. and GIARMAN, N. J. (1957) 5-Hydroxytryptamine (serotonin, enteramine) content of structures of the limbic system, *Journal of Neurochemistry*, **1,** 326–33.

RANDIĆ, M. and STRAUGHAN, D. W. (1965) Iontophoretic study of palaeocortical neurones, *Journal of Physiology* (in press).

SALMOIRAGHI, G. C., BLOOM, F. E., OLIVER, A. P. and COSTA, E. (1964) Adrenergic inhibition in rabbit olfactory bulb, *Federation Proceedings*, **23,** 152.

STEFANIS, C. (1964) Hippocampal neurons: their responsiveness to microelectrophoretically administered endogenous amines, *Pharmacologist*, **17,** 675–7.

STRAUGHAN, D. W. and LEGGE, K. F. (1965) The pharmacology of amygdaloid neurones, *Journal of Pharmacy and Pharmacology*, **17,** 675–7.

SUDAK, H. S. and MAAS, J. W. (1964) Central nervous system serotonin and norepinephrine localization in emotional and non-emotional strains of mice, *Nature* (*London*), **203,** 1254–6.

VOGT, M. (1954) The concentration of sympathin in different parts of the central nervous system under normal conditions and after the administration of drugs, *Journal of Physiology*, **123**, 451–81.

WINSBURY, G. J. (1954) Machine for the production of microelectrodes, *Review of Scientific Instruments*, **27**, 514–16.

A QUANTUM-CHEMICAL CORRELATE OF HALLUCINOGENESIS

SOLOMON H. SNYDER[1] and CARL R. MERRIL

Laboratory of Clinical Science and Laboratory of Neurochemistry,
National Institute of Mental Health, National Institutes of Health, Bethesda, Maryland

HALLUCINOGENIC drugs have been studied extensively in recent years, both as tools for the production of experimental psychosis and as possible therapeutic agents in mental disease. The striking effects of these drugs on the human mind have intrigued layman and scientists alike. Although the therapeutic usefulness and the authenticity of the "schizophreniform" state following drug ingestion has been debated, it is likely that an understanding of the mechanisms of action of hallucinogenic drugs will be of considerable heuristic value in the study of the biochemical basis of mental function.

While many drugs affect mental activity, and various drug-induced psychoses have been described, the term "hallucinogen" as used here will refer only to a restricted group of compounds, whose effects are quite similar and, in some studies, indistinguishable (Ungar, 1963). There are two major chemical classes of hallucinogens: those resembling tryptamine, such as psilocin and *d*-lysergic acid diethylamide (LSD); and those related to phenylethylamine, such as mescaline and 3,4,5-trimethoxyamphetamine, (TMA). The clinical resemblance of the syndromes produced by mescaline, psilocin, LSD, TMA and other hallucinogens suggests that these drugs, despite differences in chemical structure, may share a common mechanism of action. The fact that the psychotropic effects of TMA, a methoxylated amphetamine, are quite unlike those of amphetamine but strikingly similar to those of LSD, a complex alkaloid, illustrates the complexity of structure-activity relationships of hallucinogens. The hypothesis that hallucinogens possess a common mechanism of action is supported by findings that cross-tolerance can develop between the hallucinogens, LSD, mescaline, and psilocybin (Balestrieri and Fontanari, 1959; Isbell *et al.*, 1961), but not between hallucinogens and amphetamine (Isbell *et al.*, 1962), or scopolamine (Isbell *et al.*, 1964).

There are other structure-activity relationships of hallucinogens which are not easily explained. The introduction of bromine at carbon 2 of LSD

[1] Present address: Henry Phipps Psychiatric Clinic, Johns Hopkins Hospital, Baltimore, Maryland.

(Cerletti and Rothlin, 1955), or the reduction of a double bond between carbons 9 and 10 of LSD (Cerletti, 1959), renders the molecule devoid of hallucinatory activity. Minor structural changes in the TMA series produce marked changes in hallucinogenic activity. Shulgin (1964) has found that TMA-2 (2,4,5-trimethoxyamphetamine) is about seventeen times as potent an hallucinogen as mescaline; that TMA (3,4,5-trimethoxyamphetamine) is about twice as active as mescaline; and that TMA-3 (4,5,6-trimethoxyamphetamine) is devoid of hallucinogenic activity. Of the N-methylated tryptamines, psilocin (4-hydroxy-N,N-dimethyltryptamine) is a potent hallucinogen (Wolbach *et al.*, 1962), while bufotenine (5-hydroxy-N,N-dimethyltryptamine) is inactive (Turner and Merles, 1959; H. Isbell, personal communication).

Hypotheses for the mechanism of hallucinogenic activity of drugs ideally should explain all the structure-activity relationships described above. Since the presumed brain neurohumors, norepinephrine and serotonin, are structurally similar to phenylethylamine and tryptamine, respectively (the prototypes for the two major classes of hallucinogens), it has been thought that hallucinogens might affect synaptic transmission in the brain. One theory postulates that hallucinogens act in the brain as anti-metabolites of serotonin (Wooley and Shaw, 1954), and is based on the finding that LSD in low concentrations antagonizes the contractile effect of serotonin on smooth muscle. However, 2-brom-LSD, which has 50% more anti-serotonin activity than LSD on the estrous rat uterus, and which readily enters the brain, has no hallucinogenic activity (Cerletti and Rothlin, 1955).

The apparent lack of a simple relationship between molecular architecture and the hallucinogenic potency of drugs is perplexing. In our laboratories, molecular models of active hallucinogens and their less active analogs were constructed and compared. This comparison failed to reveal any remarkable properties of the active compounds. It was therefore considered that the critical feature of hallucinogens might reside not in their gross chemical structure but in the distribution of electrons.

An electronic, or "sub-molecular" hypothesis for the psychotic actions of drugs is not altogether novel. Karreman *et al.* (1959) had performed molecular orbital calculations for a series of psychoactive drugs. They noted that chlorpromazine is an extraordinarily potent electron donor and suggested that its efficacy as a tranquilizer may be related to an electron-donating action. Isenberg and Szent-Gyorgyi (1959) found experimentally that serotonin readily donates electrons to form charge transfer complexes. Szent-Gyorgyi (1960) speculated that schizophrenia might involve a paucity of cerebral electronic activity, reversed by chlorpromazine treatment.

Molecular orbital calculations such as those performed by Karreman *et al.* (1959) afford an approximation of the electronic configuration of pi systems of molecules. From such calculations, measures of chemical reactivity can be ascertained for a given molecule and compared with any given property in order to define a correlation between function and electronic configuration.

Molecular orbital calculations have been made for a variety of hallucinogenic drugs and their non-hallucinogenic analogs in order to seek such correlations. A striking relationship has been observed between electronic configuration and hallucinogenic potency in several series of phenylethylamine, amphetamine, and tryptamine derivatives, and for LSD.

METHODS

Molecular orbital calculations were made by the semi-empirical Hückel method (Streitweiser, 1961), using a Honeywell 800 digital computer with a program designed by Howard de Voe. The authors wish to express their appreciation to Dr. Howard de Voe for the use of his program and for assisting us in its modification. The simple Hückel molecular orbital calculations deal only with pi-bonded systems and cannot take into account sigma bonds. Since all of the compounds in this study contain sigma-bonded side chains, an approximation was made for the side chains. Comparison of reactivity indices were made between compounds with similar side chains. Parameter values were those suggested by Streitweiser (1961). The following reactivity indices were determined: pi charge, free valence, frontier electron density, superdelocalizability, and the energies of the highest filled and lowest empty molecular orbitals.

Pi charge represents the net positive or negative electrical charge measured at each atom of a molecule. This index provides a relative indication of the capacity to participate in electrostatic interactions.

Free valence (Streitweiser, 1961) measures the residual pi bonding which is available to form a weak pi bond linkage with an attacking reagent.

The energy of the highest filled molecular orbital (HFMO) is a relative measure of the ability of an electron in the highest occupied molecular orbital of a compound to be transferred to an acceptor molecule. The higher the HFMO energy, the greater will be the propensity of a molecule to donate electrons. The energy of the lowest empty orbital (LEMO) indicates the ease with which an electron can be accepted from a potential donor.

Frontier electron density is the spatial distribution of the electrons in the HFMO. Thus an atom with a high frontier electron density would have a greater density of HFMO electrons than an atom with a low frontier electron density (Fukui *et al.*, 1957).

Superdelocalizability (Fukui *et al.*, 1952) is a measure of the ability of each atom in a molecule to form a weak pi bond with an incoming attacking reagent when the pi system remains unperturbed. In the present study superdelocalizability was calculated for all atoms in each molecule, but is reported only for the atom with the highest frontier electron density.

TABLE 1. ELECTRONIC CONFIGURATION OF PHENYLETHYLAMINES

Compound	HFMO†	Highest free valence	Position	Greatest negative pi charge	Position	Greatest frontier electron density	Position	Super-delocalizability‡	LEMO†
Mescaline (3,4,5-trimethoxyphenylethylamine)	+0·5357	1·72	CH_3 at 4	−0·104	2, 6	0·5122	4	1·23	−1·12
2,3,4-Trimethoxyphenylethylamine	+0·5696	1·72	CH_3 at 4, 5, 6	−0·072	3	0·3960	4	1·05	−1·10
3,4-Dimethoxydopamine	+0·5702	1·72	CH_3 at 4	−0·074	2	0·4162	4	1·06	−1·05
4-Methoxydopamine	+0·6016	1·72	CH_3 at 4	−0·071	2	0·4341	4	1·02	−1·04
3-Methoxydopamine	+0·6184	1·72	CH_3 at 3	−0·074	2	0·4690	4	1·05	−1·05
Methoxytryramine	+0·6583	1·71	CH_3 at 3	−0·041	2	0·3894	4	0·95	−1·03
Methoxymetatyramine	+0·7240	1·71	CH_3 at 3	−0·076	2	0·3595	4	1·05	−1·03
3,4,5-Trihydroxyphenylethylamine	+0·6316	1·51	O_2 at 4	−0·097	2, 6	0·6111	4	1·16	−1·11
Dopamine	+0·6586	1·50	O_2 at 4	−0·071	2	0·5191	4	1·02	−1·04
Tyramine	+0·7209	1·49	O_2 at 4	−0·038	3, 5	0·5017	1	0·92	−1·00
Metatyramine	+0·7240	1·48	O_2 at 3	−0·072	2	0·4834	6	1·02	−1·03
Phenylethylamine	+0·8619	0·41	6, 2	−0·031	4	0·5771	4	0·91	−1·00

† Expressed in β units so that mescaline is a better electron donor and a poorer acceptor than phenylethylamine.
‡ Expressed in reciprocal β units; thus mescaline is a better electron donor than phenylethylamine.

RESULTS AND DISCUSSION

Molecular orbital calculations were performed for series of mono-, di-, and trihydroxylated and methoxylated phenylethylamines (Fig. 1; Table 1). Progressive methoxylation was found to correlate with an increase in HFMO energy. With monophenolic amines, such as tyramine and metatyramine, and the diphenolic amine dopamine, the methoxy derivatives had more energetic HFMO's than the corresponding hydroxylated derivatives. A more energetic HFMO is indicated by a lower value in β units. Moreover, additional hydroxy groups also increased the HFMO energy. Thus 3,4-dihydroxyphenylethylamine had a more energetic HFMO than the monophenolic

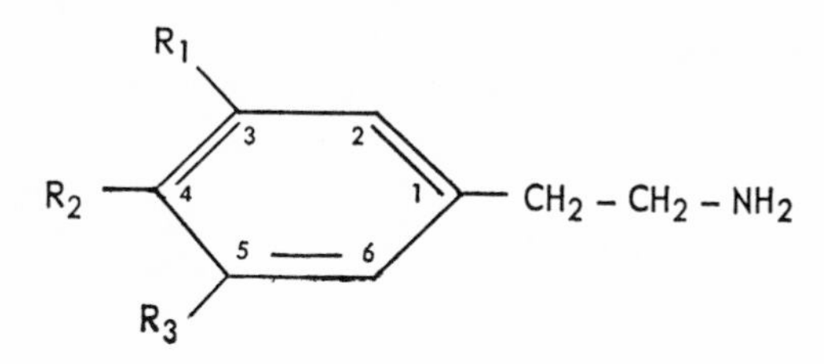

COMPOUND	R_1	R_2	R_3
Dopamine	OH	OH	–
3-Methoxydopamine	CH_3O	OH	–
3-4-dimethoxyphenylethylamine	CH_3O	CH_3O	–
Mescaline	CH_3O	CH_3O	CH_3O
Tyramine	–	OH	–
Phenylethylamine	–	–	–

FIG. 1. The structures of several phenylethylamine derivatives.

derivatives, and 3,4,5-trihydroxyphenylethylamine had the highest HFMO energy of the phenolic amines. Highest HFMO energy levels occurred in compounds with the most methoxy substituents. Mescaline, a molecule in which all three hydroxy groups are methylated, had the most energetic HFMO of the series. The second highest value was considerably less energetic and occurred in 2,3,4-trimethoxyphenylethylamine. Progressive methoxylation also correlated with superdelocalizability, which is a function of the HFMO energy related to each atom.

There was a negative correlation between the number of methoxy groups and the energy of the lowest empty molecular orbital (LEMO). This would indicate that progressive methoxylation decreases the capacity of these compounds to function as electron acceptors. No clear-cut correlation was obtained between the number of methoxy substituents and frontier electron density, free valence or pi charge.

Mescaline (3,4,5-trimethoxyphenylethylamine) is well known as an effective hallucinogen. Transposition of one methoxy group from the No. 5 position to the No. 2 position (to form 2,3,4-trimethoxyphenylethylamine) results in a molecule which is devoid of hallucinogenic activity (Slotta and Muller, 1936). Data on the effects of 3,4-dimethyoxyphenylethylamine in humans are lacking. Direct information regarding central effects of phenolic amines, such as dopamine and tyramine, is difficult to obtain, since these compounds do not cross the blood brain barrier. However, the concentration of both dopamine

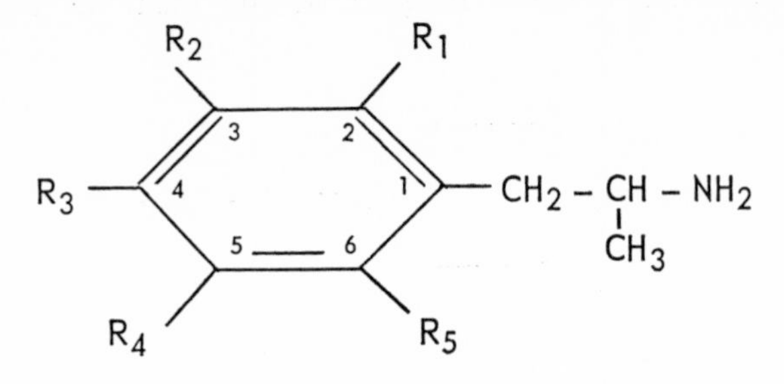

COMPOUND	R_1	R_2	R_3	R_4	R_5
TMA	–	CH_3O	CH_3O	CH_3O	–
TMA-2	CH_3O	–	CH_3O	CH_3O	–
TMA-3	–	–	CH_3O	CH_3O	CH_3O

FIG. 2. The structures of three trimethoxylated amphetamine derivatives.

and tyramine in the brain can be markedly elevated in animals following treatment with monoamine oxidase inhibitors (Kakimoto and Armstrong, 1962; Carlsson *et al.*, 1960). Brain dopamine concentration can also be increased by the administration of its amino-acid precursor, dihydroxyphenylalanine (Weil-Malherbe and Bone, 1959). Neither monoamine oxidase inhibition nor dihydroxyphenylalanine treatment produces effects comparable to those of mescaline. Yet, the characteristic effects of mescaline on mental functioning presumably occur when brain levels of the drug are less than 1 μg/g (Neff *et al.*, 1964), and thus lower than brain levels of dopamine obtained after monoamine oxidase inhibition or dihydroxyphenylalanine treatment.

There would therefore appear to be a possible relationship between the hallucinogenic activity of phenylethylamines and the ability of these compounds to donate electrons, as indicated by the energy of the HFMO's.

TABLE 2. AMPHETAMINE DERIVATIVES: ELECTRONIC CONFIGURATION AND HALLUCINOGENIC POTENCY

Compound	Hallucinogenic activity§	HFMO†	Highest free valence	Position	Greatest negative pi charge	Position	Greatest frontier electron density	Position	Super-delocalizability‡	LEMO†
TMA-2	17	0·4810	1·72	CH_3 at 2, 4, 5	−0·0854	3	0·3675	5	1·14	−1·072
TMA	2·2	0·5357	1·72	CH_3 at 4	−0·1040	2, 6	0·5122	4	1·23	−1·116
TMA-3	2	0·5696	1·72	CH_3 at 4, 5, 6	−0·0716	3	0·3960	4	1·05	−1·105

† Expressed in β units so that TMA-2 is a better electron donor and poorer acceptor than TMA-3.
‡ Expressed in reciprocal β units so that TMA is a better electron donor than TMA-3.
§ Hallucinogenic activity values are those of Shulgin (1964) and are expressed as the ratio of the effective dose of mescaline in humans (3·75 mg/kg) to the effective dose of a given drug.

To test this correlation in another series, calculations were performed for a group of trimethoxyamphetamines (Fig. 2; Table 2) of widely varying hallucinogenic activity. TMA-2 (2,4,5-trimethoxyamphetamine) and TMA (3,4,5-trimethoxyamphetamine) are respectively about seventeen times and two times more potent then mescaline as hallucinogens, whereas TMA-3 (4,5,6-trimethoxyamphetamine) appears to be inactive (Shulgin, 1964). The three drugs differ structurally only in the location of their methoxy substituents. The presence of both ring and side chain methyl groups should enable all three to enter the brain readily and to a similar extent. Calculations revealed marked differences in the HFMO energies of these three compounds which correlated with the differences in their hallucinogenic potency. Thus, TMA-2

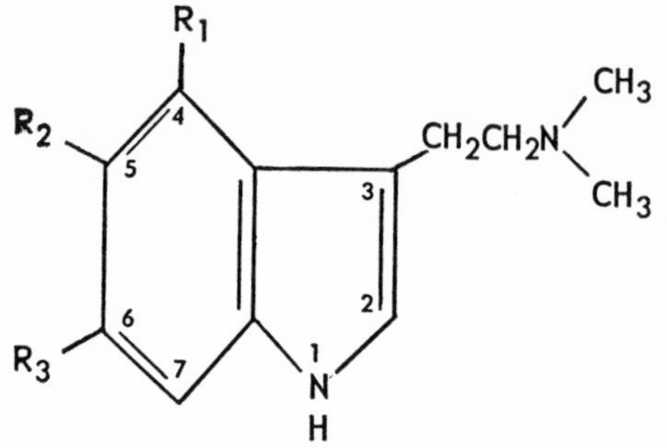

COMPOUND	R_1	R_2	R_3
Dimethyltryptamine	H	H	H
Bufotenine	H	OH	H
6-Hydroxy-N-N-dimethyltryptamine	H	H	OH
Psilocin (4-Hydroxy-N-N-dimethyltryptamine)	OH	H	H

FIG. 3. The structures of several N-alkylated tryptamine derivatives.

had the most energetic HFMO, TMA-3 the least, and TMA was intermediate. Hallucinogenic potency did not correlate with frontier electron density, pi charge, free valence, superdelocalizability, or energy of the LEMO.

Since the Hückel determinations employed here do not take into account sigma bond alterations in the side chains, the calculated electronic configurations for TMA and TMA-3, respectively, are the same as for mescaline and 2,3,4-trimethoxyphenylamine. It is, therefore, interesting that hallucinogenic potency parallels HFMO energy in the same way for these four molecules.

Several N-alkylated tryptamine derivatives produce hallucinogenic effects in human subjects which are qualitatively similar to those associated with mescaline and LSD (Szara, 1957). Calculations were performed on a series of these compounds (Fig. 3; Table 3). The energy of the HFMO was greatest

TABLE 3. TRYPTAMINE DERIVATIVES: ELECTRONIC CONFIGURATION AND HALLUCINOGENIC POTENCY

Compound	Hallucinogenic activity‖	HFMO‡	Highest free valence	Position	Largest negative pi charge	Position	Greatest frontier electron density	Position	Super-delocalizability§	LEMO†
Psilocin	31	0·4603	1·48	O_2 at 4	−0·077	9	0·5118	2	−1·53	−0·882
6-Hydroxydiethyl-tryptamine	25	0·4700	1·49	O_2 at 6	−0·080	3	0·5664	2	−1·53	−0·871
Bufotenine	—†	0·5147	1·49	O_2 at 5	−0·084	3	0·5435	2	−1·43	−0·839
Diethyltryptamine	—†	0·5164	0·99	1	−0·081	3	0·5739	2	−1·43	−0·838

† Weak or inactive as detailed in text.

‡ Expressed in β units so that psilocin is a better electron donor and poorer acceptor than dimethyltryptamine.

§ Expressed in reciprocal β units; thus psilocin is a better electron donor than dimethyltryptamine.

‖ Expressed as ratio of effective dose of mescaline to effective dose of a given drug. Values for psilocin were obtained from Wolbach *et al.* (1962) and for 6-hydroxydiethyltryptamine from Szara (1957).

for psilocin (4-hydroxy-N,N-dimethyltryptamine) and next highest for 6-hydroxy-N,N-diethyl or dimethyltryptamine.[1] Corresponding values for bufotenine (5-hydroxy-N,N-dimethyltryptamine) and N,N-dimethyltryptamine (or N,N-diethyltryptamine) were considerably lower. Psilocin is the most potent hallucinogen of these drugs (Wolbach *et al.*, 1962) and 6-hydroxy-N,N-diethyltryptamine is next most effective (Szara, 1962). The administration of N,N-dimethyltryptamine or N,N-diethyltryptamine does produce hallucinogenic effects (Szara, 1957) but the available evidence indicates that these compounds and bufotenine of themselves are weak or ineffective as compared to psilocin and 6-hydroxy-N,N-diethyltryptamine.

Fabing and Hawkins (1956) observed minor alterations in visual perception and paresthesias in normal subjects after the intravenous injection of bufotenine. There were, however, no control subjects in this study to rule out possible placebo effects. Other workers (Turner and Merles, 1959; H. Isbell, personal communication) administered a variety of drugs as well as saline controls to schizophrenics and to normal subjects. Bufotenine in doses up to twice those used by Fabing and Hawkins (1956) was without hallucinogenic effect.

The parenteral administration of dimethyl or diethyltryptamine to human subjects results in hallucinogenic experiences similar to those produced by LSD or mescaline, but of more rapid onset and shorter duration (Szara, 1957). Szara has found that these drugs are 6-hydroxylated in the liver (Szara and Axelrod, 1959) and that their psychotropic activity is closely related to the extent of 6-hydroxylation (Szara and Hearst, 1962). Moreover, 6-fluorodiethyltryptamine, a molecule which cannot be 6-hydroxylated *in vivo*, is devoid of hallucinogenic activity (Kalier and Szara, 1963). These data, as well as the observation that 6-hydroxy-N,N-diethyltryptamine in doses of 0·14 mg/kg can produce psychotropic effects comparable to those evoked by 1·0 mg/kg of N,N-diethyltryptamine (Szara and Hearst, 1962), have led Szara to conclude that the characteristic symptoms associated with diethyl- or dimethyltryptamine administration are mediated by their 6-hydroxylated metabolites.

There appears, therefore, to be an excellent correlation between hallucinogenicity of the tryptamine derivatives and the energy of their HFMO. Superdelocalizability, a function of the HFMO energy, also correlated with hallucinogenic potency. There was a negative correlation with the energy of the LEMO and no correlation with pi charge, frontier electron density, or free valence.

To provide an indication of the distribution of various electronic parameters throughout each molecule, the free valence, frontier electron density, superdelocalizability, and pi charge for mescaline appear in Fig. 4. Comparable values for TMA-2 and psilocin appear in Figs. 5 and 6 respectively.

[1] The molecular orbital calculations used in this study do not distinguish between N,N-dimethyl- or N,N-diethyltryptamines.

PI CHARGE

.0613 .0036
OCH3
-.0855
-.0107
.0036 .0615
CH3O
-.0122
-.0325
CH2 — CH — NH2
.0412
CH3
-.0220
-.0721
CH3O
.0035 .0603

FRONTIER ELECTRON DENSITY

.1628 .0452
OCH3
.0012
.3065
.0426 .1530
CH3O
.2881
.3070
CH2 — CH — NH2
.0652
CH3
.3675
.0117
CH3O
.0541 .1952

FREE VALENCE

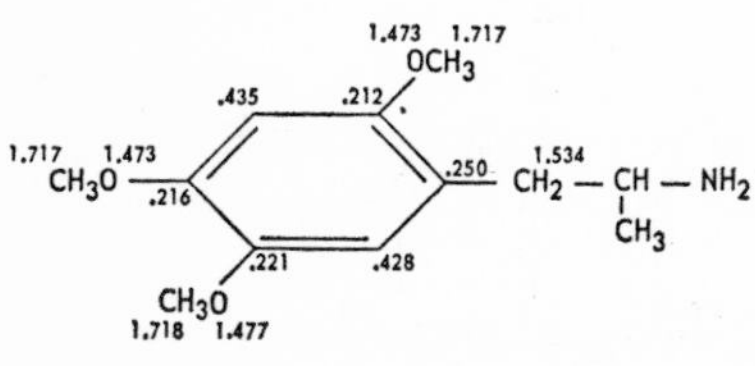

SUPERDELOCALIZABILITY

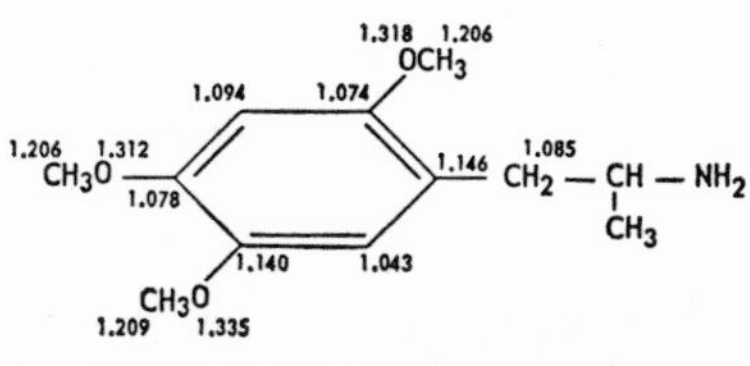

FIG. 4. Electronic reactivity indices for mescaline. Superdelocalizability is expressed in reciprocal β units.

PI CHARGE

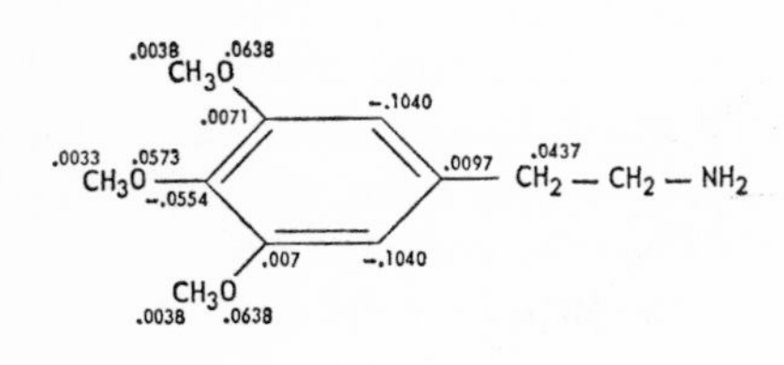

FRONTIER ELECTRON DENSITY

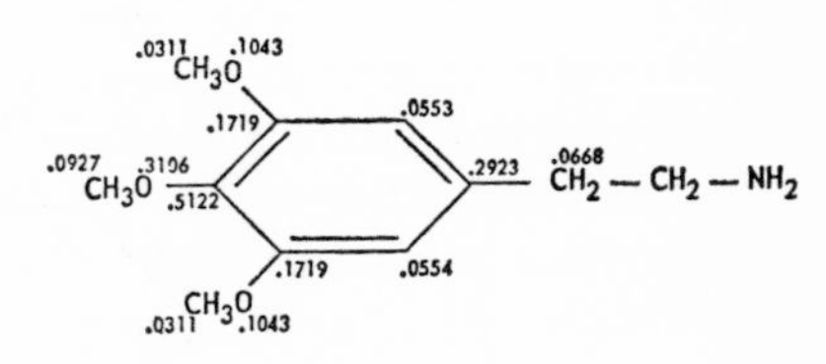

FREE VALENCE

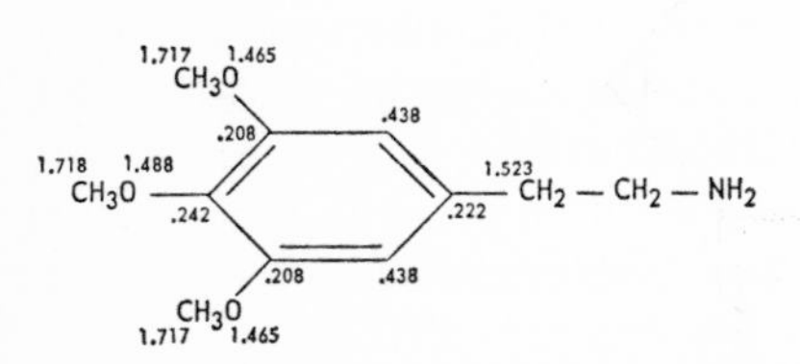

SUPERDELOCALIZABILITY

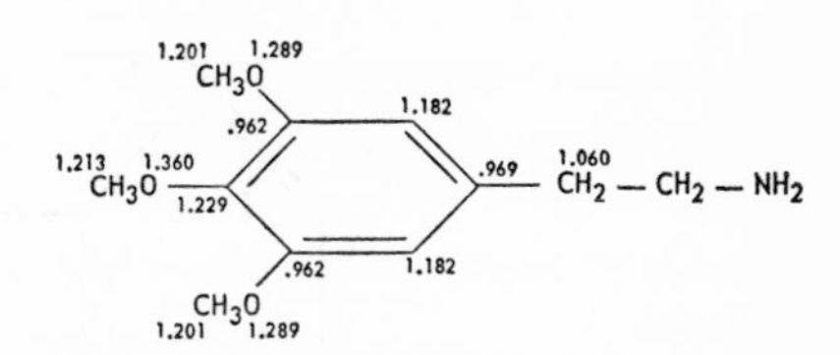

FIG. 5. Electronic reactivity indices for TMA-2. Superdelocalizability is given in reciprocal β units.

PI CHARGE

.0623 OH .0402 .0376 $CH_2 - CH_2 - N(CH_3)_2$ −.0770 −.0780 −.0769 −.0153 −.0544 .0020 N −.0650 .2245

FRONTIER ELECTRON DENSITY

.0838 OH .2727 1478 $CH_2 - CH_2 - N(CH_3)_2$ .0482 .0566 .4056 .1703 .5118 .0466 N .1830

FREE VALENCE

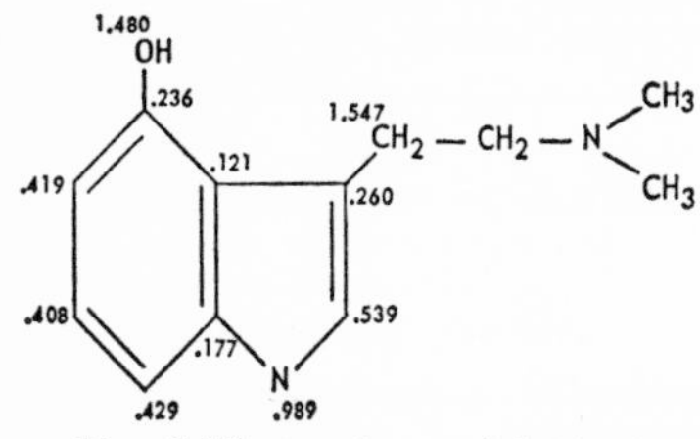

SUPERDELOCALIZABILITY

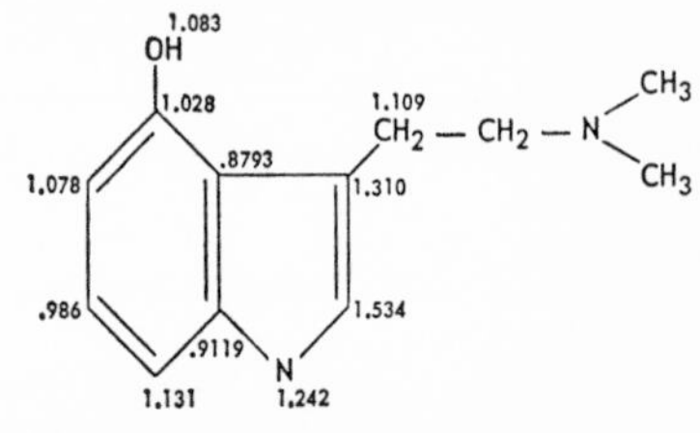

FIG. 6. Electronic reactivity indices for psilocin. Superdelocalizability is expressed in reciprocal β units.

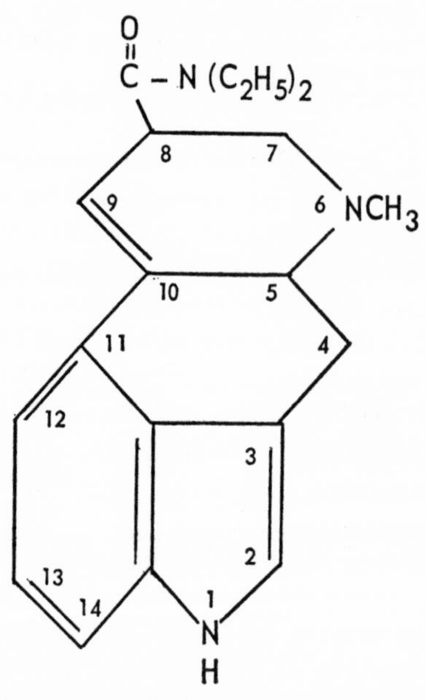

FIG. 7. The structure of *d*-lysergic acid diethylamide.

The best known and most potent hallucinogen is LSD, which is highly effective in humans at doses of 1 μg/kg. The LSD molecule (Fig. 7) contains an indole nucleus linked to two other sigma-bonded ring systems. Since the computer program used in this study to determine electronic indices cannot take into account sigma-bonded systems, a detailed electronic configuration could not be determined for LSD. If, however, the effect of the saturated ring system on the indole nucleus is approximated by the introduction of methyl groups at positions Nos. 3 and 4, a crude calculation can be performed. Such a methylated indole model of LSD has a calculated energy of the HFMO of 0·474 β units as compared to a value of 0·516 for N,N-dimethyltryptamine which contains an unsubstituted indole ring. Karreman *et al.* (1959) calculated the HFMO energy for the complete LSD molecule and obtained a value of

TABLE 4. RELATIONSHIP OF HALLUCINOGENIC POTENCY IN DIFFERENT CLASSES OF DRUGS TO THE ENERGY OF THEIR HFMO

Drug	Minimum effective dose (mg/kg)	Hallucinogenic activity†	Energy of HFMO§
LSD	0·001	3700	0·2180‡
Psilocin	0·12	31	0·4603
6-Hydroxydiethyltryptamine	0·15	25	0·4700
TMA-2	0·22	17	0·4810
TMA	1·70	2·2	0·5357

† Hallucinogenic activity is expressed as ratio of effective dose of mescaline (3·75 mg/kg as the base) to the effective dose of a given drug.
‡ As determined by Karreman *et al.* (1959).
§ Expressed in β units; thus LSD is a better electron donor than TMA.

0·218 β units, indicating an HFMO far more energetic than any of the compounds examined in this study. As with all the tryptamine derivatives examined, the region of highest frontier electron density in LSD is at the No. 2 carbon atom. The position of greatest frontier electron density in a molecule is the probable active site for charge transfer reactivity. If a charge transfer mechanism is involved in the hallucinogenic action of LSD, the No. 2 carbon should be critical for this activity. It is, therefore, interesting to note that 2-brom-LSD (Cerletti and Rothlin, 1955) and 2-oxy-LSD (Axelrod *et al.*, 1957), which contain sterically obstructing substituents at the No. 2 carbon, are devoid of hallucinogenic effect, even though they readily enter the brain.

The energy of a pi system of electrons is closely related to the extent of the resonance within the system. A major factor in increasing the HFMO energy of LSD over that of a simple indole structure such as tryptamine lies in the possibility of resonance between the indole ring and the pi electrons of the double bond at C_9—C_{10} (Fig. 4). Although we cannot perform the appropriate calculations, it is likely that reduction of the double bond at C_9—C_{10}

would markedly decrease the HFMO energy for the LSD molecule. It is important, therefore, to note that the loss of the C_9—C_{10} double bond by hydrogenation or hydration (as in dihydro-LSD and Lumi-LSD respectively) abolishes the hallucinogenic properties (Cerletti, 1959).

The correlations between electronic configuration and hallucinogenic properties discussed above have been obtained within series of structurally related compounds. It would be important if such correlations could be obtained between groups of structually dissimilar drugs. It is unlikely that such a relationship could be established in detail. The action of a drug on its receptor in the brain is certainly several steps removed from its administration. Intervening are such critical variables as relative metabolic degradation, penetration of the blood brain barrier, and concentration into presumed target areas within the brain. The amphetamine and tryptamine analogs for which hallucinogenic efficacy, minimum effective dose, and electronic configuration are reasonably well established, have been grouped in Table 4, revealing a close correlation between hallucinogenic potency and HFMO energy.

The observed relationships between reactivity indices and psychotropic activity suggests the possibility of predicting the structure of hallucinogens even more potent than those presently available. Calculations for several hypothetical tryptamine derivatives (Table 5) indicate that methoxylation and disubstitution increase the energy of the HFMO. Thus dimethoxylated derivatives, such as 4,6-dimethoxy-N,N-dimethyltryptamine have the most energetic HFMO's.

The correlative data described here suggest a common mode of action for these hallucinogens at a hypothetical receptor. To support this view are studies which indicate that cross-tolerance can develop between LSD, psilocybin, and mescaline (Balestrieri and Fontanari, 1959; Isbell *et al.*, 1961).

It would be interesting to postulate an electronic model for the interaction of an hallucinogenic drug with its receptor. The calculations performed in this study, however, do not permit a specific formulation. The energy of the highest filled molecular orbital of a compound is not a precise index; the correlation of HFMO energy with hallucinogenic activity only implies that these compounds may act as electron donors, but does not describe a mechanism for hallucinogenesis. Reactions involving electron donation cover a broad spectrum including such strong interactions of donor and acceptor as oxidation-reduction, as well as such weak interactions as charge transfer or acid-base phenomena. Moreover, the crudeness of the theoretical and pharmacological data in this study preclude a detailed delineation of the nature of the electron-donation process, as might be afforded by indices, such as free valence and superdelocalizability.

Correlation with an index of electron donation, and not with other indices of chemical reactivity is none the less useful. There are a great number of

TABLE 5. TRYPTAMINE DERIVATIVES WITH INCREASED HFMO ENERGY

Compound	HFMO†	LEMO†	Greatest frontier electron density	Position	Super-delocalizability‡	Greatest negative pi charge	Position	Greatest free valence	Position
4-Methoxypsilocin	0·4402	−0·8854	0·4753	2	1·558	−0·0822	5	1·714	CH_3 at 4
4,6-Dihydroxydimethyltryptamine	0·4231	−0·9227	0·5248	2	1·649	−0·1110	5	1·487	O_2 at 6
6-Methoxy-4-hydroxy-dimethyltryptamine	0·4099	−0·9257	0·5142	2	1·675	−0·1151	7	1·716	CH_3 at 6
4-Methoxy-6-hydroxy-dimethyltryptamine	0·4070	−0·9264	0·4972	2	1·675	−0·1156	5	1·714	CH_3 at 4
4,6-Dimethoxydimethyltryptamine	0·3954	−0·9294	0·4917	2	1·701	−0·1187	7	1·716	CH_3 at 6

† Expressed in β units so that 4,6-dimethoxydimethyltryptamine is a better electron donor and poorer acceptor than 4-methoxypsilocin.
‡ Expressed in reciprocal β units; thus, 4,6-dimethoxydimethyltryptamine is a better electron donor than 4-methoxypsilocin.

conceivable interactions between drug and receptor. The drug could sterically approximate the receptor, be bound by electrostatic interactions, form a weak covalent linkage, or act as an electron donor or acceptor. While steric factors are certainly important, they do not explain some structure-activity relationships, such as the greater efficacy of 2,4,5-trimethoxyamphetamine as compared to 4,5,6- or 3,4,5-trimethoxyamphetamines. The absence of correlation with pi charge distribution would tend to be inconsistent with an electrostatic attraction. And, if an electron transfer mechanism is involved, the negative correlation with energy of the lowest empty orbital would indicate that the hallucinogens do not exert pharmacological activity via electron acceptance.

REFERENCES

AXELROD, J., BRADY, R. O., WITKOP, B. and EVARTS, E. V. (1957) The distribution and metabolism of lysergic and diethylamide, *Annals of the New York Academy of Science*, **66,** 435–44.

BALESTRIERI, A. and FONTANARI, D. (1959) Acquired and crossed tolerance to mescaline, LSD-25, and BOL-148, *AMA Archives of General Psychiatry*, **1,** 279–82.

CARLSSON, A., LINDQUIST, M. and MAGNUSSON, I. (1960) On the biochemistry and possible functions of dopamine and noradrenaline in brain, *Adrenergic Mechanisms*, J. R. Vance, G. E. Wolstenholme and M. O'Connor, Editors, London, J. and A. Churchill Ltd. (p. 432).

CERLETTI, A. and ROTHLIN, E. (1955) Role of 5-hydroxytryptamine in mental diseases and its antagonism to lysergic acid derivatives, *Nature*, **176,** 785–6.

CERLETTI, A. (1959) Discussion, *Neuro-Psychopharmacology*, P. B. Bradley, P. Deniker and C. Kadouco-Thomas, Editors. Amsterdam, Elsevier Publishing Company (p. 117).

FABING, H. and HAWKINS, J. H. (1956) Intravenous bufotenine injection in the human being, *Science*, **123,** 886–7.

FUKUI, K., YONEZAWA, T. and SHINGU, H. (1952) A molecular orbital theory of reactivity in aromatic hydrocarbons, *Journal of Chemical Physics*, **20,** 722–5.

FUKUI, K., YONEZAWA, T. and NAGATA, C. (1957) A molecular orbital theoretical approach to the mechanism of charge transfer in the process of aromatic substitutions, *Journal of Chemical Physics*, **27,** 1247–58.

ISBELL, H., WOLBACH, A. B., WIKLER, A. and MINER, E. J. (1961) Cross tolerance between LSD and psilocybin, *Psychopharmacologia*, **2,** 147–59.

ISBELL, H., WOLBACH, A. B. and ROSENBERG, D. E. (1962) Observations on direct and cross tolerance with LSD and dextroamphetamine in man, *Federation Proceedings*, **21,** 416.

ISBELL, H., ROSENBERG, D. E., MINER, E. J. and LOGAN, C. R. (1964) Tolerance and cross tolerance to scopalamine, N-ethyl-3-piperidyl benzylate (JB 318) and LSD-25, *Neuro-psychopharmacology*, P. B. Bradley, F. Flugel and P. Hoch, Editors, Amsterdam, Elsevier Publishing Company (pp. 440–6).

ISENBERG, I. and SZENT-GYÖRGYI, A. (1959) On charge transfer complexes between substances of biochemical interest, *Proceedings of the National Academy of Sciences, U.S.A.*, **45,** 1229–31.

KAKIMOTO, Y. and ARMSTRONG, M. D. (1962) On the identification of octopamine in mammals, *Journal of Biological Chemistry*, **327,** 422–7.

KALIER, A. and SZARA, S. (1963) Synthesis and pharmacological activity of fluorinated tryptamine derivatives, *Journal of Medicinal Chemistry*, **6,** 716–19.

KARREMAN, G., ISENBERG, I. and SZENT-GYORGYI, A. (1959) On the mechanism of action of chlorpromazine, *Science*, **130,** 1191–2.

NEFF, N., ROSS, G. V., CHASE, G. D. and RABINOWITZ, J. L. (1964) Distribution and metabolism of mescaline-C^{14} in the cat brain, *Journal of Pharmacology and Experimental Therapeutics*, **144,** 1–7.

SHULGIN, A. T. (1964) Psychomimetic amphetamines: methoxy 3,4-dialkoxy-amphetamines, *Experientia*, **20,** 1–4.

SLOTTA, K. H. and MULLER, J. (1936) Über den Abbau des Mescalins in mescalina inlicher Stoffe in Organismus, *Zeitschrift für Physiologische Chemie*, **238,** 14–22.

STREITWEISER, A. (1961) *Molecular Orbital Theory for Organic Chemists*, New York, Academic Press.

SZARA, S. (1957) The comparison of the psychotic effect of tryptamine derivatives with the effects of mescaline and LSD-25 in self experiments, *Psychotropic Drugs*, S. Garattini and V. Ghetti, Editors, Amsterdam, Elsevier Company (p. 460).

SZARA, S. and AXELROD, J. (1959) Hydroxylation and N-demethylation of N,N-dimethyltryptamine, *Experientia*, **15,** 216.

SZARA, S. and HEARST, E. (1962) The 6-hydroxylation of tryptamine derivatives, a way of producing psychoactive metabolites, *Annals of the New York Academy of Sciences*, **96,** 134–41.

SZENT-GYORGYI, A. (1960) *Introduction to a Submolecular Biology*, New York, Academic Press.

TURNER, W. J. and MERLES, S. (1959) Effect of some indolealkylamines on man, *AMA Archives of Neurology and Psychiatry*, **81,** 121–9.

UNGAR, S. M. (1963) Mescaline, LSD, psilocybin and personality change, *Psychiatry*, **26,** 111–25.

WEIL-MALHERBE, H. and BONE, A. D. (1959) The effect of reserpine on the intracellular distribution of catecholamines in the brain stem of the rabbit, *Journal of Neurochemistry*, **4,** 251–63.

WOLBACH, A. B., MINER, E. J. and ISBELL, H. (1962) Comparison of psilocin with psilocybin, mescaline and LSD-25, *Psychopharmacologia*, **3,** 219–23.

WOOLEY, D. W. and SHAW, E. (1954) A biochemical and pharmacological suggestion about certain mental disorders, *Proceedings of the National Academy of Sciences*, **40,** 228–31.

STUDIES ON HOMOCYSTINURIA

S. HARVEY MUDD, LEONARD LASTER, JAMES D. FINKELSTEIN and FILADELFO IRREVERRE

National Institute of Mental Health,
National Institute of Arthritis and Metabolic Disease, Bethesda, Maryland

DURING the course of a survey of mentally backward individuals in Northern Ireland in 1962 it was discovered that the urines of two female siblings gave a positive cyanide nitroprusside test suggesting the presence of a sulfur-containing compound (Carson and Neill, 1962). Specimens were subsequently studied at the University College Hospital Medical School in London by Dr. Dent and his collaborators and it was found that the abnormal urinary substance was homocystine (Field *et al.*, 1962; Carson *et al.*, 1963). Meanwhile Gerritsen, Vaughn, and Waisman, at the University of Wisconsin Medical School, had independently discovered that an infant with congenital anomalies, mental retardation, and failure to thrive excreted an abnormal amino acid. This group presented evidence also in 1962 to identify the unusual substance as homocystine (Gerritsen *et al.*, 1962).

Since then, similar patients have been discovered in sufficient numbers to permit delineation of a clinical syndrome associated with the presence of homocystine in the urine and characterized by such relatively constant features as mental retardation, fair hair, dislocated ocular lenses, malar flush, peculiar gait, and genu valgum, and by such variable features as pes cavus, long extremities and digits, convulsions, thrombotic incidents, cardiovascular disorders and fatty liver. No accurate estimate of the prevalence of the disease is yet available, but it is already clear that the abnormality is *not* an extremely rare one (Carson *et al.*, 1963; Komrower and Wilson, 1963; Gerritsen and Waisman, 1964a; Gibson *et al.*, 1964; Carson *et al.*, 1965; Hall *et al.*, 1965).

We became interested in studying some of the biochemical features of such patients. The early reports had established that in addition to the abnormal amounts of homocystine in the urine, these persons have elevated concentrations of both methionine and homocystine in the plasma so that an abnormality in the metabolism of the sulfur-containing amino acids was suggested. Present concepts of the metabolic relationships of the pertinent compounds are presented in Fig. 1.

Very briefly, methionine is converted via S-adenosylmethionine and S-adenosylhomocysteine to homocysteine. Homocysteine may be methylated to form methionine once again. Alternatively, it may condense with serine to form the thioeither cystathionine. The latter is cleaved to yield cysteine. Most of the sulfur of cysteine is ultimately converted via a complicated set of reactions to inorganic sulfate. We tried to imagine in this diagram a single defect which would result in an accumulation of *both* methionine and homocystine and were led to postulate that the most likely site for the lesion was reaction 4, the formation of cystathionine from homocysteine and serine. In the presence of such a block, homocysteine would accumulate and be methylated to form methionine which would also accumulate. An important aspect of the reasoning was a consideration of which enzymatic reactions are

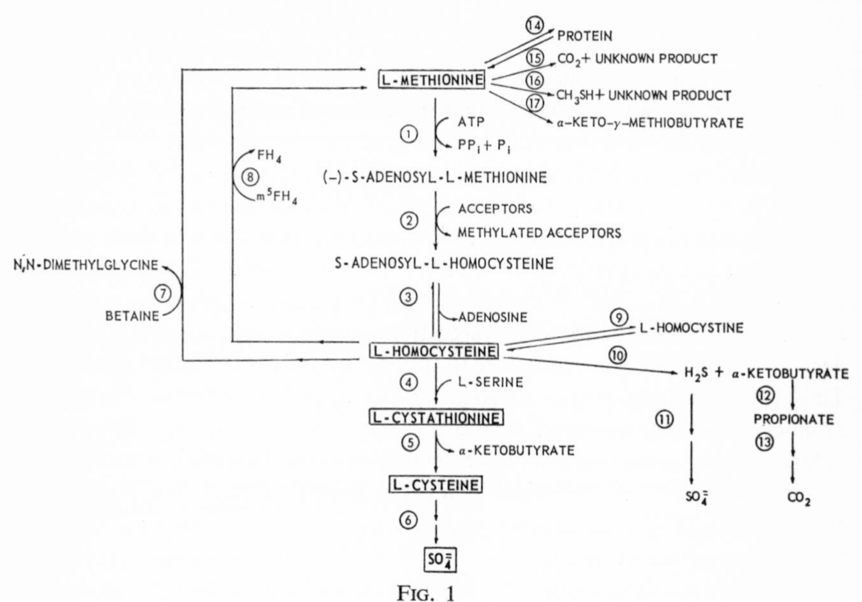

FIG. 1

essentially irreversible. For example, the physiological irreversibility of the methylation of homocysteine makes it likely that a block in methionine activation (reaction 1) would result in an excess of methionine but not homocyst(e)ine. Likewise, the irreversible nature of the overall conversion of methionine to homocysteine via S-adenosylmethionine suggests that a defect in homocysteine methylation might lead to accumulation of homocysteine, but not methionine.

An assay was developed for cystathionine synthase, the enzyme which catalyzes reaction 4. This assay was based upon the formation of radioactive cystathionine during incubation of enzyme, homocysteine, and radioactive serine (Mudd *et al.*, 1964). A preliminary survey of available tissues in the human showed that skin, erythrocytes, leucocytes and mucosa of small intestine or rectum did not contain detectable levels of the enzyme. Liver tissue was active and the sensitivity of the test was such that one could assay accurately the activity present in the relatively small amounts of liver available by percutaneous needle biopsy. Indeed, it became clear that from a single needle biopsy one would obtain material in excess of the amount needed for assay of cystathionine synthase. Therefore an assay was developed for S-adenosylmethionine synthase or methionine-activating enzyme. This assay was used as a control and to directly test a second, although far less likely, possible site of the lesion.

Appropriate experiments were carried out to gain assurance that under our conditions the assays were linear with time and proportional to enzyme, that the correct pH was used, that the enzymes had the expected dependencies, that the proper cofactors were present, that the products formed by the crude

TABLE 1. HEPATIC ENZYME ACTIVITIES IN HOMOCYSTINURIC PATIENTS AND THEIR RELATIVES

Subjects and age (years)	Methionine activating enzyme: S-adenosylmethionine, mμmole/mg/60 min†	Cystathionine synthase: cystathionine, mμmole/mg/135 min†
Controls, 32–64 years (9 patients)	Mean: 6.4 Range: 4·4–9·2	Mean: 252 Range: 133–610
C. T., 8, homocystinuria	10·3	0 (<13)
D. T., 35, mother of C. T.	6·7	86
L. T., 38, father of C. T.	5·2	88
M. A. G., 24, cousin of C. T.	4·8	31
S. M., 56, maternal grandmother of C. T.	5·6	257

† These values are normalized to 60 min and therefore differ from those previously published (Finkelstein *et al.*, 1964) which were based on a 45-min incubation. Neither enzyme was assayed at saturation with respect to substrate, so that the values for one enzyme should not be compared to those for the other.

extracts were indeed cystathionine and S-adenosylmethionine, and that these products were not being removed at significant rates by further metabolism.

Most of our assays of these enzymes in specimens of fresh liver are summarized in Table 1 (adapted from Finkelstein *et al.*, 1964). Controls with a variety of clinical conditions all had readily detectable levels of both enzymes. In marked contrast, the liver of C. T., the first homocystinuric patient studied, had no detectable activity of cystathionine synthase. Activity would have been detected had it been equal to 6% of the mean control value. C. T. did have a normal level of methionine-activating enzyme. These results then confirmed our hypothesis that the syndrome associated with homocystinuria is due to a lack of activity of the enzyme cystathionine synthase (Mudd *et al.*, 1964).

Study of the relatives of C. T. demonstrated two additional points of interest (Finkelstein *et al.*, 1964). C. T.'s parents, who are clinically normal and do not excrete homocystine in the urine, each had a concentration of cystathionine synthase in the liver below the lowest control value and equal to 35–40% of the mean control value. We have interpreted this finding as showing that cystathionine synthase deficiency is hereditary and is transmitted as an autosomal trait.

M. A. G., a paternal cousin of C. T., is not mentally retarded and is clinically normal but excretes homocystine in the urine while on a normal diet. Her hepatic cystathionine synthase activity is 31 mμmoles/mg of protein, a value between those found for the parents of C. T. and for C. T. herself. The genetic status of M. A. G. is not clear. Neither is it possible at the moment to answer the question as to why she suffers none of the pathological consequences associated with cystathionine synthase deficiency. Perhaps the residual

TABLE 2. CYSTATHIONINE SYNTHASE ACTIVITY OF LIVER EXTRACT FROM A HOMOCYSTINURIC PATIENT

Experiment	Patient	Protein, mg	Radioactivity in cystathionine fraction, c.p.m.
A	J. H. (homocystinuria)	0·34	167
	M. B. (control)	0·37	4630
	Boiled enzyme	0·26	69
	Boiled enzyme	0·26	53
	Boiled enzyme	0·26	53
B	J. H. (homocystinuria)	0·17	97
	M. B. (control)	0·37	4863
	J. H., 0·34 mg+M. B., 0·37 mg		4967
	Boiled enzyme	0·26	52
	Boiled enzyme	0·26	53
	Boiled enzyme	0·26	51

Components and volume were those of the standard incubation mixture. Incubation was for 135 min at 37°. Experiment B. Pyridoxal phosphate was raised to 0·4 μmoles for the incubation with extract J. H.

enzyme activity is sufficient to prevent damage. Perhaps environmental factors, e.g. her diet during early infancy, were responsible. Clarification of the situation in M. A. G. and other patients like her who are now being discovered will be important to further define the spectrum of this disease and to increase the chances of designing the proper therapeutic management for patients with cystathionine synthase deficiency.

I should like to discuss now some of our more recent unpublished results. We have had an opportunity to study another patient with the fully developed syndrome of homocystinuria. This patient was kindly referred to us by Drs. Neill Schimke and Victor McKusick of Johns Hopkins University. Some studies of the hepatic cystathionine synthase of this patient, J. H., are shown in Table 2. The assay has been improved since the original studies of C. T.

and her family so that we are now able to detect and quantify a lower level of activity. To illustrate this point, the immediate results of the experiments are shown. Radioactive serine was incubated with tissue extracts in the presence of homocysteine and appropriate additives. The values shown are the amount of radioactivity found in the cystathionine fraction after this fraction was separated from the remainder of the reaction mixture. The blank value was determined by the use of boiled enzyme. In experiment A, three such boiled enzyme controls were included. The range of blank values was found to be 53–69 counts per minute. An extract from M. B., a control patient, gave 4630 counts per minute whereas a similar amount of extract from the homocystinuric patient yielded 167 counts per minute. This value is extremely low relative to that found with the extract from the control patient, but there is some increase above the boiled enzyme blanks. In a further experiment, not shown here, the incubation with extracts from J. H. was repeated using serine of higher specific activity. The radioactive material in the cystathionine fraction was rigorously identified as cystathionine, confirming the fact that J. H. has a small but significant residual cystathionine synthase activity. The level is 2–3% of the mean control value.

One might ask: Is the cystathionine synthase activity low due to a lack of some necessary cofactor for the reaction? Is it low due to the presence of an inhibitor? Or is it low due to a defect in the enzyme itself? Experiment B presents evidence against the first two of these possibilities. Pyridoxal phosphate, known to be a cofactor in the reaction catalyzed by cystathionine synthase, was routinely included in all reaction mixtures. In experiment B, the cofactor was raised to a concentration far above that normally used without noticeable effect on the activity obtained with the extract from J. H. Incidentally, note that only half as much protein from the extract of J. H. was included in experiment B and the rise above the blanks was about half that obtained in experiment A. To explore the second possibility, that is the presence of an inhibitor, an experiment was carried out in which the extract from the control patient was incubated in the presence of the extract from J. H. No effect was noted, showing that the lack of activity in the extract from J. H. was not due to an inhibitor or to excessive removal of the product, cystathionine.

Another aspect of the metabolism of methionine and homocysteine which has recently occupied us is an investigation of the reactions which these and related amino acids undergo in brain tissue. An understanding of the role of these reactions in brain might throw light on the association between cystathionine synthase deficiency and mental retardation. A more specific reason for our interest was the finding, first noted in 1958 (Tallan *et al.*, 1958), that human brain is extremely rich in cystathionine. This high concentration is specific for the tissue and for the species. Brains of a variety of other mammals have lower concentrations of cystathionine. Human brain is far richer in this substance than is liver, kidney or muscle. The concentration in monkey brain also is rather high, offering the possibility that an experimental animal is available in which to study the reasons for this accumulation.

These facts raise several questions. What causes the difference between brain and other tissues? What leads to the difference between *human* brain and the brain of other mammals? To answer these questions one would like to know whether cystathionine is synthesized in the brain or whether it is transported there. One would like also to know about the further metabolism of cystathionine in the brain. Some suggestive evidence bearing on these questions has been published. In 1956 Gaitonde and Richter observed that after the intracisternal or subarachnoid injection of S^{35}-methionine to rats, S^{35}-cystine was recovered from brain proteins (Gaitonde and Richter, 1956). These workers later offered evidence that the conversion was occurring in the

TABLE 3. CYSTATHIONINE SYNTHASE CONCENTRATION IN VARIOUS TISSUES

Tissue	Cystathionine synthase, mμmoles cystathionine/mg protein/135 min Monkey	Rat	Man
Liver	323	415	252
Kidney	5	188	—
Pancreas	215	373	—
Brain	68	84	22†

† Post-mortem specimens only.

brain itself (Gaitonde and Richter, 1957). A preliminary note (Hope, 1959) reported the formation of cystathionine by rat brain homogenates incubated with serine and homocysteine. We have now searched in brain tissue for three of the enzymes involved in the conversion of methionine to cysteine. Each is present in this tissue. Methionine activating enzyme is present in rat and monkey brain at about 10% of the specific activity of this enzyme in liver. The data for cystathionine synthase are shown in Table 3. Cystathionine synthase is present in brain at concentrations about 20% of the comparable hepatic concentrations. We have found this enzyme in only a few other tissues of the rat, most of which are listed here. Certainly the brain is one of the relatively few tissues in which major amounts of cystathionine synthesis occurs.

Table 4 shows comparable figures for cystathionase, the enzyme which cleaves cystathionine to cysteine and α-ketobutyrate. Again, the enzyme is definitely present in brain. However, in contrast to the situation for cystathionine synthase, the levels of cystathionase are very low relative to the concentrations of this enzyme in the other tissues specified. Indeed, to detect activity in brain a method more sensitive than the usual colorimetric one had to be employed. This method was based upon the use of cystathionine-2-C^{14} (label in the 4 carbon moiety) as substrate and separation of the product, α-ketobutyrate-2-C^{14}, by column chromatography on Dowex-50 (H^+) (Mudd *et al.*, 1965). The values for cystathionase specific activity in brain are only about 1% of the values for liver. This observation suggests a partial explanation for the high concentration of cystathionine reported in monkey and human brain. The low level of cystathionase in a tissue which is actively making cystathionine could explain the accumulation of this thio-ether. However, since there is no striking difference in the relative cystathionase levels of the rat and the monkey brain, factors other than the low concentration of cleaving enzyme must explain the difference in cystathionine concentrations of the brains of these two species. A particularly intriguing possibility (which is entirely speculative at this time) is that cystathionine in brain

TABLE 4.
CYSTATHIONASE CONCENTRATION IN VARIOUS TISSUES

Tissue	Cystathionase, mμmoles α-ketobutyrate/mg protein/60 min Monkey	Rat	Man
Liver	57	74	25
Kidney	23	40	—
Pancreas	5·1	55	—
Brain	0·63	0·22	0·31†

† Post-mortem specimens only.

may have some fate other than to be cleaved to cysteine, its only present known metabolic role. This possibility deserves further experimental attention.

The situation in the brain of patients with the clinical syndrome associated with homocystinuria has now been explored by several techniques. Brenton, Cusworth and Gaull (1965) reported that the concentration of cystathionine was extremely low in all areas of the brains of two homocystinuric patients whereas brains from control patients contained the expected high concentrations. A similar finding was reported by Gerritsen and Waisman (1964b) for the brain of another homocystinuric patient, R. S. These facts certainly strongly support our formulation that the syndrome is due to a lack of cystathionine synthase activity.

Through the kindness of Dr. Waisman, a specimen of brain tissue obtained at post-mortem examination of his homocystinuric patient, R. S., was made available to us. Extracts of this brain tissue were assayed for cystathionine synthase, methionine activating enzyme and cystathionase. The results are shown in Table 5. The controls were also post-mortem material. Specimens D. D. and K. K. were obtained at the National Institutes of Health. Specimens

C. L., J. W. and J. D. were obtained from Dr. Waisman and had been stored under conditions more or less similar to those under which specimen R. S. was stored. Although the possibility of post-mortem artefacts cannot be excluded, it is clear that the levels of methionine activating enzyme and cystathionase in specimen R. S. were not markedly depressed relative to values on other post-mortem human brains. In contrast, the value for cystathionine synthase in the brain of R. S. was less than 1% of the mean control value. This is strong evidence for a specific lack of cystathionine

TABLE 5. ENZYMATIC ACTIVITIES IN EXTRACTS OF BRAIN TISSUE FROM CONTROL AND HOMOCYSTINURIC SUBJECTS

Patients	Methionine activating enzyme: S-Adenosylmethionine mμmole/mg/30 min	Cystathionase: α-Ketobutyrate mμmole/mg/60 min	Cystathionine synthase: Cystathionine mμmole/mg/135 min
D. D.	0·72	0·51	21
K. K.	0·80	0·17	27
C. L.	0·35	0·28	23
J. W.	1·24	0·34	20
J. D.	1·30	0·26	19
R. S. (homocystinuria)	0·22	0·21	0·03†; 0·11†

All tissues were acquired post-mortem and stored frozen. The sample from R. S. was thawed at least once.

† Duplicate determinations.

Note: Since this paper was presented, we have performed enzyme assays in extracts of brain obtained post-mortem from a second patient with the syndrome of homocystinuria. The following activities were observed: methionine activating enzyme, 0·88 mμmole/mg/30 min; cystathionase, 0·19 mμmole/mg/60 min; cystathionine synthase, none detected (<0·08 mμmole/mg/135 min). An extract of liver from this same patient had values for methionine activating enzyme and cystathionase within the control ranges whereas no cystathionine synthase activity was detected (sensitivity: 1% of mean control value for fresh tissue). We wish to thank Dr. Richard J. Allen of University Hospital, Ann Arbor, Michigan, for making these tissues available.

synthase in the brain of R. S. and we take this finding to mean that the enzymatic defect is present in the brain as well as the liver.

Therapy for patients with cystathionine synthase deficiency may be designed by consideration of the immediate consequences of their enzymatic block. These patients lack the major means by which they might form cysteine. This amino acid therefore probably becomes an essential one and care must be taken that the patients receive an adequate supply at all times. Whether abnormal accumulation of homocystine, methionine, or one of their metabolites contributes to the pathological manifestations and would thus warrant methionine restriction remains to be determined. Thought should also be given to the possibility that cystathionine itself is necessary for such patients and cannot be entirely replaced by cystine. In this case, cystathionine supplementation would be required.

This completes a brief outline of some aspects of our present work. In summary, we have shown that two patients suffering from the typical clinical syndrome associated with homocystine in the urine have very low levels of hepatic cystathionine synthase. Studies of the family of one of these patients have suggested that the enzymatic defect is inherited as an autosomal trait. A clinically normal patient who excretes homocystine in the urine has a level of enzyme intermediate to the values found in the mentally retarded patients and in the heterozygotes. All three of the enzymes of transulfuration which have been looked for in brain are present in this tissue. Brain from a homocystinuric patient displayed a specific lack of cystathionine synthase.

Although only very fragmentary therapeutic experience with this disease has been reported, it is hoped that available knowledge will soon make it possible to design rational therapy for these patients.

REFERENCES

BRENTON, D. P., CUSWORTH, D. C. and GAULL, G. E. (1965) Homocystinuria: Biochemical studies of tissues including a comparison with cystathioninuria, *Pediatrics*, **35,** 50–6.

CARSON, N. A. J. and NEILL, D. W. (1962) Metabolic abnormalities detected in a survey of mentally backward individuals in Northern Ireland, *Archives of Diseases of Childhood*, **37,** 505–13.

CARSON, N. A. J., CUSWORTH, D. C., DENT, C. E., FIELD, C. M. B., NEILL, D. W. and WESTALL, R. G. (1963) Homocystinuria: A new inborn error of metabolism associated with mental deficiency, *Archives of Diseases of Childhood*, **38,** 425–36.

CARSON, N. A. J., DENT, C. E., FIELD, C. M. B. and GAULL, G. E. (1965) Homocystinuria: Clinical and pathological review of ten cases, *Journal of Pediatrics*, **66,** 565–83.

FIELD, C. M. B., CARSON, N. A. J., CUSWORTH, D. C., DENT, C. E. and NEILL, D. W. (1962) Homocystinuria: A new disorder of metabolism, *Abstracts Xth International Congress of Paediatrics* (*Lisbon*), p. 274.

FINKELSTEIN, J. D., MUDD, S. H., IRREVERRE, F. and LASTER, L. (1964) Homocystinuria due to cystathionine synthetase deficiency: The mode of inheritance, *Science*, **146,** 785–7.

GAITONDE, M. K. and RICHTER, D. (1956) The metabolic activity of the proteins of the brain, *Proceedings of the Royal Society of London*, Series B, **145,** 83–99.

GAITONDE, M. K. and RICHTER, D. (1957) The metabolism of ^{35}S-methionine in the brain, in *The Metabolism of the Nervous System*, D. Richter, Ed., Oxford, Pergamon Press, pp. 449–55.

GERRITSEN, T., VAUGHN, J. G. and WAISMAN, H. A. (1962) The identification of homocystine in the urine, *Biochemical and Biophysical Research Communications*, **9,** 493–6.

GERRITSEN, T. and WAISMAN, H. A. (1964a) Homocystinuria: An error in the metabolism of methione, *Pediatrics*, **33,** 413–20.

GERRITSEN, T. and WAISMAN, H. A. (1964b) Homocystinuria: Absence of cystathionine in the brain, *Science*, **145,** 588.

GIBSON, J. B., CARSON, N. A. J. and NEILL, D. W. (1964) Pathological findings in homocystinuria, *Journal of Clinical Pathology*, **17,** 427–37.

HALL, W. K., CORYELL, M. E., HOLLOWELL, J. G., Jr. and THEVAOS, T. G. (1965) A metabolic study of homocystinuria, *Federation Proceedings*, **24,** 470.

HOPE, D. B. (1959) Distribution of cystathionine and cystathionine synthetase in rat brain, *Federation Proceedings*, **18,** 249.

KOMROWER, G. M. and WILSON, V. K. (1963) Homocystinuria, *Proceedings of the Royal Society of Medicine*, **56**, 996–7.
MUDD, S. H., FINKELSTEIN, J. D., IRREVERRE, F. and LASTER, L. (1964) Homocystinuria: An enzymatic defect, *Science*, **143**, 1443–5.
MUDD, S. H., FINKELSTEIN, J. D., IRREVERRE, F. and LASTER, L. (1965) unpublished material.
TALLAN, H. H., MOORE, S. and STEIN, W. H. (1958) L-Cystathionine in human brain, *Journal of Biological Chemistry*, **230**, 707–16.

GENERAL DISCUSSION[1]

Discussion after Dr. Straughan's Paper

Himwich: Dr. Straughan, a large body of evidence indicates that in general the monoamines play an activating or stimulating role in the central and peripheral nervous systems and that the exhaustion of the monoamines is followed by paralysis, for example a large dose of reserpine depletes norepinephrine and induces a chemical sympathectomy. Do you have any suggestions that would make it possible to reconcile these data with your own?

Straughan: You have put your finger on an apparent paradox. That is why, when NA and 5-HT depress central neurones, chronic depletion of the substance in the intact animals reduces peripheral, and, presumably, central sympathetic activity, rather than the reverse. I am afraid I have no real answer to this. One might speculate in terms of the relative balance between hypothalamic sympathetic and parasympathetic activity being disturbed, but I have no evidence at all on this. It is probably worth adding a cautionary note here: it could be that 5-HT and NA would produce more excitant effects on central neurones if the animals were unanesthetized, but I do not think this is likely, for we have seen similar depressant results with these monoamines with several different kinds of anesthetic. Also, most investigations using a variety of parameters have shown that monoamines are generally depressant. We are, however, very keen to try and repeat these experiments in unanesthetized brain if this is possible.

Baldessarini: Dr. Straughan, what was the pH of the solutions or drugs that you used?

Straughan: NA, 5-HT and dopamine ions were applied from solutions at an acid pH around 4·5. We have done careful pH controls, particularly in the hippocampus. To get effects from the control, saline has to be acidified with HCl to around pH 2. Then you can show excitant effects.

Baldessarini: Would you expect to see electrical changes just with acidic solutions alone?

Straughan: No. In general, though, I think it is worth remembering that the amounts of drug ion expelled are very small and the tissues probably affectively neutralize any excess acidity.

Baldessarini: Have you ever seen depression with acid then?

Straughan: No. The point I think to be remembered is the amounts that are exposed are very small and fairly extensive in the patients.

Discussion after Dr. Snyder's Paper

Kuehl: Dr. Snyder, it seems to me that in the last year or so there have been several papers that showed that 5-hydroxy-dimethyltryptamine is less a potent hallucinogenic agent than dimethyltryptamine itself.

Snyder: I used Dr. Szara as my correspondent. Would Dr. Szara care to comment?

Szara: I would like to set the record straight on the available data about the hallucinogenic activity of the 6-hydroxy derivatives of N,N-dimethyltryptamine (DMT) and N,N-diethyltryptamine (DET). On the basis of our animal experiments in rats and mice with these drugs, we suggested that the 6-hydroxy metabolites might be responsible for the hallucinogenic action of DMT and DET. We were not pursuing this notion in the case of DMT in man because of the very short duration of action presumably due to the very rapid metabolism and inactivation of this drug. Harris Isbell and his collaborators, however, tested 6-hydroxy DMT in six drug addicts and found this compound practically inactive as compared to the same dose of DMT in the same subjects. (For further discussion of N-dimethyltryptamine, see addendum to Dr. Szara's paper.)

[1] The discussion refers to the papers of Drs. Straughan, Snyder and Mudd.

In the case of DET in humans we have three bits of information suggesting that 6-hydroxylation might be important in the hallucinogenic effects of this drug. First we gave 1 mg/kg of DET to ten normal volunteers and collected their urine for 9 hr after the injection. There was a wide individual variation in the amount of 6-hydroxy DET (6-HDET) found in the specimens and this variation correlated surprisingly well with the variation in the intensity of the psychodysleptic reaction of the individuals. In another series of tests on seven patients we found that the 6-fluoro analog of DET—which cannot be metabolized through the 6-hydroxylation pathway—produced autonomic changes only without the psychodysleptic or hallucinogenic effects which are so characteristic of DET itself. These two sets of evidence strongly suggest that 6-hydroxylation is somehow involved in the hallucinogenic effect of DET.

A more direct evidence for this assumption would be to demonstrate the dysleptic effect 6-HDET which is the first step through this pathway. Unfortunately we do not have enough synthetic 6-HDET to do a complete study, but I took some 6-HDET which was prepared from DET by catalytic oxidation in the presence of Versene, ascorbic acid and $FeCl_3$ and purified the oxidation product until it was chromatographically and colorimetrically identical with synthetic 6-HDET. After ingestion of 10 mg of this derivative, I experienced hallucinogenic symptoms comparable to those produced by 60 mg of DET.

This was, of course, just one single experiment and the compound might have contained traces of isomer hydroxy DET not easily separable from 6-HDET. We have not done any further experiments because the synthetic compound has never become available in sufficient quantities and I wish somebody would synthesize some more so that this problem could be solved.

SMYTHIES: I think you can also arrange the hallucinogens in order of potency on the basis of the lipid solubility. Is there any correlation between electron-donating power and lipid solubility? LSD I understand is about fifty times as lipid soluble as psilocybin.

SNYDER: There may be some minor correlation between lipid solubility and hallucinogenic efficacy activity relationships of the amphetamines or tryptamines. However, lipid solubility could not possibly explain the structure.

As for LSD, the inactive molecules, dihydra and lumi-LSD, are more lipid soluble than LSD itself.

SMYTHIES: My other problem was the stereoisomers. When you compare the stereoisomers with LSD what is your position about their electron-donating power?

SNYDER: Molecular orbital calculations do not treat stereoisomerism.

HOLMSTEDT: I have a question for both Dr. Snyder and Dr. Szara. Dr. Snyder, in your theory here you cannot differentiate between methyl-substituted and ethyl-substituted compound, is that correct?

SNYDER: Our calculations cannot take into account side-chain alterations.

HOLMSTEDT: Dr. Szara is not quite sure whether this compound is active or not, and if I understood him correctly this morning he denied that the 6-hydroxydimethyltryptamine was active at all.

SZARA: According to Isbell's finding in patients, 6-hydroxydimethyltryptamine was not hallucinogenic when compared with the dimethyltryptamine in the same dose.

HOLMSTEDT: Well you did not find any activity at all as I understood it. One more question, Dr. Snyder. When you say that the electron energy transfer of the compounds is about twice as much for psilocybin as for LSD, is that correct?

SNYDER: The figures were 0·2180 for LSD and 0·4603 for psilocin.

HOLMSTEDT: How do you then account for the fact that pharmacologically LSD is at least 100 times more active than psilocybin?

SNYDER: It is possible, in fact, probable, that hallucinogenicity is related not lineally, but logarithmically, to molecular orbital indices.

RICHTER: Is there any relation between the quantities you computed and the stability of the picrate or dinitrobenzene compounds formed by the amines?

SNYDER: I do not know.

KUEHL: It has been quite a while since I read the paper by Rosenberg, Isbell and Miner (*Psychopharmacologia*, **4**, 39, 1963) but it seems to me that they studied a number of tryptamines in human volunteers and found that whereas N-dimethyl tryptamine caused typical hallucinations and anxiety symptoms, 6-hydroxy-N-dimethyltryptamine was essentially without effect.

SMYTHIES: I do not think I made my point clear. What I was asking was is there any necessary connection between lipid solubility and the energy of the highest filled orbitals? Do compounds with a high energy tend to be more lipid soluble?

SNYDER: No.

HORWITT: It seems to me that one should differentiate between the correlation of hallucinogenic activity with lipid solubility and the kind of correlation which Dr. Snyder reported because if one were to range the compounds in general upon their lipid solubility, one would find a very poor correlation between that and their hallucinogenic activities whereas it seems that the correlations Dr. Snyder suggests are much more striking not only in the degree of hallucinogenicity but in differentiating hallucinogens from other compounds.

SMYTHIES: Would you say that in the case of the LSD/mescaline series of hallucinogens the solubility is correlated with their lipid solubility? The higher the lipid solubility the more potent they are.

In comparing LSD, bufotenin, 5-methoxy-N,N-dimethyltryptamine and tryptamine, we find that 5-methoxy-N-dimethyltryptamine does not have that 5-hydroxy group so it is going to be more lipid soluble and tryptamine without that will be more lipid soluble. LSD is fantastically lipid soluble. Those are the things that are related. Those are fairly simple considerations, for example how well it will pass the blood brain barrier. The more difficult ones which I was worried about include the position of putting methyl groups in positions where lipid solubility should not be affected or whether a 4-hydroxy or 5-hydroxy position is more potent—why should psilocin be different from bufotenin or why should reducing a double-bond in LSD make it less potent? That should make it more lipid soluble.

FRIEDHOFF: I want to reiterate something that Dr. Snyder said that I think is an important contribution in understanding the mechanism of action of these drugs. It is properly not Dr. Snyder's concern whether the drug gets to a site of action. The degree of correlation which he finds seems to be phenomenally high when we take into consideration all of the factors that go into whether or not a drug is a hallucinogen. I think that his contribution may be to help us understand what happens at the final point when the drug gets to the site of action.

DISCUSSION AFTER DR. MUDD'S PAPER

LASTER: I would like to add a few comments regarding clinical aspects of homocystinuria. Homocystinuria is a relatively common disorder; more cases are discovered daily. Recently Carson and her associates (*J. Pediat.* **66,** 565, 1965) reported that in a survey of urine samples from 2920 mentally defective individuals in Northern Ireland they discovered sixty-nine cases of phenylketonuria and ten cases of homocystinuria. The latter ranked as the second most common inborn error of metabolism in the group. Because the clinical features of homocystinuria may resemble those of the Marfan syndrome (Gibson, Carson and Neill, *J. Clin. Path.* **17,** 427, 1964), Schimke *et al.* (*J. Amer. Med. Assoc.* **193,** 711, 1965) examined patients who had been presumed to have that syndrome and they discovered that a significant number of them had homocystinuria. They also discovered a rather large number of homocystinuric subjects by screening patients who had ectopia lentis without mental retardation (Schimke *et al., J. Amer. Med. Assoc.* **193,** 711, 1965). It is apparent that the clinical expression of the complete biochemical defect can vary; for example, the patient need not be mentally retarded. To complicate the situation even further, the biochemical defect may be partial—as was shown for M. A. G. in Dr. Mudd's presentation—and a patient with a partial deficiency of cystathionine synthase may excrete abnormal quantities of homocystine in the urine but may show none of the clinical features of the disorder. Such asymptomatic patients can be detected only by chemical examination of the urine, and there may be many such individuals in the population who will go unrecognized. The heterozygous subject shows neither homocystine in the urine nor clinical manifestations of the disease and at present the heterozygous state can be demonstrated only by enzyme assay of a sample of liver.

Let us turn to some metabolic consequences of the biochemical defect in homocystinuria (Laster *et al., J. Clin. Invest.* **44,** 1708, 1965; Laster *et al., Ann. Intern. Med.* **63,** 1117, 1965).

There is abundant evidence suggesting that the pathway represented by reactions 1 to 6 in Fig. 1 of Dr. Mudd's presentation is a possible route for the conversion of the sulfur of methionine to inorganic sulfate in mammals. The evidence that this is the predominant route is less convincing. The availability of patients who are human mutans blocked at reaction 4, the step catalyzed by cystathionine synthase, afforded us the opportunity to test whether that step is an obligatory one in the major pathway for methionine metabolism. When a normal individual is fed a dose of methionine, 80 to 85% of it is excreted in the urine as inorganic sulfate; similarly, ingested cysteine is also converted to inorganic sulfate. A patient with cystathionine synthase deficiency would be unable normally to increase urinary excretion of inorganic sulfate in response to a dose of methionine, but would respond normally to cysteine administration, if several conditions were met. First, reaction 4 would indeed

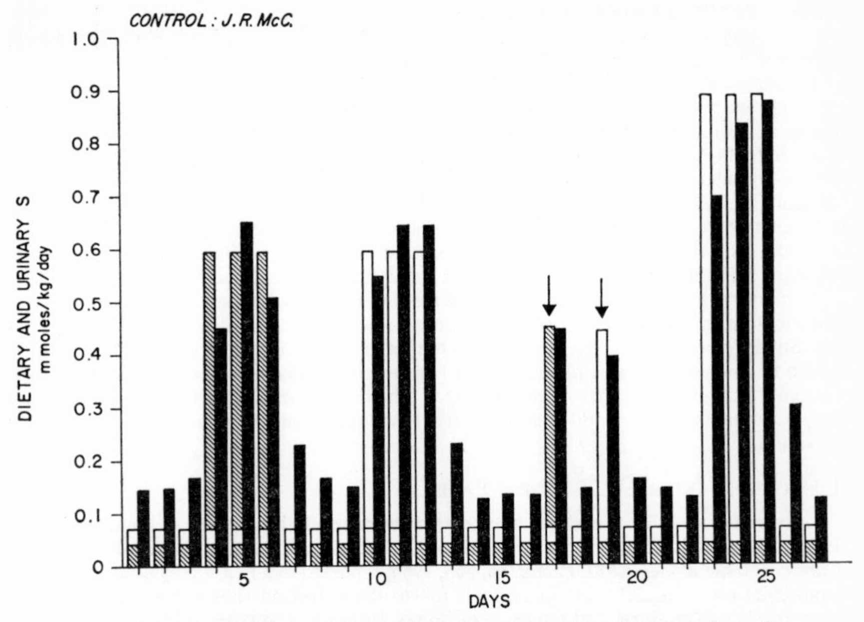

FIG. 1. Urinary excretion of inorganic sulfate after the administration of L-methionine or L-cysteine to a control subject. The symbols are defined in the text. The urinary excretion of inorganic sulfate rose when supplementary doses of cysteine (hatched rectangles) or methionine (open rectangles) were fed repeatedly for several days or in single doses (arrows). Fig. 1 through 5 have been published previously (4) and are reprinted here with the permission of the Editor of the *Journal of Clinical Investigation.*

have to be an obligatory step in the major pathway for conversion of methionine to inorganic sulfate; second, the pathway beyond reaction 4 would have to be intact; and third, the detection of a reduced activity of cystathionine synthase in the liver would have to reflect a generalized impairment in the body's ability to convert homocysteine to cystathionine. These considerations were tested and found to be so, by the administration of doses of methionine or cysteine to control subjects and homocystinuric patients and by determination of the subsequent urinary excretion of inorganic sulfate.

A study of a control subject is summarized in Fig. 1. Each day is represented by two bars; the left-hand bar represents intake of sulfur as methionine or cysteine in the diet or in supplementary doses of pure amino acid. The open rectangles represent methionine, the hatched rectangles represent cysteine. The right-hand bar, in black, represents urinary

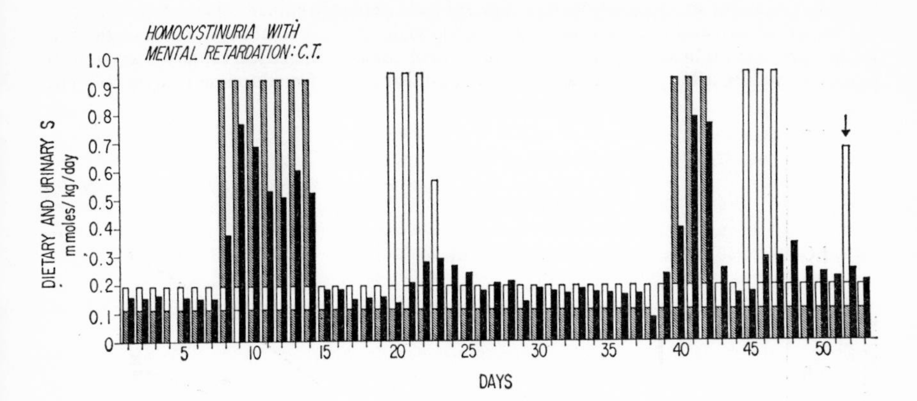

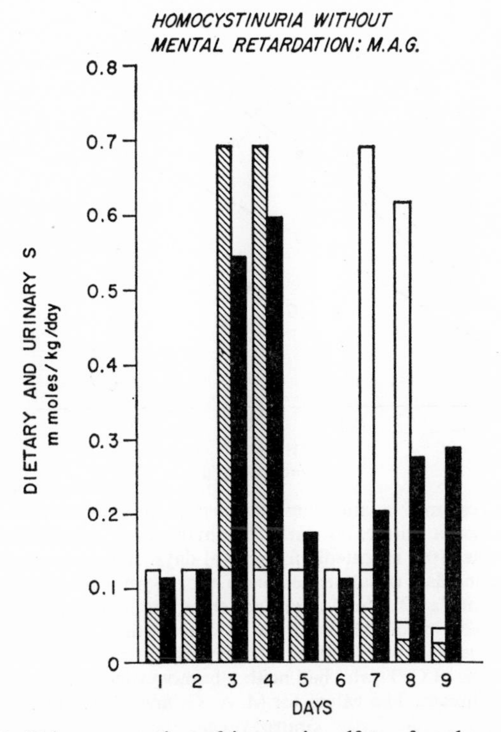

FIGS. 2 and 3. Urinary excretion of inorganic sulfate after the administration of L-methionine or L-cysteine to patients with cystathionine synthase deficiency. In each case the response to cysteine administration was not abnormal whereas the response to methionine administration was much lower than was observed for a group of control subjects.

excretion of sulfur as inorganic sulfate. The subjects were maintained on constant diets and fed one of the two amino acids repeatedly in divided doses for several days or as a single dose in the morning (indicated by arrows). The control subjects increased urinary excretion of inorganic sulfate after the chronic or acute administration of methionine or cysteine. The

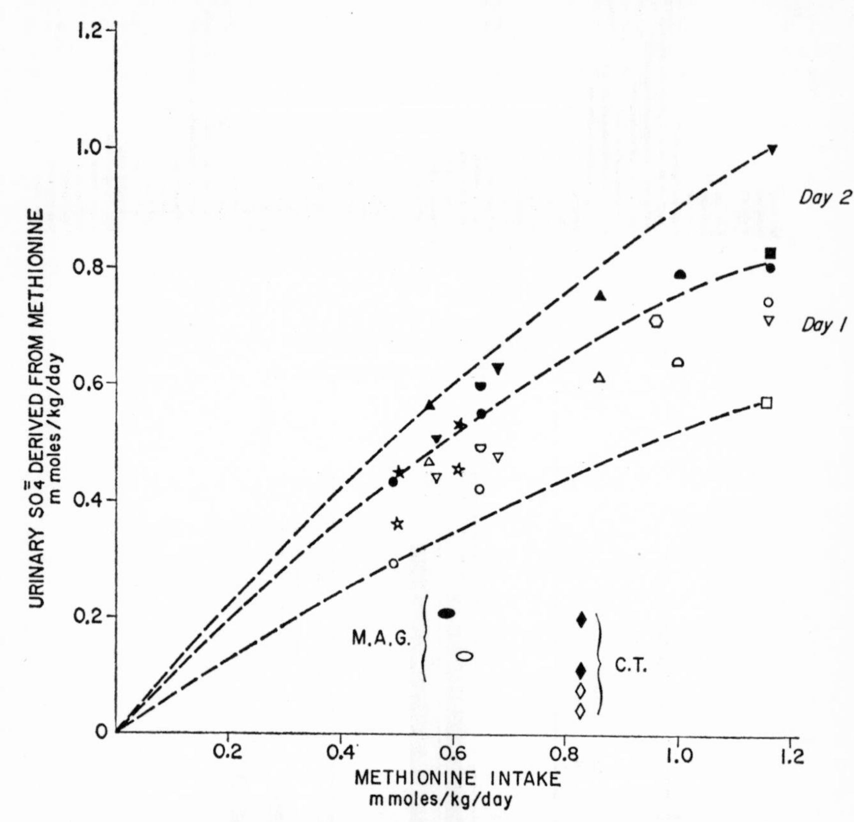

FIG. 4. Dose–response relationship between methionine intake and urinary excretion of inorganic sulfate. The data are from the studies in which supplementary L-methionine was given repeatedly for several days. Responses are presented for the first and second days of supplementation. Open symbols represent day 1; black symbols represent day 2. The dotted lines show the limits of the control range. The control subjects included four normal volunteers, S. M. (Table 1 of Dr. Mudd's paper), who has been shown to have normal hepatic cystathionine synthase activity, and three relatives of C. T. who had neither homocystine in the urine nor clinical features of the disease. The values for M. A. G. and C. T. are clearly below the control range.

patient with barely detectable hepatic cystathionine synthase activity, C. T., showed a markedly depressed response to the administration of methionine but her response to cysteine administration was within the range of responses observed for the control subjects (Fig. 2). The cousin of C. T., M. A. G., whose hepatic cystathionine synthase activity was lower than that of the heterozygous parents of C. T. but significantly higher than that of C. T., the homozygous patient, also showed an impaired response to methionine feeding and a normal response to cysteine feeding (Fig. 3). The entire group of studies is summarized in Fig. 4 where urinary excretion of inorganic sulfate is plotted as a function of methionine intake for the first and second days of methionine administration. The values for C. T., tested twice, and for M. A. G. fell below the control range. A similar graph of the data obtained after cysteine administration (Fig. 5) shows that the data for C. T. and M. A. G. fell within the control range. Thus, patients with cystathionine synthase deficiency have a generalized reduction in the body's activity of that enzyme, and appear to be able to metabolize cysteine normally. Furthermore, reaction 4 of Fig. 1 in Dr. Mudd's paper

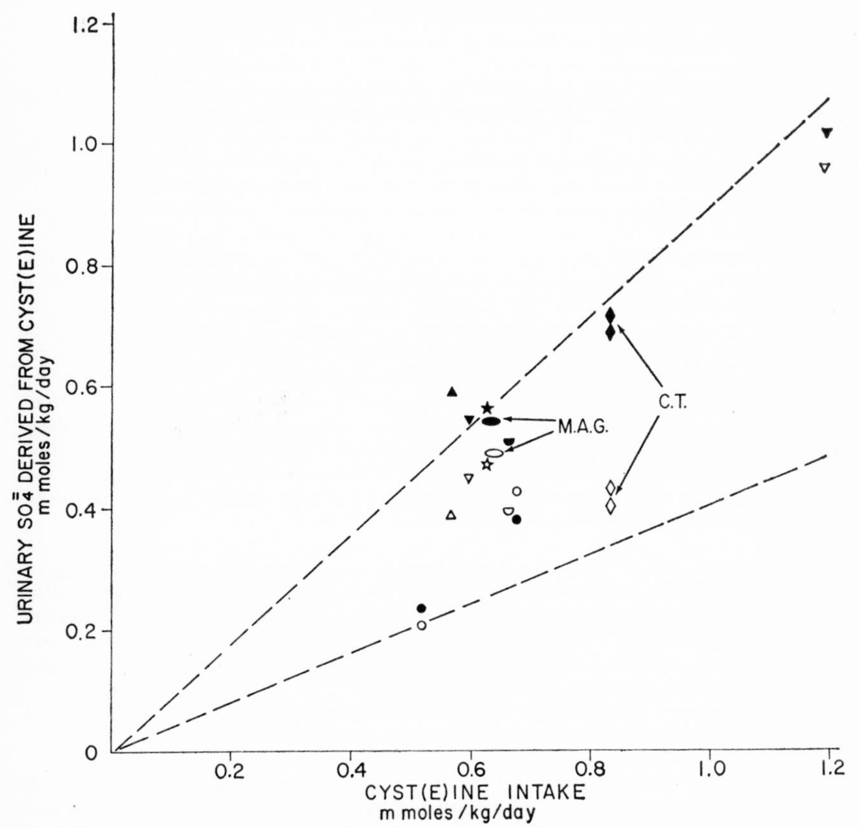

FIG. 5. Dose–response relationship between cyst(e)ine intake and urinary excretion of inorganic sulfate. The symbols of this figure are identical to those in Fig. 4. The values for M. A. G. and C. T. are within the control range.

appears to be an obligatory step in the predominant pathway for the conversion of the sulfur of methionine to that of inorganic sulfate.

We had hoped that it would prove possible to distinguish heterozygous individuals from normal ones by means of their response to methionine administration. Unfortunately the parents of C. T. increased the urinary excretion of inorganic sulfate after methionine ingestion to the same degree as the control subjects. Thus, at present the biochemical detection of the heterozygous states requires a liver biopsy and assay of the tissue for cystathionine synthase activity.

We also obtained evidence in these studies that when a patient with homocystinuria is fed methionine, homocysteine is not necessarily the most abundant abnormal sulfur-containing compound excreted in the urine. Excessive amounts of a bound form of methionine and of unidentified neutral sulfur were detected in the urine in quantities exceeding that of the homocysteine.

WAISMAN: Mudd, Laster *et al.* have left very little to discuss because they presented the subject very well indeed. I have a few things on which I would like to comment, however. As far as I know there are about thirty or thirty-five patients with homocystinuria now and most recently Dr. V. McKusick at Johns Hopkins has studied a few additional cases in several families which makes it interesting, and I am glad that Dr. Mudd and Dr. Laster had a chance to study these too. We had only one real patient and while the second one excreted homocysteine in decreasing amounts as time went on during our study, he was not typical. So there are patients who excrete the amino acid but do not have the full-blown disease. It is very easy to test for the homocysteine by using the well-known prusside reagent. We became curious because of dislocated lenses in these patients and went to a blind school for children in Wisconsin and tested 180 children. We were certain we would find some homocystinurics but of these, six were Marfan's and none of these patients had positive test for homocysteine. The relationship between these diseases is not yet clear. The homocystinuric patients and the Marfan's have dislocated lenses but the circumstance of homocysteine excretion apparently does not always occur in Marfan's disease. The liver of a child appears to have greater enzyme activity, at least in certain ages. Dr. Mudd's data confirms that the highest cysthationine synthetase activity is found in the liver of children rather than the adult, and I think this is typical of many enzymes in the liver of children. As the child gets older the enzyme activity decreases as adulthood is attained. Obviously not enough biopsies have been made so that we can be sure about this. There are several methods by which one can produce homocystinuria in animals. We fed monkeys L-methionine in dosages of 3 g/kg per day for over a year and we could always find homocysteine in the urine. Unhappily this is a very toxic amino acid and after a time these animals were so debilitated that we lost all four monkeys. There is a relationship, as pointed out by Dr. Mudd, on the ability of the liver to provide chemicals for the brain which the brain itself may not make. Many diseases in which the liver is damaged account for concurrent brain damage and there are many examples which are known to you.

There are many unanswered questions in this disease and I think it is going to be an interesting one to observe because one might expect to find the full spectrum of enzyme activity and clinical signs of symptoms. The fact that patients with homocystinuria can be found who are not mentally retarded, of course, is not impossible. This has a precedent in phenylketonuria in which a few patients of the many hundreds that are known do have normal intelligence. I think this is another challenging area for investigation since no understanding of this circumstance is presently available.

Homocystinuria is a disease which has no known relationship to certain populations or ethnic groups, but it is interesting that when we analyzed urines from about 1500 patients in the entire institution, we found no cases of homocystinuria, whereas the Irish investigators and I think some other Englishmen in Birmingham tested some 1200 patients and found ten such patients. Whether our Norwegian and Swedish population in Wisconsin differs genetically from the Irish or other English population, I do not know for sure, but I believe more case finding should be done in order to do additional studies on patients that will provide meaningful information or prevention or treatment of the diseases.

PERRY: We have recently found seven patients in three unrelated families in British Columbia and we also get the impression that there are probably a lot of patients with homocystinuria not being diagnosed in the pediatric age group. We recently saw a pathetic example of what beings will do. While trying some methionine loading experiments on the parents of two homocystinuric children in an effort to develop a test for heterozygosity, we explained to them very carefully that we strongly advised them not to have any more children, because the chances were 1 in 4 that their next child would also have homocystinuria. Apparently they reacted by being extremely encouraged and they figured one chance in four was odds they were quite willing to accept. The mother promptly became pregnant, and we are now faced with the problem of what to do if our pessimistic view of the odds proves to be correct. We have had a special low-methionine diet prepared, and we are concerned about whether, and how much, cystathionine we should add to the diet. I would like anybody who knows to tell me whether if one gives cystathionine by mouth there is any evidence that it will find its way into the brain. Are there any ideas as to how much cystathionine one should give to a homocystinuric infant because it is very expensive?

In one of our homocystinuric patients who was already severely retarded and too old to make it worth while trying any permanent treatment, we found that temporary use of a diet providing only ½ g of protein per kilo per day significantly lowered serum concentrations of methionine and homocysteine as well as the urinary excretion of methionine and homocysteine. I think that use of a modified low-methionine diet, based on small amounts of dietary protein derived from vegetable sources, might be valuable in avoiding, if not the mental defect, at least some of the other difficulties we have seen, particularly the tendency to have intravascular thromboses.

The other question I wanted to ask is what people here know about the possibility that

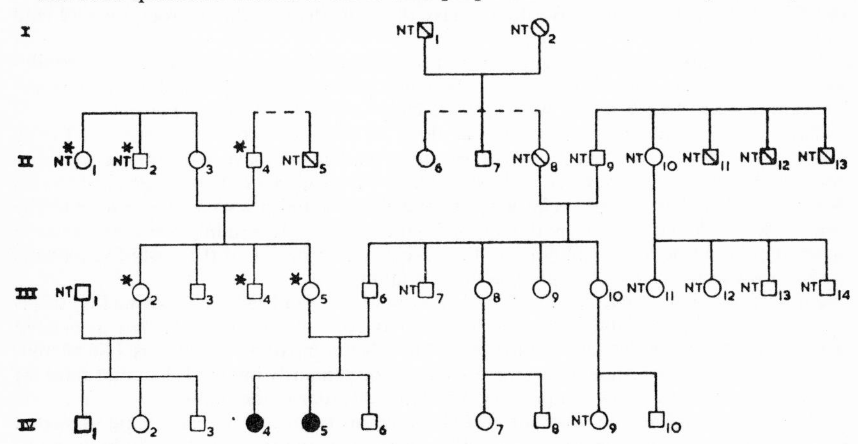

FIG. 6. Family tree. The two affected sibs (IV 4 and 5) are shown in black. Urine was obtained and analysed from all the subjects except those who have died, or those marked as not tested (NT). Subjects marked * have suffered from schizophrenia. The main mental manifestations in each case were: II 1, auditory hallucinations, restlessness; II 2, visual and auditory hallucinations, persecutory delusions; II 4, auditory hallucinations, delusions, agitation; III 2, auditory hallucinations, hallucinations, delusions, agitation; III 2, auditory hallucinations; III 4, auditory and visual hallucinations; III 5, auditory hallucinations, paranoia.

mental disease in later life is more common among the relatives of homocystinurics. We were very struck by the pedigree presented by the British discoverers of homocystinuria for the family of their index cases. This pedigree shows that there is alleged schizophrenia in the two generations before the homocystinuric children. In our Canadian homocystinuric patients, in two of the three families there is an appreciable incidence of mental illness with a number of psychotic individuals going back three generations, but unfortunately only on one side of the family so that the other side of the family contains no mentally ill subjects. In our third homocystinuric family there is one first cousin who has a severe behavior disorder. What are the experiences of the people here who have worked with homocystinuria? Have they found or have they not found an increased incidence of mental illness among relatives, and could heterozygosity for homocystinuria be a possible cause for mental illness?

SNYDER: I think this is just a pedigree from the first family found in Ireland and reported by Carson *et al.* (*Arch. Dis. Childhood*, **38**, 425, 1963). He simply showed that the mother of the patient as well as her brother and her sister are schizophrenic and the maternal grandfather and the three maternal great uncles and aunts are schizophrenics. It would seem rather a striking incidence of it. The only trouble is that in the three families we have one does not find it on the other side and it should be on both sides presumably.

WAISMAN: I would like to try to answer Dr. Perry's question. If one would ask what is the best way to give treatment for a child with homocystinuria as young as Dr. Perry's patient, I think I would tend to give cystathionine because it is apparent that the homocystinuric brain does not contain it, at least in the one patient we had, and perhaps others will find the same thing. It is much easier to give cystathionine than to give a low methionine diet. Since methionine is an essential amino acid we should use a lowered protein intake.

I have the feeling that cystathionine does cross the blood brain barrier. This is based on some preliminary data we have, and I think what is missing is some real information in animals, and we would love to do it on monkeys if we had labelled homocysteine—we just cannot get anybody to make S^{35}-homocysteine for us. Because this is an obvious compound to use in such experiments we would like to inject it or feed it and then take a piece of brain out and see what is going on. We do not have that information. But anyway, I would tend to give cystathionine.

I think one can calculate the requirement for cystathionine using the methionine requirements per day. The requirement would be some place between $\frac{1}{4}$ and $\frac{1}{2}$ g per day for newborn babies. This is taking weight of the baby and amino-acid requirement.

There are so many things that could be done on patients with this disease that I envy Dr. Perry and with the one honest-to-goodness patient we have had among so many patients. Unfortunately, our one patient died and was illegitimate. Despite great efforts on our part, using sheriffs and social workers and doctors and priests and everyone in the county, we could get no information on or from the family. It certainly seems as though a summary should be forthcoming of all the parents and relatives of the thirty-five patients with known incidents of schizophrenia in their families.

RICHTER: I would like to ask Dr. Mudd two questions. Am I right in believing that this is the first time that any kind of mental disorder has been shown to be *definitely* associated with a primary metabolic defect in the brain? In other comparable conditions, like phenylketonuria, the liver or some other organ seems to be primarily involved. I cannot think of any other case where there is a primary metabolic disorder in the brain.

MUDD: I do not know of other instances in which metabolic disorders leading to mental retardation have been shown to be associated with an enzymatic defect in the brain itself.

WAISMAN: We took the brain of a phenylketonuric child we had and analyzed it for cystathionine and it was normal. The analysis on one brain does not mean anything, but apparently the inferences from this great amount of data implies that at least cystathionine is not the common factor in all cases of mental retardation.

SPRINCE: Our findings with rats on excess dietary methionine, homocysteine, or cysteine lead me to suggest that it might be of interest to test for N^1-methylnicotinamide and indoleacetic acid in the urine of children with homocystinuria to see if there are differences in the levels of these metabolites from normal children. The elevated plasma level of methionine found in homocystinuria might have the same effect on tryptophan metabolism in the homocystinuric child as excess dietary methionine was found to have in our rats fed our experimental diets (Sprince *et al.*, *Fed. Proc.*, **24**, 169, 1965).

HIMWICH: Did you give large amounts of homocysteine to your rats?

SPRINCE: Yes, at a level of about 4% in the diet.

HIMWICH: What were your results?

SPRINCE: Homocysteine was actually more toxic than methionine or cysteine. With excess homocysteine the rats actually lost weight and the output of urinary N^1-methylnicotinamide was markedly decreased. The effect on urinary indoleacetic acid was not quite as marked as it was with methionine. With excess methionine, the urinary N^1-methylnicotinamide was decreased and the urinary indoleacetic acid was markedly increased. One point which strikes me as important is the possibility that homocysteine by virtue of its sulfhydryl group may act as a metabolic inhibitor of oxidative enzymes along the tryptophan-nicotinic acid pathway.

KETY: I was wondering whether Dr. Smythies or anyone else has any speculation at all on this incidence of schizophrenia in this one family. How does this tie in with the disturbance of methionine and cysteine. . . . ?

SMYTHIES: I heard that there was some doubt that this family really was schizophrenic.

KETY: If it is called schizophrenia in England, it is much more likely to be schizophrenia than what is called schizophrenia here.

BALDESSARINI: I have a rather wild speculation about that question. I noticed that the level of the methionine activating enzyme in one patient was 7. Were enzyme activity studies done in any controls or in other members of this family? I wonder whether S-adenosylmethionine levels in the families in question might be elevated? To speculate wildly, if S-adenosyl is in fact elevated in the relatives, they might be making methylated psychotogens!

MUDD: The value for methionine activating enzyme which we reported for our first homocystinuric patients (Mudd, S. H., Finkelstein, J. D., Irreverre, F. and Laster, L., *Science*, **143,** 1443, 1964) was indeed slightly higher than the control values reported at that time. It is difficult to interpret this finding because (a) for obvious reasons we have no control values on completely normal children of the same age, and (b) since that time we have found comparable or higher specific activities for methionine activating enzyme in liver specimens obtained from patients undergoing laparotomy for other conditions.

LASTER: I would like to comment on some problems involved in attempting to treat homocystinuria by manipulation of the diet. It is not clear at present whether the clinical abnormalities that accompany the biochemical defect in homocystinuria are due to the accumulation of a metabolite prior to the blocked reaction or to a deficiency of one or more of the compounds generated beyond the blocked reaction. Thus, do you restrict methionine, feed such compounds as cystathionine and cysteine, or do both? Furthermore, the evaluation of the efficacy of a diet will be difficult. If one assumes that our patient M. A. G. excreted excessive amounts of homocystine in the urine as an infant, she would have been diagnosed as having homocystinuria on the basis of chemical analysis of her urine. If she had been maintained on a special diet one might have been inclined to have attributed her normal mental capacity to the dietary regimen. However, that would have been totally misleading because, as we now know, she grew into adulthood without any mental retardation though on a normal diet. It will be necessary to keep patients such as M. A. G. in mind when studying the question of whether a particular diet can prevent any or all of the clinical manifestations of cystathionine synthase deficiency.

PERRY: Well this is exactly the thing that is bothering us. In homocystinuria one has mental defect, one has abnormality of the suspensory ligament of the lens, abnormal development of cartilage and bone, possibly increased platelet adhesiveness. A host of things are going on and it is very difficult to say which of these are due to the lack of cystathionine, which are due to relative deficiency of cysteine, and which are due to excess of homocysteine and/or excessive methionine. It is likely that all three of these factors are involved and it would be good to learn the relative importance of each of them.

GENERAL DISCUSSION

HIMWICH: To start this portion of our general discussion not necessarily associated with the presentation of any given paper, I would like to learn Dr. Holmstedt's idea concerning the comparative activities of the various psychotomimetic indoles and catechols.

HOLMSTEDT: Since some years it has been said that indoles are psychotomimetic only if they are substituted in the 4 position. This goes for LSD, it goes for psilocin and psilocybin, it goes also for the later discovered psychotomimetics that Hofmann found in *Rivea corymbosa*. They are also LSD-like compounds. Discovery by Szara and his associates in Hungary and in this country that DMT could produce lasting psychotic-like episodes brought up the question whether this would be due to the compound itself or to some metabolites. I do not think the question is definitely settled yet, would you agree to that, Dr. Szara?

SZARA: Yes, I would agree.

HOLMSTEDT: In my opinion the methoxy-substituted indoles will have to be investigated in the near future for their effect on the CNS. In some behavioral experiments by Page, 5-methoxydimethyltryptamine has been found next to LSD in potency. Maybe the whole concept for psychotomimetic indoles as being substituted only in the 4 position has to be revised.

SNYDER: It is interesting that methoxylation of bufotenin would markedly increase the energy of its highest occupied molecular orbital.

SPRINCE: How about the methoxylation of the 6-hydroxylated compound, in other words N-dimethyl-6-methoxytryptamine?

SNYDER: This should be still more active.

SMYTHIES: I think there is something odd about one of the compounds we showed yesterday, the N-dimethylmescaline. Its effects are almost purely excitation. Why should this be so?

I was really wondering if anybody had the idea of why this compound, which is merely N-methylated mescaline, tends to act like amphetamine and not mescaline itself. The other point I want to raise is the problem raised by Block, Block and Patzig back in 1952 (Hoppe Seyler's *Zeitschr. physiol. Chem.* **291**, 119, 1952) who showed that mescaline is attached to liver protein which hangs around for a long time in the body.

There are well-documented clinical results of giving mescaline to people and you get the mescaline effect lasting on and off for several weeks. In one of our cases there was only a mild reaction at the time to 400 mg mescaline—just a mild euphoria with hardly any hallucinations. Three weeks later the subject went to Spain and after a long and tiring trip he did not sleep and wandered around until about 4.00 in the morning, when he suddenly developed a full-flown mescaline hallucinosis lasting for about 8 hr. This could not be a learned reaction since his first reaction had been minimal. In some way the mescaline seems to linger in the body and a superadded sleep deprivation can be converted thereby into a typical severe mescaline hallucinosis.

SPRINCE: Normetanephrine and metanephrine are known to be the *monomethoxy* metabolites which are usually formed in the metabolism of norepinephrine and epinephrine. One wonders if the *dimethoxy* derivatives of norepinephrine and epinephrine are known to exist and if they could arise by a metabolic process.

BALDESSARINI: Dr. Friedhoff, might you comment on the very high percentage of DMPEA found in a very wide variety of diagnostic types? This seems to be somewhat in conflict with the idea that there are some specific subdivisions within schizophrenia which might have specific biochemical peculiarities.

FRIEDHOFF: I do not know that I am convinced that schizophrenia is or is not a single syndrome. I think the evidence one way or the other is rather meager. My own hunch would be that there probably are a number of disturbances that we would call schizophrenia but that none the less there is a large group of patients that all have the same disorder. We so often see transformation of symptoms from one type of schizophrenic to another we call a catatonic patient one day and paranoid the next. While this is not exclusive evidence it indicates a relationship of a number of clinical syndromes.

SMYTHIES: I could answer Dr. Baldessarini's question this way: If you got a metabolic disorder in the stress mechanism, e.g. adrenaline production, then clearly there will be a necessary interrelationship between all manner of psychological and social stress-reducing factors and the subsequent biochemical disturbance. This would also clearly lead to a vicious circle, as Dr. Osmond and I pointed out in 1952, and this might account for the malignant prognosis of the illness.

FORREST: I would like to try and draw a distinction between a superimposed psychosis due to a drug like isoniazid, with which I have had some experience in the treatment of schizophrenic patients having pulmonary tuberculosis. Some of these got toxic psychoses with isoniazid, which was interesting because it seemed to be possible to distinguish between the underlying schizophrenia and the superimposed organic illness. They got confused, with distortion of time sequences and impaired recent memory, and we just regarded it as an organic illness, whereas I have seen some toxic psychoses in schizophrenic subjects apparently due to amphetamine and imipramine. In regard to Dr. Szara's remark, I thought these patients became more excited and more actively psychotic, whereas the temporal distortion and alteration of the level of consciousness was very much less marked.

SPRINCE: The possibility of a speech disorder in schizophrenia and its relationship to biochemical factors brings to mind the work of H. Ghadimi *et al.* (*New England J. Med.* **265,** 221, 1961) who have reported a new familial disorder of histidine metabolism characterized by speech retardation and abnormally high levels of histidine in the urine and blood. The metabolism of histidine leads to the formation of histamine. Schizophrenics are known to tolerate much larger doses of histamine than normal individuals (Luch, J. D., *AMA Arch.*

Neurol. Psychiat. **71**, 629, 1954). The question that now arises from Dr. Forrest's comment is as follows: Could there be a relationship between Ghadimi's congenital histidinuria (or histidinemia) and schizophrenia? Such a study might well be worthy of further consideration.

SCHILDKRAUT: I wish to comment on the problems involved in clinical psychiatric diagnosis at the present time. Recognizing these problems, I think there may be considerable value in the utilization of longitudinal research designs, especially in studies of those patients in whom changes in clinical state might reasonably be anticipated. Of course, such longitudinal studies involve the assumption that biochemical changes occur in relationship to change in clinical state. It should be pointed out, however, that cross-sectional studies which compare patient populations to control groups, without considering the clinical state of the individual patient at the time of the study, involve the equally unproved assumption that biochemical abnormalities will persist independent of changes in the clinical state. Either of these two possibilities may, in fact, be true in different conditions and, in the present state of our knowledge, both research approaches seem indicated.

The problems involved in the clinical classification and groupings of psychiatric patients may, in part, be obviated by the longitudinal study since, in a sense, the patient may be used as his own control and the need for classification and comparison across groups is reduced. This approach has been quite rewarding in studies of the affective disorders where changes in steroid, electrolyte and catecholamine metabolism have been found to be associated with changes in clinical state. The possible relationship of these changes to etiology raises a question which, I think, must be left open for the present. Irrespective of the question of etiology, however, this approach can provide knowledge about pathophysiological changes occurring in mental disorders. What we learn in this regard may be of importance even if it should turn out not to be etiologically significant and, moreover, such pathophysiological data may ultimately contribute to our capacity to meaningfully classify the psychiatric disorders. As a clinical psychiatrist, I thus feel it important to support Dr. Forrest's position since I think that attempts by the clinician to dissect pure homogeneous subgroups from the heterogeneous groupings of psychiatric disorders offered by our current systems of classification, is to try to extend our clinical diagnostic skills beyond their present-day capacities.

SUMMARY

THE HYPOTHETICAL RELATIONSHIPS BETWEEN AMINES AND MENTAL ILLNESS; A CRITICAL SYNTHESIS

SEYMOUR S. KETY

Chief, Laboratory of Clinical Science,
National Institute of Mental Health, Bethesda, Maryland

LET me begin with some considerations of epistemology. I should like to ask: What does one require of a good hypothesis? We would want it to be plausible, and to be capable of explaining phenomena parsimoniously; to be heuristic, that is, be testable, stimulate good research and the acquisition of new and useful knowledge. We would ask that it have predictive value, and that it continue to be compatible with new data which it stimulates and with other information which becomes available. We should want it to be capable of being modified and elaborated in line with new information without losing its parsimonious qualities. We would also want it to be capable of being rejected and ourselves willing to scrap it when crucial evidence against it is obtained.

Numerous current hypotheses have formed the basis of this meeting, some have been broad and general, and others have been subsidiary to these. Have any of them been proven? I think we will agree that no hypothesis in this Symposium was proven except, perhaps, the very specific hypothesis that there may be a reduction of cystathionine synthase in the liver of patients with homocystinuria which Mudd *et al.* (this Symp., p. 247) seem to have proven rather rigorously.

But we did not really expect to prove any hypotheses in so short a time. What we must ask ourselves and answer, not so much as a group but each individually, with regard to any of these hypotheses is simply this: Is there enough evidence to reject it? And, having satisfied ourselves on that point: Is it sufficiently attractive, plausible or relevant to our own interest and competence to motivate us to devise and carry out appropriate tests of it? The answers to these questions do not demand the same kind of rigorous proof that the hypothesis itself requires. There have been no statistical techniques worked out to establish when a hypothesis is worth entertaining or when it is viable, interesting, or plausible enough to make it worth one's effort to test it.

The discovery of the psychotomimetic effects of mescaline and later of LSD was responsible for a broad and rather ill-defined hypothesis that chemical substances, or more specifically, certain amines may be crucially involved in the symptomatology of some forms of schizophrenia. It was pointed out by Smythies this morning, and others have emphasized as well, that these agents are not properly described as hallucinogens because they produce true hallucinations in only a small percentage of individuals. The interesting thing about them is that they produce a wide variety of mental changes, including delusions, hallucinations, thought disturbances, paranoid states, affective changes, in different individuals at different times. All of these are found in patients with schizophrenia. That there are differences between the effects of these drugs and schizophrenia is undoubtedly true, but one wonders exactly what the logical implications of the psychotomimetic drugs are to a toxin hypothesis of schizophrenia: dissimilarities do not disprove it since the drug is administered to the patient at different times and in different situations from those which might attend an endogenous toxin. But even if such substances were to produce a syndrome indistinguishable from schizophrenia (which I believe amphetamine may sometimes do), that, in itself, would not prove the hypothesis although it would be compatible with it.

About 15 years ago Smythies, Osmond and Harley-Mason (*J. Ment. Sci.* **98,** 309, 1952) went further with this broad hypothesis and, recognizing that mescaline was a threefold-methylated congener of the normal metabolite, dopamine, they proposed the hypothesis that an alteration in biological transmethylation, resulting in the production of abnormal methylated products, played a crucial role in some forms of schizophrenia. I may have added a few modifiers to their hypothesis, but they are not very important. This hypothesis is parsimonious in that it can incorporate within a single concept the bulk of hallucinogens which are methylated compounds. It is heuristic in that many of the studies which were discussed here resulted from that hypothesis and, as I mentioned before, if that hypothesis did no more than stimulate some of the research which we heard today—research on some of the basic aspects of S-adenosylmethionine metabolism in the brain (Baldessarini, this Symp., p. 199), the development of neurophysiological (Himwich, this Symp., p. 137) or behavioral tests (Smythies, this Symp., p. 5) for hallucinogenic activity, correlations between hallucinogenic activity and quantum molecular properties (Snyder and Merril, this Symp., p. 229)—the hypothesis would have served a valuable purpose. The hypothesis, in addition, however, has been predictive and seems capable of being compatible with new information. Harley-Mason, in what was a remarkable insight, predicted before anyone had demonstrated it, a methylation of catecholamines—in fact, he needed it as part of his hypothesis—and we have since seen only recently, through the work of Axelrod, that O-methylation is one of the most important pathways in the metabolism of catecholamines. Interestingly enough, Harley-Mason (*J. Ment. Sci.*, **98,** 309, 1952) also suggested that 3,4-dimethyoxyphenylethylamine was a provocative compound in connection with this hypothesis. He based this on its similarity to mescaline and the report by Noteboom, who observed that DMPEA was most potent in producing a catatonia-like state in animals. When a prediction as far out as that is followed by a report, 10 years later, that such a compound occurs in the urine of schizophrenics (Friedhoff and Van Winkle, *J. Nerv. Ment. Dis.* **135,** 550, 1962) a greater credence is attached to the hypothesis.

There is the report by Holmstedt (this Symp., p. 151) of the discovery of a new compound which is probably hallucinogenic and, interestingly enough, both N- and O-methylated. I must confess that I find it interesting that this new hallucinogen, which could have had any structure in all of organic chemistry, turns out to be another methylated compound. There has been reviewed considerable evidence which can be taken to support a transmethylation hypothesis of schizophrenia. The evidence does not rigorously support the hypothesis, but much is at least compatible with it. We have heard about the effects of methionine administration which can produce an exacerbation of psychosis in some schizophrenic patients (Pollin, Cardon and Kety, *Science*, **133,** 104, 1961), an observation which appears to have been confirmed in other laboratories (Brune and Himwich, *J. Nerv. Ment. Dis.* **134,** 447, 1962; Alexander *et al.*, ibid., **137,** 135, 1963). I feel that there are few more aware of the deficits in those observations than the investigators who have made them. Much remains to be done to rule out alternative hypotheses to the one that methionine exacerbates psychosis by stimulating transmethylation. As a matter of fact, we freely admitted that it was rather naïve to expect a simple increase in the ingestion of methionine to stimulate so basic a process as transmethylation. *A priori* it would seem strange that nature would have permitted a process so important in the biology of the organism to be sensitive to alterations in the nutritional intake of methionine.[1] Although the idea seemed somewhat far-fetched biochemically, it seemed at least worth while to test the effects of methionine along with a number of other amino acids which were precursors of centrally occurring amines. As I have indicated, the psychotic activation by methionine is certainly compatible with the hypothesis. The ability of betaine to do the same thing, which was demonstrated by Brune and Himwich (in *Recent Advances in Biological Psychiatry*, N.Y., Plenum Press, **5,** 144, 1963), is also compatible with the hypothesis and, as a matter of fact, as Smythies mentioned yesterday, restricts the number of alternative explanations. That methionine causes an increase in S-adenosylmethionine in the brain, as reported by Baldessarini (this Symp., p. 199),

[1] On the other hand, since methionine does not occur in nature unassociated with other amino acids in proteins, nature may not have been required to protect against overriding doses of simple methionine.

is most interesting as is his finding that monoamine oxidase inhibitors depress the concentrations of that methyl donor. On the basis of these findings, perhaps, our speculation that transmethylation could be facilitated by methionine loading may not have been naïve; at least the procedure seems capable of increasing the brain concentrations of the important methyl donor. Axelrod's finding (*Science*, **134,** 343, 1961) of what appears to be an enzyme present in mammalian tissue and capable of converting tryptamine to dimethyltryptamine, is also compatible with the transmethylation hypothesis but hardly constitutes very strong evidence since he found this in normal rabbit lung, which simply suggests that some mammalian tissues can, with a methyl donor, under certain conditions methylate a normal metabolite to a psychotomimetic compound.

Himwich's group (Berlet *et al.*, this Symp., p. 69) has reported increases in tryptamine excretion with exacerbations of schizophrenia and although this requires one or two more steps, it can certainly be made compatible with a transmethylation hypothesis in terms of providing more substrate for the formation of methylated indoles. Sprince (this Symp., p. 97) found increased tryptamine excretion in activated schizophrenics under the influence of methionine loads and he indicated why this finding was compatible with the transmethylation hypothesis. The presence of schizophrenia in the family of a homocystinuric patient (this Symp., p. 247) I find rather interesting. It could possibly be made compatible with the transmethylation hypothesis of schizophrenia, as Baldessarini valiantly attempted to do. This family could have shown many diseases—why did they have to pick on schizophrenia, if not simply to tantalize us?

Finally, we had the report by Friedhoff and Van Winkle (this Symp., p. 19) of the presence of 3,4-dimethyoxyphenylethylamine, the compound which Harley-Mason had indicated as being of special interest, with a much greater frequency in the urine of schizophrenics than in normals. This observation and Friedhoff's subsequent contributions to the problem have received careful scrutiny at this meeting. Although we do not know whether this particular compound is psychotomimetic in man, we have the interesting evidence of Noteboom, which one need not take very seriously, since what is catatonia in cats may be quite different from schizophrenia in man. But we have in addition the interesting predictions made independently by Smythies, Himwich and Snyder (this Symp., that this particular compound, whether by behavioral changes, physiologic effects, or structure, should have psychotomimetic activity. In any case, Friedhoff's observations have been confirmed by Kuehl (this Symp., p. 23) and very cogently by Bourdillon and Bridges (this Symp., p. 43), although Bourdillon was careful to point out that he has not clearly established his pink spot, which correlates so well with the probable incidence of schizophrenia in his various samples, as 3,4-dimethoxyphenylethylamine. Perry (this Symp., p. 31), on the other hand, has not found this substance in either normal urine or that of schizophrenic patients on plant free diets. That evidence is not as cogent as it would have been had he found the compound equally in both types of urine and then shown it to disappear by dietary means.[1] If its excretion is more frequent in schizophrenics, finding that it depended on dietary factors would not indicate that it was unimportant. The excretion of phenylpyruvic acid in phenylketonuria requires the presence of phenylalanine in the diet.

Further research appears to be indicated. We need more blind studies with attention to diagnostic classification, like Bourdillon's, reinforced by rigorous control of diet, drugs and of every other non-disease variable which could conceivably have been operating. Such studies could help to establish whether or not the excretion of this compound was characteristic of certain forms of schizophrenia. We have heard the reasons which indicate that dimethoxyphenylacetic acid or other metabolites of DMPEA may be more significant or more readily identified. It would seem worth while to learn whether these or other methylated compounds are excreted to a greater extent by schizophrenics during methionine loading and whether this correlates with the mental changes. Interestingly enough, the transmethylation hypothesis is in a relatively unassailable position here. If the validity and relevance to schizophrenia of DMPEA should become clearly established, that would clearly support the transmethylation hypothesis. If DMPEA is eventually found to be a will-o'-the-wisp, that does not necessarily force rejection of the transmethylation hypothesis which can then go merrily on to another metabolite which could become methylated.

This conference has provided an opportunity to present and discuss much of the evidence relevant to that hypothesis and for each line of evidence many alternative interpretations can and must be formulated in addition to the one which we would like to believe. Yet, though each bit of supporting evidence has only a small chance of being valid and relevant, it would be rather surprising, to paraphrase Dr. Richter, if all of this were unrelated to the hypothesis of transmethylation in schizophrenia. That hypothesis has by no means been proven nor is it likely to be proven very easily. It remains, however, a remarkably parsimonious explanation of a mass of otherwise disparate information and, for that reason, appears to be worth entertaining and testing.

[1] Such a report has now appeared (Studnitz, W. von and Nyman, G. E., Excretion of 3,4-dimethoxyphenylethylamine in schizophrenia, *Acta psychiat. scand.*, in press). These workers found a substance which they identified as 3,4-dimethyoxyphenylethylamine in the urine of two out of three mentally healthy hospital patients and in four out of six schizophrenics, and demonstrated its disappearance from the urine when the same subjects were placed upon an exclusively carbohydrate diet. The numbers in both samples were not large enough, however, to constitute definitive evidence against the thesis that the compound appears more frequently in schizophrenics, although its disappearance from the urine in all of six individuals on a restricted diet strongly suggests that its presence requires some dietary factors.

But we have discussed other hypotheses at this conference which relate amines to human behavior. One of these is the possibility that amines may be important in mood. We may briefly summarize the evidence which has suggested it: the correlation between the depressant drug reserpine and its ability to diminish the amines in the brain, and the almost predictable property of any monoamine oxidase inhibitor which gets into the brain and retards the degradation of amines there to act as an antidepressant drug. Straughan (this Symp., p. 219) has thrown a little cold water on even this very general hypothesis in pointing out that by micro-injection of amines into various sites in the brain, the only effect which seems to be produced is inhibition. One would expect *a priori* to see some kind of stimulatory activity, although it is not impossible that selective inhibition could result in stimulation. In addition, microinjection may not constitute a crucial test, since such application into the brain substance may not exactly simulate the manner by which these substances are actually released and the site at which they act in the nervous system.

Other hypotheses were discussed which were more specifically related to the relative importance of indoleamines or catecholamines with respect to mental state. Richter (this Symp., p. 169) reviewed considerable evidence which suggested that indoleamines had something to do with mental state, mood, or depression: the tryptamine excretion studies by Brune, Himwich and Pscheidt, the low levels of 5-hydroxyindoleacetic acid in the cerebrospinal fluid of depressed patients, what appeared to be a decrease in 5-hydroxy-tryptophan decarboxylation in clinical depression which was reversed by treatment, and finally the ability of tryptophan in conjunction with lower doses of monoamine oxidase inhibitors to restore the mood of depressed patients; all of which evidence is clearly compatible with a hypothesis that one or another of the indoleamines plays an important role in the regulation of mood. There has not been as much opportunity to discuss the corresponding hypothesis for catecholamines, some of the evidence for which was presented by Schildkraut (this Symp., p. 213). This includes the antagonism of reserpine depression in animals by dopa which is remarkable and prompt, Everett's compelling correlation between brain dopamine level and the behavioral effects of either a monoamine oxidase or a dopa precursor. I should like to mention very briefly some new data which bear on the relationship between catecholamines in the brain and mood. First let me recall for you the findings of Kopin and Gordon (*J. Pharmacol.* **140,** 207, 1963), who labeled the norepinephrine stores in the sympathetic nerve endings of the isolated heart with tritiated norepinephrine and studied the effects of certain drugs and of sympathetic stimulation. When norepinephrine was released by nerve stimulation or by tyramine, both of which are associated with a sympathetic effect on the heart, there was an increase in O-methylated derivatives. When the norepinephrine was released by reserpine which has no sympathomimetic effect, the O-methylated derivatives were unchanged and the deaminated derivatives were increased. On the basis of these findings it was reasonable to suggest as a tentative generalization that O-methylation of norepinephrine is associated with its release at functional sites while deamination occurs when it is released in a non-functional way. Now, it would be very interesting to know what was happening to norepinephrine in the brain under different circumstances, but until quite recently that was not possible. Recently, however, Jacques Glowinski, a young man who had developed a technique for injecting materials into the lateral ventricle of the rat brain, came to work with Axelrod and, with him, injected tritiated norepinephrine into the lateral ventricle. They found evidence that the radioactive substance was labeling rather faithfully the endogenous norepinephrine of the brain and by using such a preparation it was possible to study the metabolism of norepinephrine in the brain and to test the effects of various drugs (*J. Neurochem.* **12,** 25, 1965). It was found that reserpine causes an increase in deaminated products while, on the other hand, monoamine oxidase inhibitors, imipramine and amphetamine, were all associated with an increase of O-methylated products in the brain. If one is permitted to draw an analogy between what was found in the brain and what was known about the heart, one could suggest that the functionally active release of norepinephrine in the brain was a mechanism by which the antidepressant drugs acted while a diversion of normal norepinephrine through monoamine oxidase accounted for the depressant actions of reserpine.

Fortunately, as I have mentioned before, we are not forced to accept any one of these hypotheses at the present time. They are all sufficiently plausible and heuristic that it seems sensible to keep entertaining and evaluating them. I, for one, would be surprised if some increased understanding of schizophrenia, normal mood or abnormal affective states does not emerge from that process.

INDEX